Structural Concepts in Immunology and Immunochemistry

Holt, Rinehart and Winston
Molecular and Cellular Biology Series

ELVIN A. KABAT
Departments of Microbiology and Neurology, Columbia University
and Neurological Institute, Presbyterian Hospital, New York

Structural Concepts in Immunology and Immunochemistry

HOLT, RINEHART AND WINSTON, INC.
New York Chicago San Francisco
Atlanta Dallas Montreal
Toronto London

Library of Congress Catalog Card Number: 68-16789

ISBN: 0-03-066770-4

1234 090 9876543

Printed in the United States of America

Cover: DNA from phage lambda, prepared by freeze-etching. Electron micrograph by E. J. DuPraw, Department of Cell Biology, University of Maryland School of Medicine.

Preface

The teaching of immunology has been associated largely with medical schools, predominantly with microbiology and occasionally with biochemistry departments. While this association has proved of enormous benefit, it has also tended to isolate immunologists and, later, immunochemists from biologists and chemists—especially since most medical schools are physically separated from their main university campuses. As such, immunology has tended to develop a terminology and language that seem unfamiliar and often frightening or bizarre to the usual undergraduate science major.

The recent contributions of genetics, biochemistry, and molecular biology to problems of storage and transmission of information in relation to cell growth differentiation, survival, and evolution have brought workers in these areas closer to problems of immunological specificity and to the recognition mechanisms involved in antibody formation. At the same time, the medical student is having to adjust to learning a more theoretical and scientific approach to basic science in order to prepare himself to practice the medicine that will emerge from these developments.

A main aim of this book is to introduce the advanced undergraduate and beginning graduate student to modern thinking in immunology and immunochemistry. It assumes some background in organic chemistry and cell biology and some acquaintance with molecular biology at a level such as that developed in Loewy and Siekevitz's *Cell Structure and Function* and in Watson's *Molecular Biology of the Gene*. It assumes, further, an interest in learning and a willingness to acquire a somewhat different vocabulary—that of immunology and immunochemistry—and to become familiar with the basic design of immunochemical experimentation. To ease the way, similarities between immunological concepts and those in biology and biochemistry are emphasized. The chapters on the biological effects of antibodies on cells and tissues and on immunological tolerance, while closely allied to medicine, nevertheless present unusual instances of specificity which may offer important problems to the biologist and biochemist. While not especially directed to the medical student, this book will be of interest to those who look forward to a career in investigative work and in teaching; it is not inconceivable that it might even be of use to those whose primary motivation is the practice of medicine.

The problem of literature citation has been very difficult to someone accustomed to writing very closely documented books and scientific papers. For this book, however, such documentation would not have been useful or even possible. Moreover, the nature and size of the book have necessitated selection of only a few of the many examples of antigen-antibody systems, and all the lines of evidence for any point could not be presented. In the Suggested Readings at the end of each of the fifteen chapters an effort has been made to remedy this by citing review articles, books, and papers that, in addition to providing supplementary information or details about methods, contain references by which the sources and individuals involved may be identified. Specific experimental papers have been given when they seem to have special interest or if they had not yet been covered in reviews. Often, the purpose in citing the reference is given in a short sentence.

The author is indebted to Professor Ariel Loewy of Haverford College for arousing his interest in this project, to the National Science Foundation for a grant (GB-3675) making it possible for the author to spend a Sabbatical year in Paris, to Dr. Pierre Grabar of the Institut Pasteur for making the facilities of his department available, to the library at the Institut Pasteur, and Mme Claude Avrameas for typing the manuscript. He is also indebted to Drs. Stratis Avrameas, Jean Dausset, and Claude Lapresle and to Jonathan Kabat for suggestions on going over the entire manuscript; to Professor Manfred M. Mayer for reading the chapter on complement; to Professor Otto Bier both for his comments on the chapters on antibody formation, allergy, and tolerance and for reading page proof; to Professor Bernard F. Erlanger, Dr. Kenneth O. Lloyd, Kathleen Vetere, and Sally Kabat for their assistance in proofreading and checking; and to those individuals, journals, and publishers who provided illustrations, tables, or data, as acknowledged where these appear.

ELVIN A. KABAT

New York
December 1967

Contents

1

What is Immunological Specificity? An example of complementarity involving weak interactions

The biosynthetic machinery of the living cell, for its metabolic processes and its reproduction, makes use in many ways of interactions involving relatively weak binding forces as distinct from the much stronger covalent bond. These weak forces—hydrophobic and hydrogen bonds, van der Waals forces, and ionic interactions—are able to act effectively only when the two reacting molecules can approach very closely to each other and indeed so closely that the projecting constituent atoms or groups of atoms of one molecule can fit into complementary depressions or recesses in the other. This principle of complementarity—often compared to the fitting of a key in a lock*—underlies such diverse phenomena as the combination of an enzyme with its substrate, the affinity of certain proteins like serum albumin for

*This analogy was introduced by Emil Fischer for enzyme-substrate and by Paul Ehrlich for antigen-antibody interactions.

various substances such as dyes and fatty acids, the enzymatic replication of the double helix of deoxyribonucleic acid (DNA) by copying each strand, the formation of messenger ribonucleic acid (RNA) by the copying of portions of a DNA strand and the formation of a complex between messenger RNA or oligonucleotides with ribosomes and amino-acyl-s-RNA.

By x-ray diffraction studies, the enzyme lysozyme from egg white has been shown to have a three-dimensional structure containing a cleft or crevice that accommodates its substrate, a polysaccharide made up of alternating sequences of β-(1⟶4)-linked *N*-acetyl-D-glucosamine.

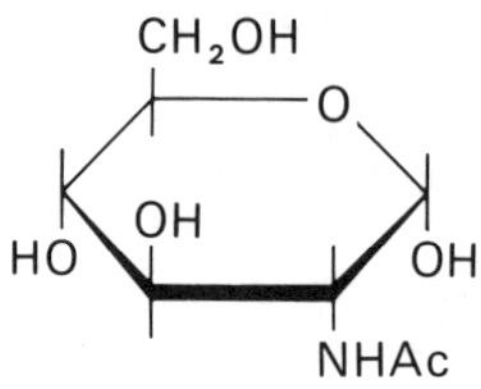

and of *N*-acetyl-muramic acid

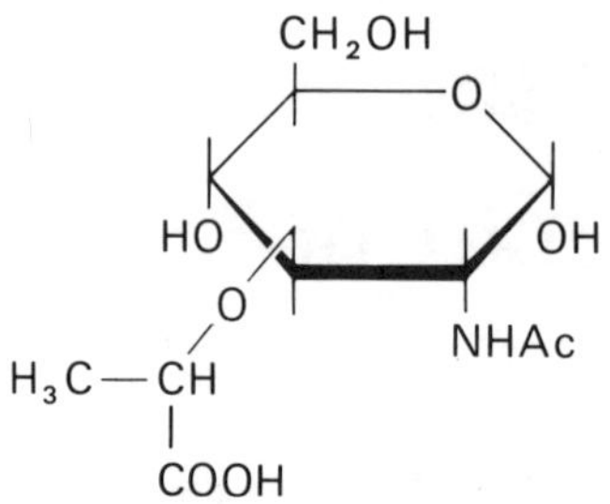

which is *N*-acetyl-D-glucosamine substituted on carbon 3 with a molecule of lactic acid in ether linkage. Six sugars rings of the substrate fit into the crevice. The methyl-β-D-glycoside of *N*-acetyl-D-glucosamine, a β-(1⟶4)-linked dimer, chitobiose, and a similarly linked oligosaccharide, the trimer chitotriose

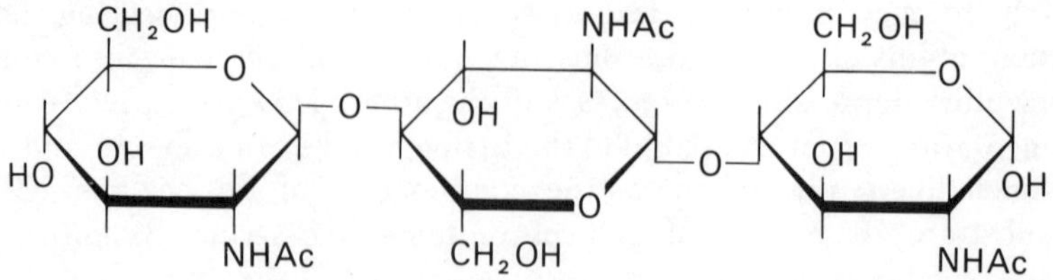

are all bound by the enzyme. They occupy very definite positions in the crevice; the fitting of each atom of each sugar residue is critically adapted to and has a definite orientation relative to the atoms forming the crevice. The trisaccharide fills the top half of the cleft and is held by hydrogen bonds and by apolar bonds. The cleft itself appears to alter its conformation slightly upon contact with the substrate so as to provide better complementarity.

Complementarity is also at the basis of the immunological reactions, that is, reactions developed during evolution of vertebrates which aid in the elimination from the body of agents causing infectious disease–bacteria, viruses, and other parasites–and which often result in the development of resistance or immunity to the infecting agent. This resistance is generally a consequence of the formation in the animal of certain types of serum proteins called ANTIBODIES, the molecules of which possess small areas of their surface that are complementary to small chemical groupings on certain protein or polysaccharide components (ANTIGENS) of the infectious agent. These complementary regions (called the ANTIBODY COMBINING SITES) of which there are at least two per antibody molecule, and in some types of antibody molecules as many as five (see Chapter 6), may react with their corresponding complementary region on the antigen (called the ANTIGENIC DETERMINANT) to link several molecules of multivalent antigen together to form a lattice. The fit of the antigenic determinant within the antibody combining site is probably of the same character as that of β-(1 $\longrightarrow$4)-linked-*N*-acetyl-D-glucosamine oligosaccharides with lysozyme. If the reaction takes place *in vitro* between a soluble macromolecule extracted from a bacterium and the antibody generally contained in whole serum from the immunized or convalescent animal (ANTISERUM), a precipitate may form (PRECIPITIN REACTION). A molecule of antibody may also serve to link two bacteria (or two virus particles) together by reacting with the antigen on their surfaces and many molecules of antibody may thus hold a large number of bacteria together as a clump (AGGLUTINATION) (Fig. 1.1). Paramecia are IMMOBILIZED by the addition of small amounts of antibody which hold their cilia together and prevent their movement (Fig. 1.2). Bacteria may also be immobilized by antibody that binds their flagella together (Fig. 1.3). Proteins such as diphtheria toxin may be NEUTRALIZED by antibody and prevented from reacting with cells to exert their harmful effects. The infectivity of viruses may also be neutralized by specific antibodies. Antibodies belong to the classes of serum protein known as IMMUNOGLOBULINS, but not all immunoglobulins are known to be antibodies (see Chapters 3 and 9).

Since the development of immunology and immunochemistry began in the latter portion of the nineteenth century and modern biochemistry and molecular biology is largely a mid-twentieth-century product, immunologists and immunochemists had already developed their own terminology for describing the phenomena with which they worked. This terminology has tended to keep immunology apart from the other fields and has often discouraged efforts to utilize immunological principles and concepts in biochemical work. Modern immunochemistry bridges the gap between the two areas.

Antigen-antibody interactions show a high degree of SPECIFICITY. This specificity is manifested at many levels. Historically it was first perceived when it was recognized that recovery from one disease such as smallpox was attended by long-lasting immunity, but that such

Fig. 1.1 (A) Electron micrograph of negatively stained wart virus particles. Substructure of virus is clearly evident × 178,500. (B) Wart virus in the presence of rabbit antibody to wart virus. Substructure of the virus is obscured by a halo of antibody around each particle, and virus particles are linked together (agglutinated) by antibody molecules × 178,500. (C) A loop of antibody with both antibody combining sites attached to a single virus particle × 1,200,000. (From Almeida, J., B. Cinader, and A. Howatson. J. Exp. Med. **118**: 327[1963]; the photograph reproduced from printed halftone copy inevitably shows a loss of detail, and the quality of the results is not representative of the original. By permission of The Rockefeller University Press.)

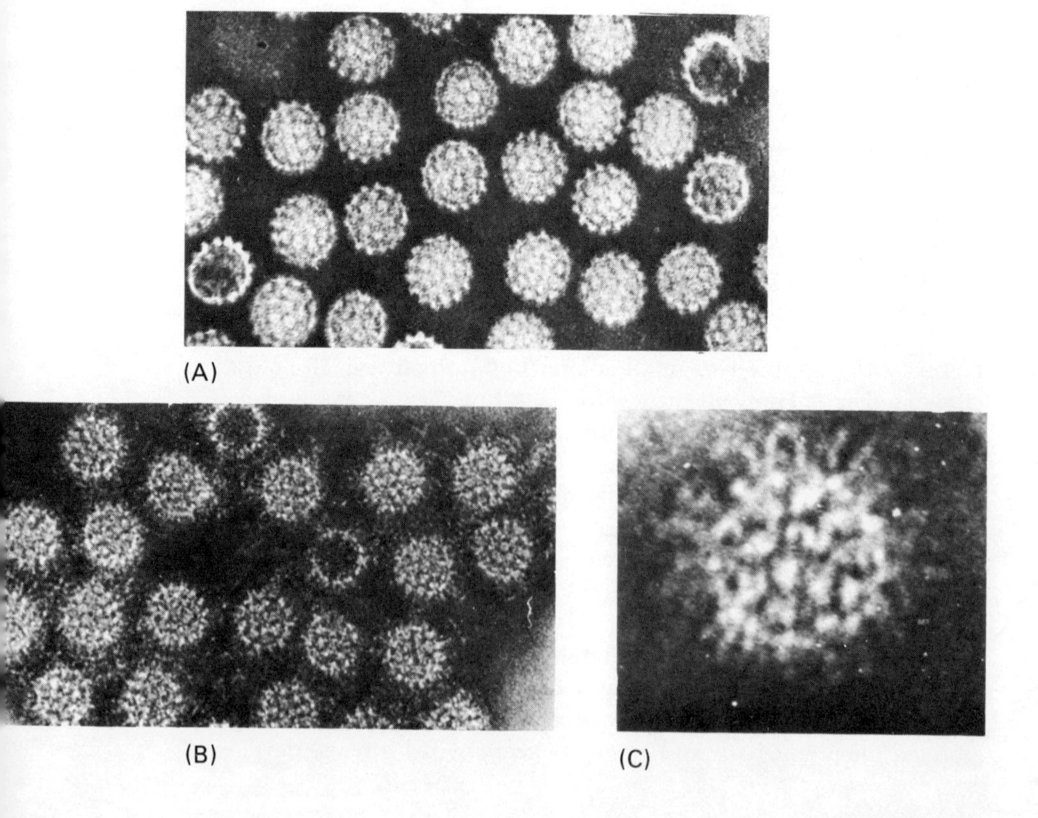

Fig. 1.2 (A) Unimmobilized paramecium × 375. (B) Paramecium immobilized by antibody × 375; note clumping of cilia. Both preparations fixed in osmic acid and photographed in phase contrast microscope. (From Beale, G. H. and H. Kacser. J. Gen. Microbiol. **17**: 68 [1957].)

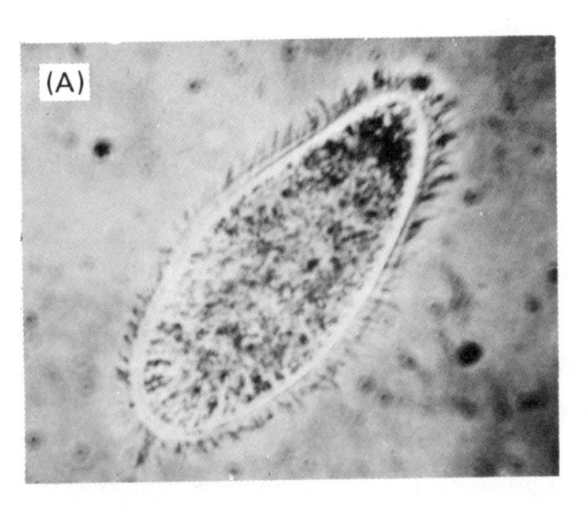

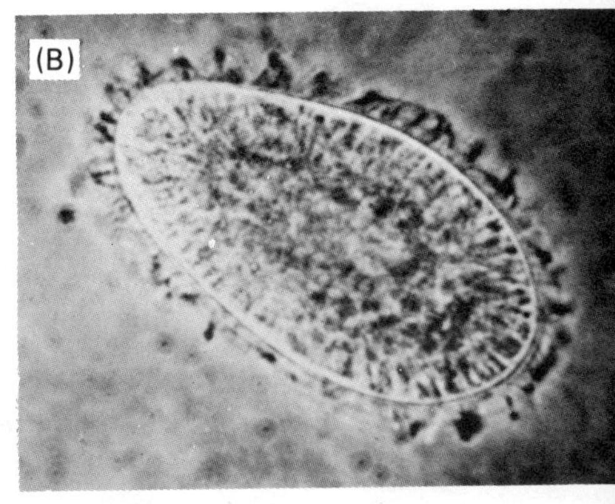

Fig. 1.3 (Left) Two flagella held together by antibody molecules giving a "rope ladder" effect × 60,000. (Right) Control showing flagella without antibody × 60,000. Flagella are from *Salmonella enteritidis*, γG antibody to *Salmonella enteritidis* prepared in rabbits was used. (Courtesy Dr. K. E. Gillert, Robert Koch Institut, Berlin.)

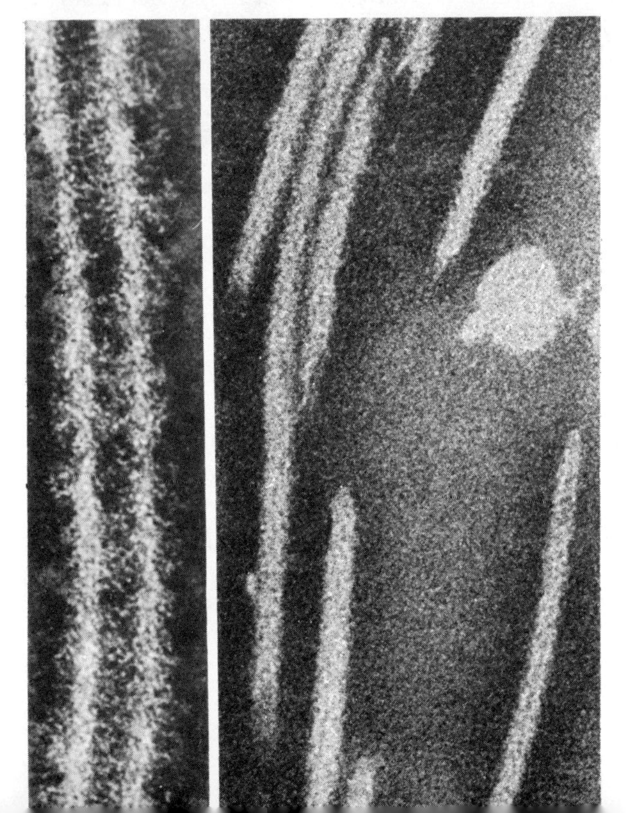

immunity did not protect against another disease, for instance measles or chicken pox. Brought down to the molecular level, specificity means that the combining sites of antibodies to the protein antigens of the virus of smallpox have a complementarity not at all similar to the antigenic determinants of the measles virus. As we shall see, whenever antigenic determinants of two different antigens have some structural similarity, some degree of fitting of one determinant into the combining site of some antibodies to the other may occur; this phenomenon gives rise to what are known as CROSS REACTIONS. Thus, only a portion of the antibody molecules formed to one antigen may precipitate with the other related antigen. Cross reactions are of major importance in understanding the complementarity or specificity of antigen-antibody reactions.

The early studies of antigen-antibody interaction were generally carried out with very complex mixtures of antigens such as microorganisms. It was soon recognized that the ability to cause disease was in no way essential for antigenicity and that a complex mixture of protein antigens–for example, serum from one animal species injected into another–would induce the formation of antibodies to the various protein constituents of the injected serum. It was also found that each antigen would precipitate only with its respective antibodies. Similarly, erythrocytes, leucocytes, tissue extracts, milk, egg white, and other complex mixtures were found to be antigenic–that is, were found to induce the formation of specific antibodies with which they react.

It took several decades and the development of modern protein chemistry for immunologists to appreciate the importance of using purified single proteins as antigens, so as to reduce the complexity of the systems with which they were dealing. During this period the standard physicochemical methods for resolving mixtures of proteins, methods such as ultracentrifugation, electrophoresis, and solubility measurements, came into widespread use. A variety of immunochemical methods was developed which permits the detection and even the quantitative measurement of the amounts of impurities in a given preparation; contaminations of 1 percent or less may readily be measured. It thus became standard practice to use well-characterized antigens for immunochemical studies and to be aware of the extent of contamination with other antigenic substances. One need only pick up a bottle of any reagent grade chemical, even one such as sodium chloride, to be reminded that there are no *pure* substances; manufacturers always specify on the label the maximum amounts of the various impurities that may be present.

It is immunological specificity or complementarity that makes possible the detection of such contaminations among antigens. Even a protein such as highly purified recrystallized human serum albumin may contain small amounts of other proteins that were present in the serum from which it was prepared. One frequent contaminant is serum gamma globulin. As antigens, these two proteins are completely different. Antibodies to one will not react with the other; for example, the antibody combining sites on molecules of antibody to human serum albumin show no complementarity for any antigenic determinants on human gamma globulin (and vice versa). Thus, if the human albumin is free of gamma globulin, it will not react at all with antibody to gamma globulin, while if the albumin contains a small amount of gamma globulin as an impurity, the molecules of gamma globulin will react with the antibody to gamma globulin. Naturally, the experimental conditions involved in detecting such contaminants are of utmost importance and will be described later.

The reaction of even the most highly purified protein antigen with the antibodies formed to it, is highly complex. Each molecule of an antigen like human serum albumin contains several antigenic determinants; the exact number is not known. If human serum albumin is injected into a group of rabbits to stimulate the formation of antibodies, each rabbit may produce antibody to any or all of the antigenic determinants on the albumin molecule. The proportion of antibody to any determinant to the total may vary from rabbit to rabbit and may change even in a single rabbit as the injections of antigen are continued; occasional animals may fail to form antibody to one or more determinants. Thus, at the molecular level the antibody molecules in a given antiserum differ from one another in the nature of their antibody combining sites, some showing complementarity to one determinant while others have structures complementary toward another determinant. We speak of this as one of the several manifestations of the HETEROGENEITY of antibodies. The extraordinary magnitude of this heterogeneity is the unique characteristic of antibodies (and of immunoglobulins) which distinguishes them from all other types of proteins. We shall soon discover that even to a single antigenic determinant, the antibody molecules formed are not uniform with respect to their combining sites, but that individual antibody combining sites may be complementary toward only a portion of the determinant while others may be specific for the whole determinant. Heterogeneity of antibody does not involve the antibody combining sites alone; there are many other parameters by which immunoglobulin molecules have been found to differ from one another, even when these molecules are not known to have the properties of antibodies. If any mechanism for the formation of antibodies at the cellular and molecular levels is to be taken seriously, it must provide a reasonable explanation for this heterogeneity.

The combination of antigen with antibody may be an event of great consequence to the individual. Antibodies may act in a beneficial manner by directly neutralizing the infectivity of viruses and the damaging effects of bacterial toxins and snake venoms. A coating of antibody on a microorganism may promote the phagocytosis and destruction of the bacteria by the white blood corpuscles and by tissue phagocytes and thus lead to recovery from infection. Antigen-antibody interactions are not always beneficial—indeed, they are the basis of many allergic and tissue-damaging reactions. These interactions may trigger the release of pharmacologically active substances like histamine, and other compounds involved in allergic reactions such as hay fever. Complexes of antigen and antibody may cause injury to cells in the presence of certain accessory substances called COMPLEMENT (or sometimes without these substances). The mechanisms of these and other biological effects of antigen-antibody interaction will be treated in subsequent chapters.

SUGGESTED READINGS

Watson, J. D. The molecular biology of the gene. (1965) W. A. Benjamin, Inc., New York; *Chapter 4 for a good discussion of weak interactions.*

Karush, F. Immunological specificity and molecular structure. Advances in Immunology **2**:1 (1962). [Academic Press, New York]; *for the importance of hydrophobic bonding in antigen-antibody reactions.*

Kabat, E. A. Kabat and Mayer's Experimental immunochemistry (2d ed.; 1961) Charles C. Thomas, Publisher, Springfield, Ill. [Chapter 1]; *for additional definitions and a discussion of other immunological reactions.*

Humphrey, J. H. and R. C. White. Immunology for students of medicine. (1963) F. A Davis Company, Philadelphia, Pa.; *for more medical aspects of immunology.*

Loewy, A. G. and P. Siekevitz. Cell structure and function. (1963) Holt, Rinehart and Winston, Inc. New York; *Chapter 8 for a survey of protein structure and how it is established*; *Chapter 9 for enzyme-substrate relationships.*

Phillips, D. C. Three-dimensional structure of an enzyme molecule. Scientific American **215**:78 (1966).

Davis, B. D., R. Dulbecco, H.N. Eisen, H. S. Ginsburg and W. B. Wood, Jr. Microbiology (1967) Hoeber Medical Division, Harper and Row Publishers. New York; *an excellent source of information on medical aspects of microbiology and immunology.*

2

Antigens

We must now consider what kinds of substances may be antigenic, that is, will induce the formation of antibodies when introduced into an animal and will then react with these antibodies. Our ideas in this area have been changing rapidly as a consequence of (1) the ability to detect smaller and smaller amounts of antibody, (2) the studies on synthetic polypeptides in which the amino acid composition may be varied, (3) the addition of various accessory substances termed ADJUVANTS which results in increased antibody formation, and (4) the detection of antibodies that do not give precipitates with antigen.

Traditionally, an overwhelming proportion of immunological information has been derived (1) from investigations using the rabbit as a convenient laboratory animal, (2) from the necessity for large-scale immunization of man to prevent infectious disease, and (3) from clinical observations of people having various diseases in whom antibody formation was taking place naturally. In those instances in which antibodies had proven of therapeutic value, for example, antibodies to diphtheria and tetanus toxins (antitoxins) and antisera to certain microorganisms such as the pneumococcus and meningococcus, large animals were considered desirable and horses were used. Recently, other animals—notably mice, rats, guinea pigs, chickens, goats, pigs, sheep, and so forth—have been fairly extensively studied.

PROTEINS

Early studies empirically established that proteins were good antigens when injected into a species other than the one from which they originated. Thus, rabbit serum proteins did not stimulate antibody formation if injected into rabbits unless the proteins had been altered or denatured in the course of purification, while serum proteins of another species–for example, human, mouse, and so forth–would readily induce the formation of antibodies in the rabbit. Indeed, it was shown very early in this century that rabbit serum proteins injected into even as closely related a species as the hare would yield antibody (and vice versa). No difficulties were encountered in preparing antibodies to protein antigens from remotely related sources such as bacteria, viruses, and egg, milk, and plant proteins. In most of these studies it sufficed to immunize the animal (an animal receiving injections of an antigen is being immunized) with a solution of the antigen or, preferably, with the protein antigen adsorbed on floccules of aluminium hydroxide (ALUM PRECIPITATE), since the use of antigens in particulate form had been shown to give a better antibody response. It was generally thought that these studies showed "foreignness" was a requirement for a substance to be antigenic, that is, that the antibody forming system recognized its own proteins as being not foreign and hence did not react with them. This concept was not strictly valid, since it was known that certain tissue extracts from brain, kidney, testis, and the crystalline lens of the eye were antigenic even when injected into animals of the same species from which they originated, and the concept of "foreignness" had to be restricted to "foreign to the circulation" or "foreign to the antibody forming cells." Even this restriction is not without its exceptions, as diseases were known in which autoantibodies were formed. One of these, hemolytic anemia, may result from the presence, in a person, of autoantibodies to his own red blood cells. Another, called HASHIMOTO'S THYROIDITIS, is associated with autoantibodies to thyroid proteins of the diseased individual and has been experimentally produced in rabbits by injecting them with a portion of their own thyroid glands that had been surgically removed (certain adjuvants must be used, as explained in Chapter 3). The concept of recognition of "self and non-self" is therefore a complex and important one in immunology and will be given further attention in subsequent considerations of antibody formation and of immunological tolerance.

There exists among all species a class of antigens called ISOANTIGENS. These are present in certain members of a species and are lacking in others; they are inherited according to Mendelian genetics. The most important classes of isoantigens are the well-known blood group substances such as the A, B, and Rh (D)* antigens which determine an individual's blood group. Antibodies may be formed to any isoantigen if it is injected into a member of the same species who lacks it. In the case of the blood group A and B substances, anti-A and anti-B are

*The D antigen is the most important of the Rh antigens, since it is responsible for most of the cases of isoimmunization.

normally present in the serum of individuals who lack the corresponding antigen, presumably because A and B substances are so widespread in various animal and plant tissues and in bacteria that antigenic stimulation may have resulted from previous contact with these materials. Thus individuals of blood group O or B generally contain anti-A in their serum, and the injection of A substance into such people may cause a rise in the anti-A level. Naturally occurring anti-Rh antibodies are very rare, but the injection of D-positive erythrocytes into a D-negative (Rh negative) individual may induce the formation of anti-D antibodies. Such isoimmunization may occur naturally during pregnancy in that a D-negative female carrying a D+ fetus that inherited the D antigen from the father may be isoimmunized by fetal red cells entering the maternal circulation. The antibodies formed may then pass through the placenta into the fetal circulation to damage the red cells of the fetus, causing the disease ERYTHROBLASTOSIS FETALIS.

Another very important class of isoantigenic differences are those present on the γG immunoglobulins of various species. In the rabbit these are generally called ALLOTYPES ; and in the human they are of two types, generally known as the Gm and Inv factors. These appear to involve small differences in the amino acid sequence on the γG globulin chains; in one instance, only a single amino acid substitution (see Chapter 9) is associated with an isoantigenic difference. These differences are often recognized by injecting γG globulin possessing an allotypic or isoantigenic determinant into an animal of the same species lacking it, and so raising antibodies specific for it. Some allotypic antisera may also be obtained by the injection of a heterologous species; and some human sera from normal individuals or from patients with a disease called rheumatoid arthritis may also contain antibodies recognizing Gm or Inv determinants.

POLYSACCHARIDES

Another class of substances that were readily shown to be antigenic is the polysaccharides. These have proved extraordinarily useful in immunochemical studies because, although complex, they nevertheless provide antigens of relatively simple structure by which many of the detailed structural aspects of antigenic determinants and antibody combining sites have been worked out. Polysaccharide antigens are unusual in that in purified form they can stimulate antibody formation only in certain species and not in others. Thus, while the rabbit and the guinea pig, which are excellent antibody producers for protein antigens, do not respond at all when purified polysaccharides are injected, humans and mice respond well to polysaccharide antigens; and human antibodies to various polysaccharides are indispensable for immunochemical investigations.

The simplest polysaccharide antigens are dextran and levan. These are exocellular products produced by bacterial enzymes from sucrose according to the reaction

$$n\,C_{12}H_{22}O_{11} \xrightarrow[\text{dextransucrase}]{} \underset{\text{dextran}}{(C_6H_{10}O_5)_n} + n \text{ fructose}$$

$$n\,C_{12}H_{22}O_{11} \xrightarrow[\text{levansucrase}]{} \underset{\text{levan}}{(C_6H_{10}O_5)_n} + n \text{ glucose}$$

Dextran is a polymer composed entirely of glucose, and levan is composed entirely of fructose. The predominant linkage in dextran is α-$(1 \longrightarrow 6)$, that is, a glycosidic bond from carbon 1 of one glucose to carbon 6 of the second glucose which gives long chains, while in levan the fructoses are chiefly linked α-$(2 \longrightarrow 6)$ in long chains. Individual strains of microorganisms have been found to produce dextrans of different structure in which other types of linkages are present; these may be α-$(1 \longrightarrow 2)$, α-$(1 \longrightarrow 3)$, or α-$(1 \longrightarrow 4)$ (Fig. 2.1), and their proportions may vary substantially among different dextrans. Some of these linkages constitute branch points, for example, they serve to attach chains of α-$(1 \longrightarrow 6)$-linked glucoses to one another, others may possibly occur within chains of $(1 \longrightarrow 6)$ linkages or at the ends of chains.

The dextran of simplest structure, called NRRL B512, has 96 percent of its glucoses linked α-$(1 \longrightarrow 6)$, with the remaining 4 percent linked α-$(1 \longrightarrow 3)$. If each α-$(1 \longrightarrow 3)$ linkage serves to connect two chains of α-$(1 \longrightarrow 6)$-linked glucoses, the average chain length $(96 \div 4)$ would be about 20 : 1. Actually, it is well established that a sizable proportion of the α-$(1 \longrightarrow 3)$ linkages join only a single glucose to an α-$(1 \longrightarrow 6)$ chain in this dextran. Thus the average length of α-$(1 \longrightarrow 6)$ chains is probably well over 20 : 1. It must be borne in mind that this is a statistical value and that there may well be a random distribution of α-$(1 \longrightarrow 6)$ chains of various lengths, depending upon where in the molecule the α-$(1 \longrightarrow 3)$ linkages occur. Figure 2.2 shows a portion of a dextran molecule; the chains are probably somewhat longer on the average, than the ones shown in the figure.

As synthesized by the microorganisms, dextrans may have molecular weights in the tens of millions (native dextran). Unlike proteins, they are not of uniform molecular weight, but are polydisperse and vary about a mean value. Since they are so simple in composition, by mild acid hydrolysis one may obtain dextrans of any desired molecular weight range. One important use for dextran is as a plasma volume expander in the treatment of shock, by virtue of its capacity to keep fluid in the blood vessels through its osmotic pressure. For this purpose, after partial hydrolysis, dextran of the desired molecular weight range, 75,000 ± 25,000, is purified by fractional precipitation with ethanol (clinical dextran). By more extensive hydrolysis, oligosaccharides with two to seven or more glucose units in α-(1 ⟶ 6) linkage are formed (Fig. 2.3); these may be obtained in highly purified form and have been of great use in immunochemical studies. It is important to remember that each glucose residue is free to rotate around the α-(1→ 6) glycosidic bond so that the schematic representation in Fig. 2.3 for isomaltose is not rigid. It may well be that the molecules prefer certain conformations in solution, conformations in which the planes of the ring bear a definite orientation to one another.

Another very important group of polysaccharide antigens are the capsular polysaccharides of pneumococci. Pneumococci have been classified into over eighty different types, each of which synthesizes under genetic control a different type of capsular polysaccharide.

Fig. 2.1 The four α-linked disaccharides of glucose occurring in dextrans.

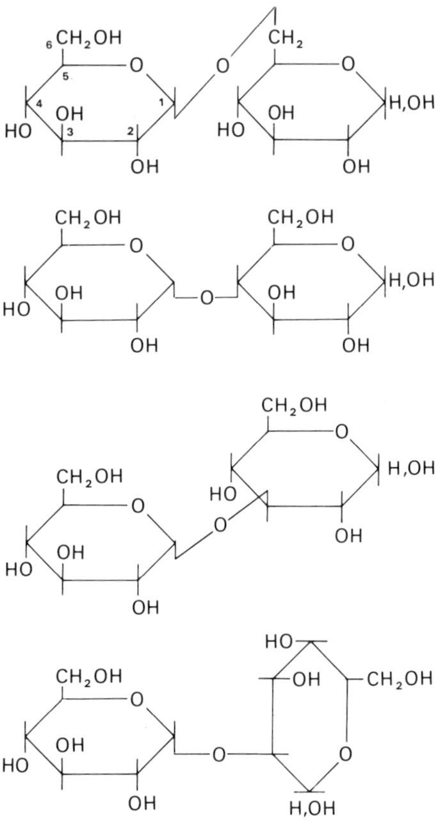

ISOMALTOSE
α-D-glucosyl-(1 ⟶ 6)-D-glucose

MALTOSE
α-D-glucosyl-(1 ⟶ 4)-D-glucose

NIGEROSE
α-D-glucosyl-(1 ⟶ 3)-D-glucose

KOJIBIOSE
α-D-glucosyl-(1 ⟶ 2)-D-glucose

These polysaccharides may be purified from culture filtrates. Not only are they antigenic in man, but antibodies to these polysaccharides moreover have been shown to protect animals against infection with pneumococci. They have proved effective in the immunization of man, each polysaccharide protecting, however, only against infection with the type of pneumococcus from which it was obtained. Although the purified polysaccharides are not antigenic in rabbits and guinea pigs, antibodies to them may be obtained by injection of whole encapsulated pneumococci.

Complex lipopolysaccharide antigens are found in a large variety of microorganisms, notably in Gram-negative enterobacteriaceae such as Salmonella and Shigella; and studies in this area are of great importance in bacterial genetics.

Fig. 2.2 Schematic representation of a small portion of a molecule of NRRL B512 dextran.

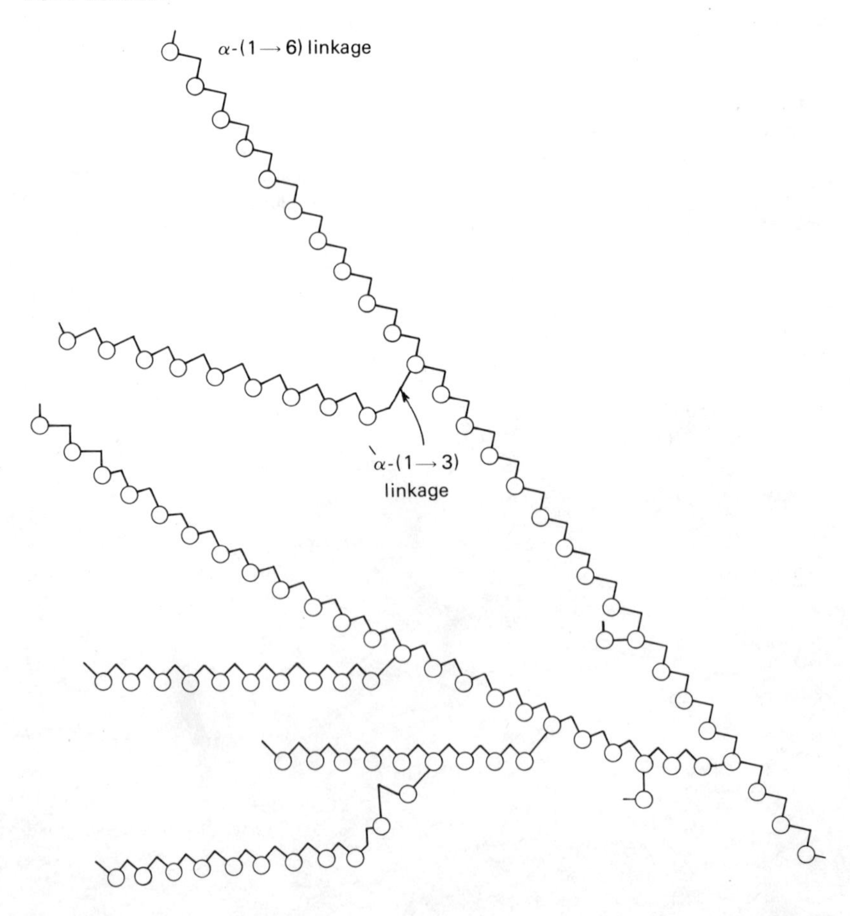

Glycoproteins and glycopeptides (carbohydrate-containing proteins or peptides) also may be antigenic and in some instances their specificity is determined by the carbohydrate moiety. The best-known and most extensively studied glycopeptide antigens are the soluble blood group A and B substances that are synthesized in mucosal cells of certain tissues and secreted (see Chapter 3 and Fig. 3.14). They are present in the secretions of only about 80 percent of individuals whose red cells show the corresponding blood group antigens, and their synthesis is controlled by a gene called the SECRETOR GENE. The 80 percent are termed SECRETORS, and the remaining 20 percent are termed NONSECRETORS. Another blood group glycopeptide called H substance is also found among secretors of A and B substances, as well as in the secretions of 80 percent of individuals of group O. H substance is considered to be a biosynthetic precursor of A and B substances. The 20 percent who do not secrete A, B, and H substances produce another kind of blood group substance, the Lewis ^{a} or Le ^{a} substance, which is thought to be formed earlier in the biosynthesis of the H substance. The secretions containing blood group substances include saliva, gastric juice, amniotic fluid, seminal fluid, and cervical mucus. Small amounts are also present in serum. All these antigenic determinants–A, B, H, and Le ^{a}–are under genetic control, each of the four genes determining the presence of a specific enzyme that can add the sugar involved in its determinant sequentially onto a precursor

Fig. 2.3 Schematic representation of isomaltose oligosaccharides.

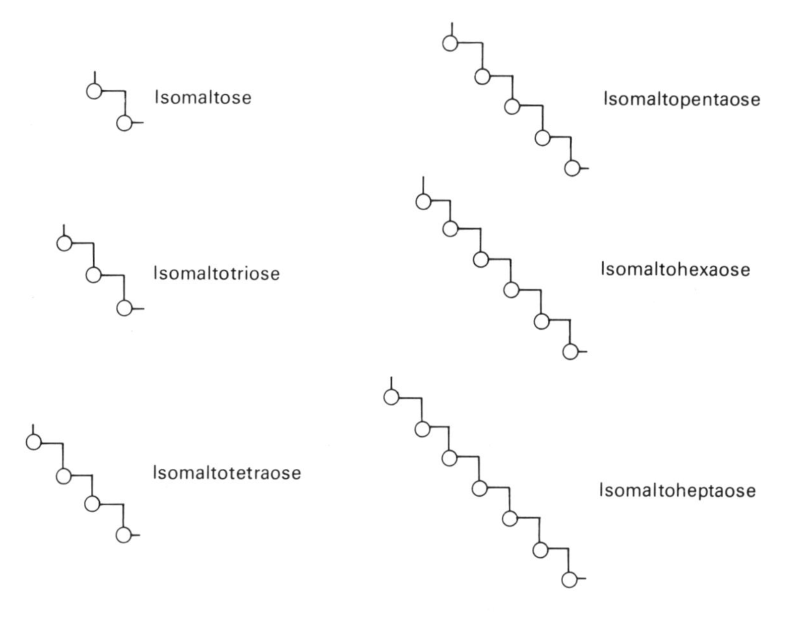

substance made up of a polypeptide chain with some sugar side chains attached to serine and threonine.

SYNTHETIC POLYPEPTIDES

Synthetic polypeptides provide a series of antigens of any desired specifications, within certain limits, for studies of antigenicity and on the complementarity relationships of antigen-antibody interaction. Synthetic methods now permit the preparation of the various types of poly-α-amino acids:

1. Homopolymers or polymers of a single amino acid
2. Block copolymers in which short peptides of known sequence are linked together
3. Random copolymers in which several amino acids are polymerized together but the sequence is determined strictly by chance
4. Multichain copolymers in which a polypeptide backbone has multiple receptor sites onto which polypeptide side chains of any of the three other types of polymers can be grown.

The reagents for the preparation of the synthetic polypeptides are the N-carboxy-α-amino acid anhydrides, many of which are available commercially and whose polymerization takes place as follows:

$$n\left[\begin{array}{l}\quad\ \ \mathrm{R}\\ \quad\ \ |\\ \mathrm{HN{-}CH{-}CO}\\ \ |\qquad\quad\ |\\ \mathrm{OC{-\!-\!-}O}\end{array}\right] \longrightarrow -\left(\begin{array}{c}\mathrm{R}\\ |\\ \mathrm{HN{-}CH{-}CO}\end{array}\right)_n - \ + \ nCO_2$$

The preceding reaction may also be used to couple side chains of amino acids onto the ϵ-amino group of the lysines in proteins to give polypeptidyl proteins. The reaction proceeds in water, or if a suitable initiator such as a strong base or an amine is present, it takes place in inert solvents as well.

The tremendous value of the synthetic polypeptides for immunological studies results from the investigators' ability to control composition and molecular weight within close limits; to prepare polypeptides with D- or L-amino acids or D,L mixtures; and to determine in the multichain copolymers which amino acids will be close to the main chain and which will be most exterior to it. It has thus become possible to evaluate the role of these factors on antigenicity and on immunogenicity; this latter term is employed to denote the capacity to induce the formation of antibodies regardless of their specificity. Thus, for example, the addition of small amounts of tyrosine to gelatin increases its immunogenicity even though the tyrosine does not act as an antigenic determinant. The major limitations of synthetic polypeptides as antigens result from inability to control the sequence of addition of any amino acid in the random copolymers so that a very heterogeneous population of molecules is formed—a population having about the same average composition with respect to the amino acids present, but with sequences that may differ sharply from one molecule to another and from one part of each molecule to another. Thus an animal immunized with such a polymer is exposed to a very large number of different antigenic determinants. In addition, in preparing multichain copolymers it is impossible to control the length of the side chains so that, for example, when alanine side chains are grown on to a polylysine backbone, each side chain may have a different number of alanines attached to it. If additional amino acids are now added on to the alanines, these too will add on, at random, to give chains of various lengths. This also creates extensive heterogeneity.

Recently, a procedure called solid-phase peptide synthesis, in which the reactions are carried out on an insoluble support, has permitted the rapid synthesis of oligopeptides of almost any desired sequence.

One very important concept developed by the use of synthetic polypeptides is that the antigenically important regions must be accessible to the antibody forming mechanism. This is best illustrated as follows: Two multichain copolymers of similar composition were prepared, each containing lysine, alanine, and a peptide of glutamic acid and tyrosine. Both had a polylysine backbone. In one, polyalanine side chains were grown on the lysine backbone and the glutamic acid-tyrosine peptide chains were then substituted on the alanines; in the other, the order of addition was reversed so that the glutamic-tyrosine peptide was in the interior of the molecule. (A schematic representation is given in Fig. 2.4). Only the polymer with the glutamic acid-tyrosines on the outside was found to be antigenic in rabbits. If the polypeptide backbone was made up of a copolymer of lysine and alanine, however, so that more space existed between the ε-amino groups of lysine onto which the side chains were attached, then a polymer with glutamic acid-tyrosine attached directly to the lysines with alanine side chains at the outside was found to be a good antigen. Therefore, accessibility does not absolutely require a position at the ends of chains.

Extensive studies have been carried out on the immunogenicity of polypeptides composed entirely of D-amino acids. For example, it

Fig. 2.4 Schematic representation of a multichain copolymer in which L-tyrosine and L-glutamic acid residues are attached to multipoly-DL-alanyl--poly-L-lysine (left) and of a multichain copolymer in which tyrosine and glutamic acid are directly attached to the lysine backbone (right) and then elongated with alanine peptides. (Reprinted with permission of the copyright owner, The Regents of the University of Wisconsin, from Mark Stahmann, ed. Polyamino Acids, Polypeptides, and Proteins, 1962.)

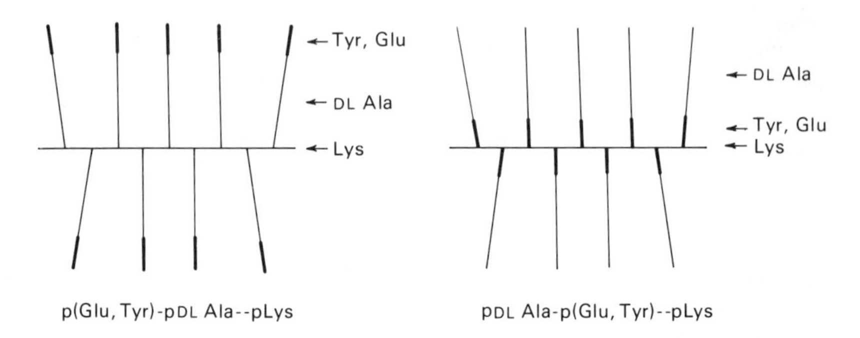

is possible to prepare two polypeptides with the same amino acid composition, one with L-amino acids and one with only D-amino acids. In most instances, no antibody to the D-polypeptides was formed. However a polypeptide* consisting of D-Glu^{55}-D-Lys^{39}-D-Tyr^{6} was found to be a fairly good antigen, and more recently good antibodies have been obtained to poly-D-lysine by injecting it as a complex with phosphorylated serum albumin (see below). Although in immunology a positive result, for instance, finding that antibody is formed specific for a given substance, establishes that the substance is antigenic or immunogenic, the inference of nonantigenicity from negative data is far more difficult to validate conclusively.

NUCLEIC ACIDS

For many years, efforts to obtain antibodies to nucleic acids were unsuccessful. However, antibodies to nucleic acids were found in rabbits that had been injected with lysates of T4 bacteriophage. Also, it was established that humans suffering from a fairly rare and generally fatal disease of connective tissue called LUPUS ERYTHEMATOSUS had antibodies in their sera which reacted with single-stranded DNA prepared by thermal denaturation. Reactions occur with DNA from many

*Superscripts represent percent composition of the amino acids.

sources including bacterial DNA; some sera also react well with double-stranded DNA. It became possible to prepare antibodies to DNA readily when it was shown that if DNA, denatured by boiling and cooled rapidly so that the strands of the double helix remained separated, was mixed with methylated bovine serum albumin (BSA), a complex was formed which upon injection with adjuvants (see Chapter 3) resulted in good antibody formation to the nucleic acid. The carboxyl groups in the methylated BSA are esterified and the remaining positively charged NH_3^+ groups complex with the negatively charged phosphates on the denatured DNA. A similar complex between methylated BSA and the polysaccharide of the Type III pneumococcus, which contains many negatively charged carboxyl groups, made it possible to obtain antibodies in rabbits to this polysaccharide. The reverse procedure of phosphorylating BSA to introduce a series of negatively charged groups which formed a complex with the positively charged poly-D-lysine, was used to obtain antibodies to this polypeptide.

Antibodies with a specificity for ribonucleic acids have been obtained by intravenous injection of ribosome suspensions.

CHEMICALLY MODIFIED ANTIGENS

A substantial part of our earlier knowledge of the relationships of the structure of antigenic determinants came from the finding that it was possible to attach groupings of known structure onto protein antigens by covalent bonds and thereby obtain antibodies with complementarity directed toward the grouping introduced. Landsteiner, who did the pioneering work in this field, coupled his low molecular weight substances to protein by using a diazonium salt; this procedure is still in general use. During the last few decades a variety of other techniques have been developed, and it is now possible to attach almost any type of molecule to a protein or synthetic polypeptide and obtain antisera in which the antibody has some specificity for the group introduced. The types of determinants introduced include aromatic rings, sugars, steroids, peptides, purines, pyrimidines, drugs such as penicillin, fluorescent compounds such as fluorescein and rhodamine, and electron-dense materials such as the iron-containing protein ferritin. The low molecular weight compounds introduced which are not antigenic by themselves are often called HAPTENS, and the grouping in the protein may be called the HAPTENIC GROUP; it functions as an important part of the antigenic determinant (IMMUNODOMINANT GROUP).

The main reactions used to introduce these groups into protein are as follows:

1. **Iodination** Iodine dissolved in KI is used. A soluble complex I_3^- forms in equilibrium with free iodine according to the equation

$$I_3^- \rightleftharpoons I_2 + I^-$$

Only the I_2 reacts to iodinate the tyrosine residues and it reacts as H_2OI^+, which exists in aqueous KI solution:

$$I_2 + H_2O \rightleftharpoons H_2OI^+ + I^-$$

The reaction with the tyrosine of the protein is

$$H_2OI^+ + \text{(}p\text{-}O^-\text{-}C_6H_4\text{-}CH_2\text{—protein)} \rightleftharpoons \text{(}O^-\text{-}C_6H_3I\text{-}CH_2\text{—protein)} + H^+ + H_2O$$

A second H_2OI^+ may also react to give:

$$O^-\text{-}C_6H_2I_2\text{-}CH_2\text{—protein}$$

This reaction at pH 9.3 is widely used to introduce small quantities of radioactive iodine I^{131} or I^{125} into proteins for tracer studies, but it may also be used to introduce large amounts and to prepare iodoproteins.

2. **Diazotization and coupling** Any compound with an aromatic amino group such as arsanilic acid may be used.

$$AsO_3H_2\text{-}C_6H_4\text{-}NH_2 \xrightarrow[HCl]{NaNO_2} AsO_3H_2\text{-}C_6H_4\text{-}\overset{+}{N}{\equiv}N + HO\text{-}C_6H_4\text{-}CH_2\text{—protein} \longrightarrow$$

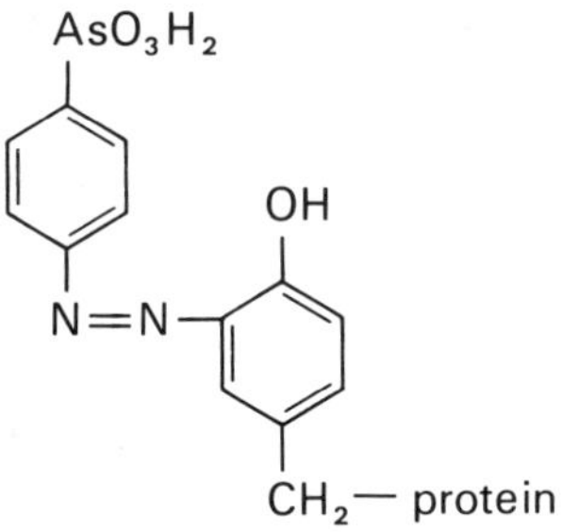

AsO_3H_2

OH

N=N

CH_2— protein

Coupling takes place on the tyrosine of the protein. A second mole of diazonium compound may couple to the other ortho position if suitable amounts of reagent are used.

3. **Reaction with isocyanates** (**R−N=C=O**) **and isothiocyanates** (**R−N=C=S**) Reaction is with the free amino groups of the protein.

Fluorescein −N=C=S + H_2N-CH_2 . . . protein

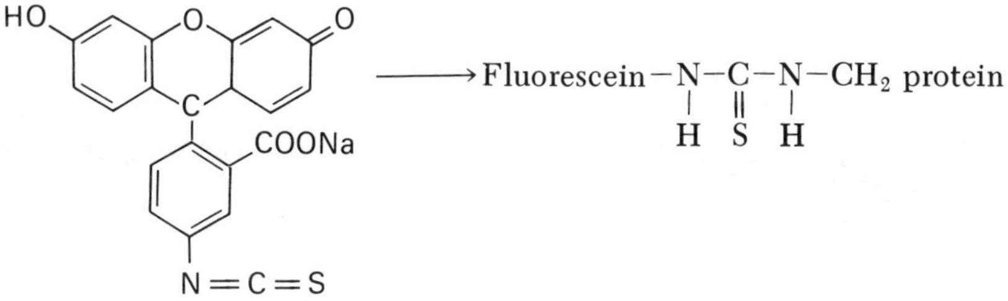

HO O O

C COONa

N=C=S

$\longrightarrow$ Fluorescein−N(H)−C(=S)−N(H)−CH_2 protein

4. **Dinitrophenyl derivatives** These are readily produced by reaction with dinitrofluorobenzene. Reaction is with the free amino groups of proteins. The same reaction is used in determining the *N*-terminal amino acid in proteins.

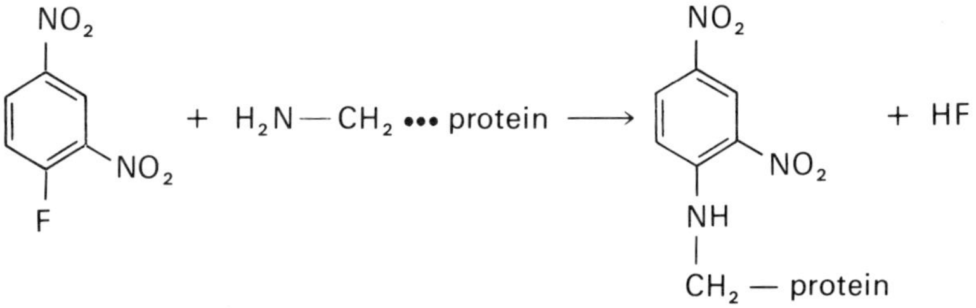

NO_2 NO_2 F + H_2N-CH_2 ••• protein $\longrightarrow$ NO_2 NO_2 NH CH_2 — protein + HF

5. **Mixed anhydride reaction** This is used in coupling compounds with a carboxyl group to the amino groups of proteins. It has been used with steroids and with sugar acids.

$$R{-}COOH + O{=}C(Cl){-}O{-}CH_2{-}CH(CH_3)_2 \xrightarrow{\text{tributylamine}} R{-}C({=}O){-}O{-}C({=}O){-}O{-}CH_2{-}CH(CH_3)_2 + HCl$$

$$+ \; H_2N{-}CH_2{-}\text{protein}$$

$$\downarrow OH^-$$

$$(CH_3)_2CH{-}CH_2OH + CO_2 + R{-}C(=O){-}N(H){-}CH_2{-}\text{protein}$$

6. **Reaction with carbodiimides** These reagents of the general type RN=C=NR are widely used to couple carboxyl to amino groups and form peptide bonds at room temperature. It has been very useful in the preparation of nucleoside antigens by coupling them to polypeptides and for coupling protein antigens to red cells. The primary hydroxyl of the nucleoside is first oxidized to a COOH group

$$\text{RCOOH} + \underset{\text{carbodiimide}}{R{-}N{=}C{=}N{-}R'} \longrightarrow \left[RC(=O){-}O{-}C(=N{-}R'){-}NH{-}R \right]$$

$$+ \; \text{protein}{-}NH_2$$

$$R{-}NH{-}C(=O){-}NH{-}R' \longleftarrow$$

$$+$$

$$\underset{\text{coupled product}}{R{-}C(=O){-}NH{-}\text{protein}}$$

7. **Reactions with penicillin** Penicillin is a very highly reactive molecule which may combine with the amino groups of proteins as well as with the sulfhydryl groups. The reactions are as follows:

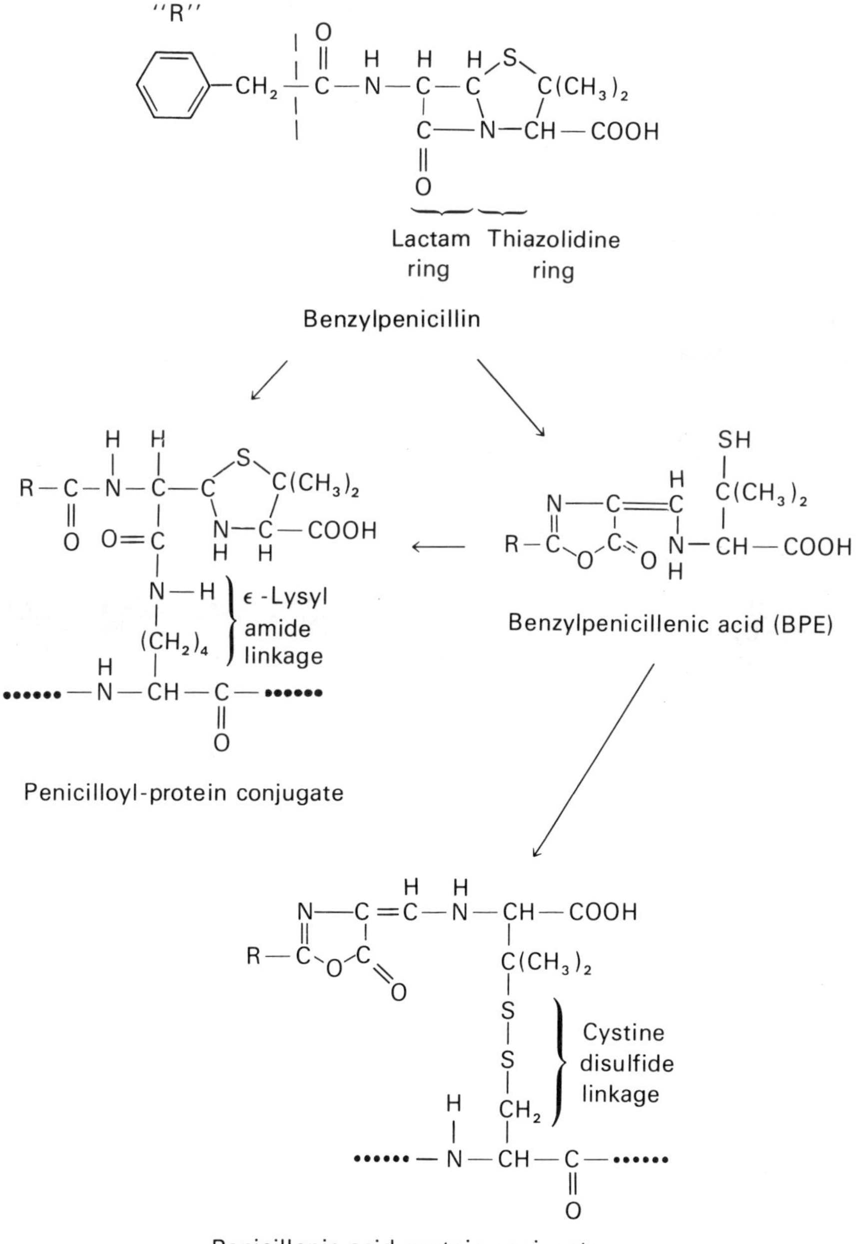

"R"

C_6H_5–CH_2–CO–NH–CH–CH(S–$C(CH_3)_2$)–N–CH–COOH (β-lactam C=O)

Lactam ring Thiazolidine ring

Benzylpenicillin

R–C(=O)–NH–CH(C(=O)–NH–$(CH_2)_4$–protein)–CH(S–$C(CH_3)_2$)–NH–CH–COOH

ε-Lysyl amide linkage

Penicilloyl-protein conjugate

R–C(oxazolone)=CH–NH–CH(COOH)–$C(CH_3)_2$–SH

Benzylpenicillenic acid (BPE)

R–C(oxazolone)=CH–NH–CH(COOH)–$C(CH_3)_2$–S–S–CH_2–CH(–NH–)(–C(=O)–)

Cystine disulfide linkage

Penicillenic acid-protein conjugate

It appears that penicillenic acid is not the only intermediate, but that only the lactam ring may open and react directly with the free amino groups. This preserves the stereospecificity of the molecule, which is lost if both rings open as in penicillenic acid. These reactions are responsible for penicillin allergy, the most important being the one with the ϵ-amino groups of lysine to give benzylpenicilloyl derivatives (Chapter 15).

8. **Coupling of ribonucleosides and nucleotides to proteins** The reaction involves oxidizing the ribose ring of the nucleoside or nucleotide with periodic acid to give a dialdehyde that couples to the free amino groups and is stabilized by reduction with sodium borohydride

$\xrightarrow{HIO_4}$ $\quad$ pH 9-9.5, H_2N—protein $\quad$ $\xleftarrow{NaBH_4}$

(P-purine or pyrimidine; R is H or $-\overset{O}{\overset{\|}{P}}(OH)_2$)

SIDE REACTIONS

One must always remember that while the reactions given in the preceding paragraphs are the major reactions that take place, almost all the reagents can react with other groups on the protein molecule. Iodination of tryptophane occurs, and sulfhydryls (SH) may be oxidized; the diazonium compounds may react with histidine and with free amino, sulfhydryl and guanido groups; isocyanates react with sulfhydryl groups; dinitrofluorobenzene reacts with tyrosine hydroxyls, with imidazole groups of histidine and with the SH of cysteine. In the mixed anhydride and carbodiimide reactions, the reagents may remain attached to the protein and in both instances may effect coupling of the carboxyl groups of one protein molecule to the amino groups of another to cause aggregation. Moreover, antibodies may be produced to determinants on the protein which have not reacted with the reagent.

LOW MOLECULAR WEIGHT SUBSTANCES

Recent studies have revealed that low molecular weight substances such as α-DNP-(lys)$_7$ or arsanilic acid azo-D or L-tyrosine with Freund adjuvant (Chapter 3) can induce antibody formation in animals. They do not contain reactive groups as do penicillin or dinitrofluorobenzene, and the way in which they induce an antibody response is not clear. Being monovalent, these substances do not precipitate directly with the antibody, but the antibody will precipitate with proteins onto which several haptenic groups have been introduced to give multivalence (see Chapter 13). The immunogenicity of such small molecules opens up an entirely new area for immunological investigation. Lipids have not been definitely shown to be antigenic. However, they are capable of functioning as haptens when mixed with proteins such as pig or human serum, and injected into rabbits. Antibodies to lecithin, cephalin, and cholesterol have been produced by this means. The foreign serum or serum protein is said to act as a carrier, but nothing is known about its mode of action.

CARDIOLIPIN, the specific hapten of the Wassermann antigen, is an important lipid. It is universally used in serological tests for syphilis, as patients with this disease produce antibody that reacts with cardiolipin under appropriate conditions. Cardiolipin is present in a large variety of plant and animal tissures and it is usually extracted from beef heart. It is built up of three glycerol molecules esterified with two phosphates and has four molecules of unsaturated fatty acids esterified on the hydroxyls and represented by R as follows:

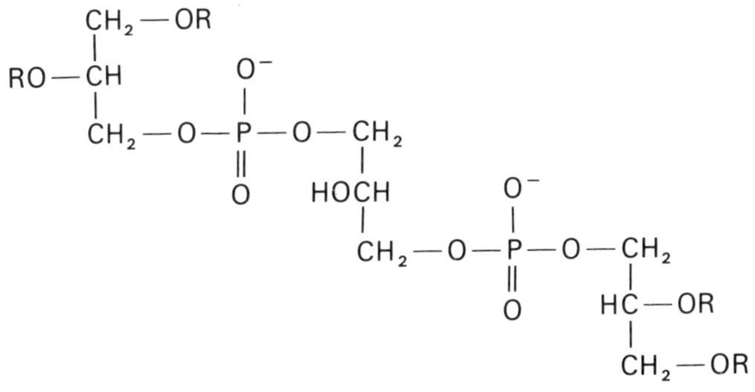

```
       CH2—OR
       |
   RO—CH          O⁻
       |          |
       CH2—O—P—O—CH2
                 ||     |
                 O    HOCH          O⁻
                        |           |
                        CH2—O—P—O—CH2
                                ||    |
                                O   HC—OR
                                      |
                                      CH2—OR
```

Another group of lipid haptens are the cytolipins. These are made up of sphingosine $CH_3{-}(CH_2)_{12}{-}CH{=}CH{-}CHOH{-}CHNH_2{-}CH_2$-

OH; fatty acid linked to the NH_2 group and mono- or disaccharide may be substituted on the terminal OH of the sphingosine. One of these, cytolipin H, has a lactose group; and this disaccharide determines the specificity of the cytolipin. Antibodies to cardiolipin do not react with it unless it is prepared as an emulsion with lecithin and cholesterol. Under these conditions, flocculation (agglutination) and complement fixation (see Chapter 3) may be obtained. With cytolipin H, only lecithin is needed for optimal reactivity.

SUGGESTED READINGS

Landsteiner, K. The specificity of serological reactions. (2d ed.; 1945) Harvard University, Press, Cambridge, Mass. [Reprinted in paperback, Dover Publications, New York, (1962)]; *the basic early studies on immunological specificity and the introduction of small haptenic groups into proteins to modify antigenicity.*

Kabat, E. A. Kabat and Mayer's Experimental immunochemistry (2nd ed.; 1961) Charles C. Thomas, Publisher, Springfield, Ill.; *for methods of introducing haptenic groups onto protein and for further details and references about antigens.*

Sela, M. Immunological studies with synthetic polypeptides. Advances in Immunology **5**: 1 (1966). (F. J. Dixon, Jr., and J. H. Humphrey, eds.). [Academic Press, New York]; a *comprehensive survey of the use of synthetic polypeptides in immunochemistry.*

Levine, B. B. Immunochemical mechanisms involved in pencillin hypersensitivity in experimental animals and in human beings. Federation Proceedings **24**; 45 (1965); *the reactions of pencillin with protein.*

Goodfriend, T. L., L. Levine, and G. D. Fasman. Antibodies to bradykinin and angiotensin: A use of carbodiimide in immunology. Science, **144**: 1344 (1964).

Erlanger, B. F. and S. M. Beiser. Antibodies specific for ribonucleosides and ribonucleotides and their reaction with DNA. Proceedings of the National Academy of Sciences **52**: 68 (1964); *a general method for attaching ribonucleotides to protein by oxidizing with periodic acid.*

Merrifield, R. B. Solid-phase peptide synthesis. Endeavor **24**: 4 (1965); *a review of this very powerful technique of rapid synthesis of peptides of any desired sequence.*

Kabat, E. A. Blood group substances—their chemistry and immunochemistry. (1956) Academic Press, New York.

Watkins, W. M. Blood group substances. Science **152**: 171 (1966).

Race, R. R. and R. Sanger. Blood groups in man, (4th ed.; 1962) Blackwell, Oxford.

Three references for additional reading on blood groups and blood group substances.

Rapport, M. M. Lipid haptens of animal cells. Journal of Lipid Research **2**: 25 (1961); *a survey of this important class of substances.*

3

The Reagents of Immunology—Detection of Antigen-Antibody Interaction

PREPARATION OF ANTISERA

Having surveyed the various kinds of antigens, we must now turn to the methods of obtaining antibodies. In studying a new substance for antigenicity the investigator can never be absolutely certain he will get antibody, but over the years a number of empirical methods have been developed which make it probable that antibodies will be formed even to relatively poor antigens. Much immunological research is carried out with antigens which are readily available and with which extensive experience has been gained so that one can prepare potent antisera quite easily. A large number of purified proteins and specific antisera to many antigens are commercially available, and antisera prepared to human serum proteins as well as to bacteria are widely used for diagnostic purposes.

In principle one injects a number of animals with the antigen. Protein antigens in solution may be injected intravenously, intraperitoneally, or subcutaneously; but it is generally considered advantageous to precipitate the protein with alum and inject it in a particulate form. This has been shown in many laboratories to give better antibody formation than the same quantity of antigen injected as a

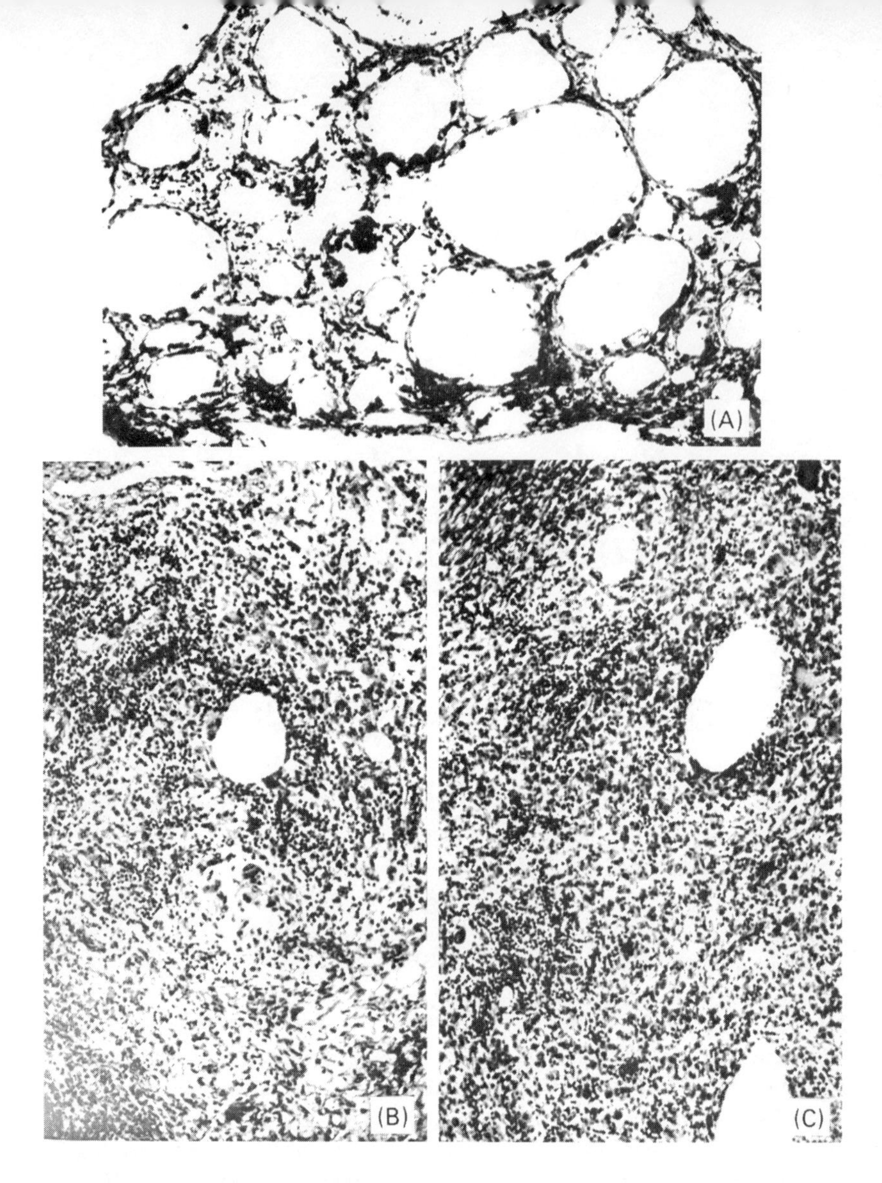

Fig. 3.1 (A) Histological section of the site of inoculation of brain antigen with Freund incomplete adjuvants (no tubercle bacilli or mycobacteria). Large pockets of oily emulsion with very little cellular reaction are seen. (B) and (C) Granulomas produced by addition of the emulsion of killed tubercle bacilli (Freund complete adjuvants). Massive infiltration and proliferation of cells, with multinucleoted giant cells, epithelioid cells. A few droplets of emulsion are seen. (From Kabat, E. A., A. Wolf, and A. E. Bezer. J. Exp. Med. **88**: 417 [1948]; by permission of The Rockefeller University Press. The photograph here reproduced from printed copy inevitably shows a loss of detail, and therefore the quality of the results is not representative of the original.)

solution; excretion is minimized when the material is particulate. Such suspended antigens are taken up by phagocytic cells, and this is believed to be a necessary step in antibody formation. In the immunization of children against diphtheria and tetanus, alum-precipitated antigens are used; these antigens are the purified toxins that have been detoxified by treatment with aqueous formaldehyde; toxins that retain their antigenic properties but have lost their toxicity are called TOXOIDS.

A good schedule for injection of rabbits is to give three or four intravenous injections per week (each injection consisting of 1 or 2 ml) for four weeks, using 0.5 mg of protein initially and going up to between 2 and 5 mg, the total being 20 to 30 mg per rabbit. About 40 ml of blood is obtained from the ear artery or vein, or by cardiac puncture of the rabbits on the fifth, sixth, and seventh days after the last injection. The blood is allowed to clot and is centrifuged to obtain the supernatant serum. To obtain a large volume of antiserum the samples from the three successive daily bleedings are pooled. Since serum is a good culture medium for bacteria, it is desirable either to keep it frozen at −20°C or to add a preservative if it is kept at refrigerator temperatures—0.25 percent phenol plus 1 :10,000 merthiolate or 0.1 percent sodium azide are widely used. Since phenol in high concentration denatures protein, a 5 percent solution of phenol in saline is added drop by drop while the serum is constantly mixed to avoid local excess of phenol. For studies on complement and for various types of tissue culture, and so forth, preservatives are not desirable. After a week or two of rest, a second course of intravenous injections may be given and a second series of bleedings carried out in the same time sequence. Repeated immunization and bleeding in this manner may frequently be continued for from six months to a year, and the antisera obtained generally increase in potency.

Perhaps the most widely used method for immunizing animals involves the preparation of the antigen as an emulsion in mineral oil with the use of an emulsifying agent such as lanolin or several commercially available products (Aquaphor, Falba, Arlacel); killed tubercle bacilli or other mycobacteria are frequently added to the mineral oil. These accessory substances are referred to as the FREUND ADJUVANT. They may be purchased in a form suitable for direct addition of the antigen. If tubercle bacilli or other mycobacteria are present, the Freund adjuvant mixture is designated as complete and if they have been omitted, as incomplete. The Freund adjuvant induces a very powerful antibody reponse after but a few injections. This is thought to be a consequence of several effects:

1. The emulsified antigen constitutes a depot that persists longer.

2. The tubercle bacilli cause the migration of many cells to the site of the injected emulsion, so that intimate contact of antibody forming cells with antigen is assured. Indeed, the number of cells brought to the site is so great that the entire area is made up of dense masses of cells called a GRANULOMA (Fig. 3.1).

3. Small droplets of the adjuvant-antigen mixture drain to the regional lymph node, which in turn is stimulated to form antibody.
4. Droplets of adjuvant-antigen mixture enter the circulation and are deposited in antibody forming organs such as the spleen and bone marrow.

Animals are generally injected into each of the four footpads or into four toepads with about 0.10 ml of antigen at a concentration of 1 to 5 mg per ml in Freund adjuvant at weekly intervals over a period of three weeks. Bleedings are carried out as already described. The animals are rested for one week and then given an intraperitoneal injection of about 2 to 5 mg of alum-precipitated antigen; the bleeding schedule is repeated. Additional injections and bleedings may be carried out as desired.

In any type of investigative work with an antigen whose properties have never been studied, it is of fundamental importance to obtain a generous sample of serum from each animal before starting injections of antigen. This permits the investigator to exclude the presence of preformed antibody to the antigen and also to exclude the presence of nonspecific interactions of serum constituents with the antigen. Many initially exciting observations have turned out to be of little significance when controls of this type were employed. The use of the Freund adjuvant provides so great an antigenic stimulus that antibodies are often formed to small amounts of antigenic impurities that may be present in the antigen. Each animal may respond differently to a given antigen, producing different proportions of antibody to the various antigenic determinants as well as varying quantities of antibody to impurities. Therefore antisera should not be haphazardly pooled.

REACTION OF ANTIGEN WITH ANTIBODY

The two readily visible reactions resulting from the combination of antigen with antibody are the precipitin reaction if the antigen is in a soluble form, or agglutination if the antigen is particulate. Visible precipitation or clumping of the particles occurs with most antigens because the antigen is multivalent (has several antigenic determinants per molecule) and the antibodies are at least bivalent so that large aggregates or lattices of antigen and antibody are formed. In instances in which the antigen is only bivalent or monovalent—for example, has but one or two determinant groups per molecule—precipitation may not occur and soluble complexes of antigen and antibody may be formed. Such complexes may also occur with antibodies of relatively weak binding affinity or with monovalent fragments of antibody. Under these circumstances the interaction of antigen and antibody must be detected by other methods, which will be subsequently discussed.

Precipitin reactions and agglutination are reversible and can be carried out under essentially equilibrium conditions. They may be considered as two component systems

$$\text{Ag} + \text{Ab} \rightleftharpoons \underset{\text{large aggregates}}{(\text{AgAb})\downarrow} + \underset{\text{excess}}{\text{Ag}} \rightleftharpoons \underset{\text{soluble}}{\text{Ag}_2\,\text{Ab}}$$

In the presence of a large excess of antigen, soluble complexes are formed which decrease in size with increasing antigen concentration and have the limiting composition Ag_2Ab. For many studies one takes advantage of this reversibility by adding a low molecular weight hapten or the specific antigenic determinant that in suitable concentration can displace the antigen from the complex to cause dissolution of the precipitate:

$$\underset{\text{large aggregates}}{(\text{AgAb})} + \underset{\text{large excess}}{\text{H}} \rightleftharpoons \underset{\text{soluble}}{\text{H}_2\text{Ab}} + \text{Ag}$$

In this instance too, a large number of intermediate complexes may be formed such as H-Ab-Ag.

One may also readily demonstrate the binding of a hapten or an antigenic determinant to an antibody site:

$$\text{H} + \text{A} \rightleftharpoons \text{HA}$$

If the concentration of free and bound hapten can be determined, the association constant of the hapten-antibody bond can be calculated (see chapter 5).

The precipitin reaction is basic to all immunological and immunochemical understanding. It permits the detection and quantitative estimation of antigens or antibodies in solution, in tissues, and even in individual cells or regions of cells. It may be carried out in liquid media; in gels of agar by allowing one or both constituents to diffuse into or toward the other; or on tissue sections by using antibody or antigen labeled with a fluorescent, electron-dense, radioactive, or enzymatic label that can be visualized.

Agglutination tests are more sensitive for detecting small amounts of antibody, since the interaction of a relatively few molecules of antibody effectively joins together large numbers of bacteria or erythrocytes into grossly or microscopically visible clumps while the sensitivity of the precipitin test is limited by the amount of antigen-antibody aggregate which can be seen. Accordingly, substantial increases in sensitivity may be achieved by coating erythrocytes, bacteria, or polystyrene spheres with an antigen and then using these coated cells in agglutination tests to detect antibody to the antigen coat; such tests are called PASSIVE agglutination tests to distinguish them from tests in which the antigen occurs naturally on the erythrocyte or the bacteria. Tannic acid-treated erythrocytes have been found to adsorb protein antigens and are widely used. For many purposes, it is preferable to attach the antigen to the erythrocytes by a covalent bond; *bis*-diazotized benzidine is often used, one diazo group being coupled to the protein and the other to the erythrocyte. Under these conditions desorption of antigen cannot occur. Some polysaccharide antigens, especially the lipopolysaccharides of Gram-negative bacteria, are taken up by untreated erythrocytes.

The standard design for qualitative agglutination and precipitin tests in detecting antibody and in making rough comparisons of the antibody content of different sera involves preparing a series of two-fold dilutions of the antiserum to which is added a suspension of particulate antigen for agglutination tests or of soluble antigen for precipitin tests. Since reagents are valuable, very small volumes ranging from 25 to 100 μl or less are used and precipitin tests are frequently carried out in capillary tubes in which antiserum is layered under antigen by capillarity, and the presence or absence of precipitate at the interface is noted. A very convenient device for making doubling dilutions for agglutination tests is the Takatsy microtitrator (Fig. 3.2). It consists of a coiled wire or of metal prongs calibrated to take up 25 μl of liquid. It is used with a plexiglass rectangular block that contains eight rows of 12 small wells, each 5 mm in diameter. By means of a calibrated dropper, 25 μl of physiological saline is added into each well in a given row. The microtitrator is then filled by dipping it into the undiluted antiserum. It is then inserted into one of the wells and mixed by rotation with the 25 μl of saline; this produces a dilution of 1 : 2; the titrator now contains 25 μl of 1 : 2 diluted serum as does the first well. It is now transferred into the next well and mixed with the saline; the result is a 1 : 4 dilution of the original serum. By repeating the process, 8-, 16-, 32-, 64-, 128-, 256-, and 512-fold dilutions of antiserum are obtained in the successive wells. The second row can be used for making a similar series of dilutions of another antiserum. A drop of suspension of erythrocytes is then added to each tube, the contents of the wells being mixed by gentle rotation or tapping of the plexiglass block. After 1 hour at room temperature or at other desired conditions, the degree of agglutination is noted either by observing the patterns of the settled cells or by examining the result with a hand lens after gently resuspending the settled cells. The degree of agglutination is generally graded visually from negative to ++++ (Fig. 3.3). The highest dilution showing detectable agglutination is taken as the end point and is called the TITER. An antiserum

Fig. 3.2 Apparatus for serial dilution titrations including plastic tray with eight rows of 12 wells, a dropping pipette, and the Takatsy microtitrator. The insert shows a magnified view of the circled portion of the titrator. (Courtesy of the Cooke Engineering Company, Alexandria, Va.)

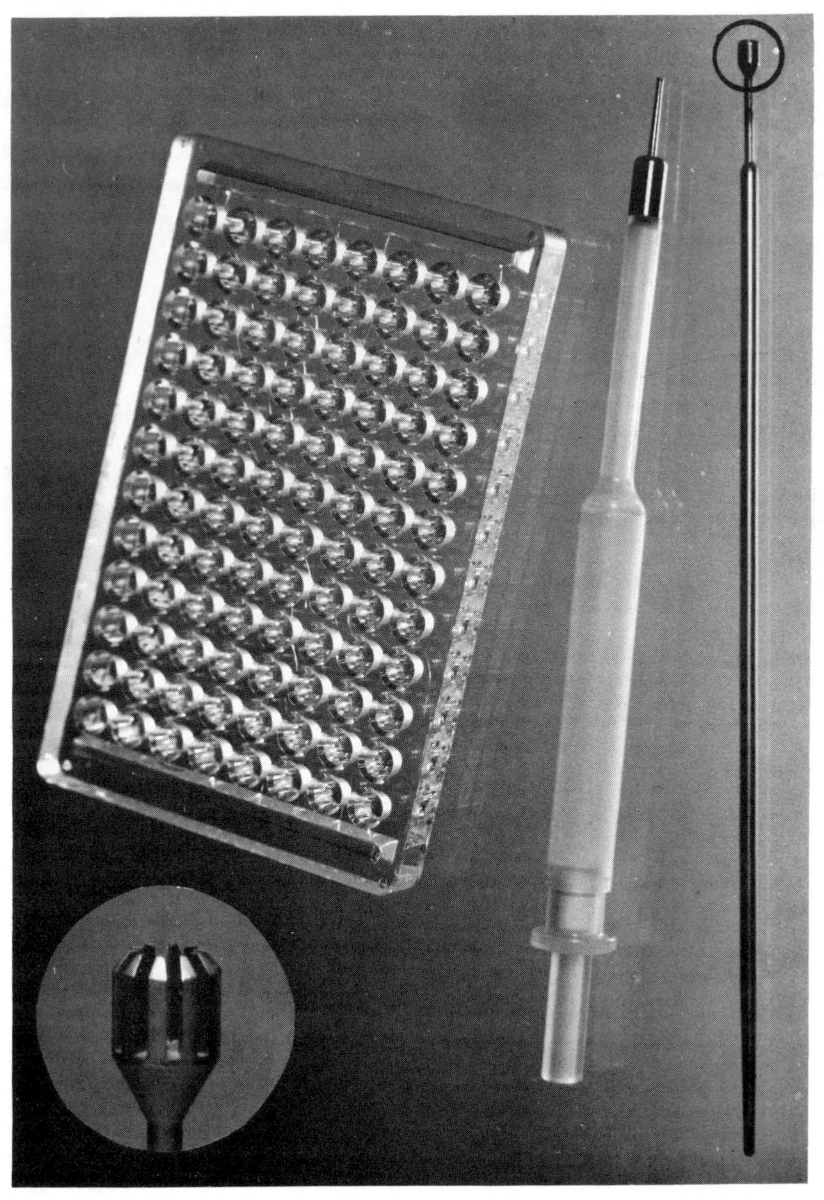

Fig. 3.3 Settling patterns of hemagglutinated erythrocytes at magnification 1 : 2. Patterns 1 and 2 are negative reactions; the inner light disc in Pattern 2 is a consequence of slight convexity in the bottom of the tube. Pattern 3 is a faintly positive reaction; Pattern 4 is a weak reaction. Patterns 5 and 6 are typical positive reactions. (From Landsteiner K., and A. S. Wiener. J. Exp. Med. **74**: 309 [1941]; the photograph here reproduced from printed halftone copy inevitably shows a loss of detail, and the quality of the results is not representative of the original. By permission of The Rockefeller University Press.)

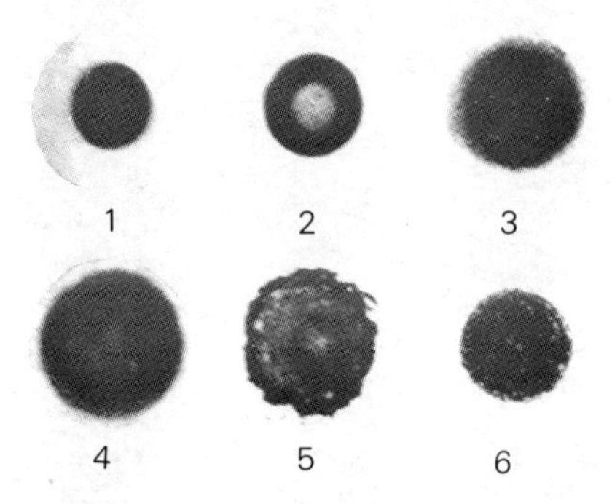

Fig. 3.4 Hemagglutination titration of anti-A and anti-B with A, B, and O erythrocytes. Strong agglutination of A cells by anti-A can be seen in the first four wells from the left and weak agglutination, in the fifth. With anti-B and B red cells the first three wells at the left are strongly agglutinated, the next three weakly, the seventh and eighth doubtful. All others are negative. (Courtesy of Mlle Janine Courcon, Institut Pasteur, Paris.)

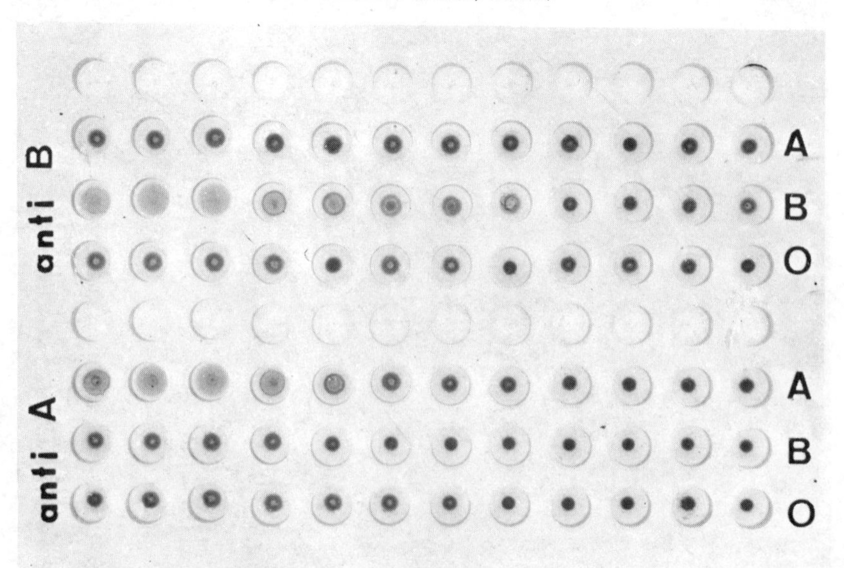

showing detectable agglutination to a titer of 16 (that is, a 16-fold dilution of the original serum) is considered to be about one fourth as potent as one with a titer of 64. These values are of course merely approximate, since the reading of the end point is subjective and the titers may change somewhat if tests are carried out on different days. The error may be ± a factor of 2. When direct comparisons are made, the ratio of the two titers tends to be more uniform; accordingly, the best comparisons of titers are always made by including a given antiserum as a reference standard. Fig. 3.4 shows a hemagglutination titration of a human anti-A and a human anti-B serum with red cells of groups A, B, and O. The specificity of the anti-A for A red cells and of anti-B for B red cells is evident.

PRECIPITIN REACTIONS IN GELS

There are several basic types of precipitin reaction in gels.

1. **Simple diffusion** (only antigen or antibody diffuses) The antiserum is uniformly dispersed in the agar and placed in a tube; it is allowed to harden, and the antigen is layered on top. Alternately the antiserum agar mixture is poured as a layer on a microscope slide, and allowed to harden; then, small holes are punched in the agar into which the antigen solution is placed. These basic designs are illustrated in Fig. 3.5 and represent diffusion in one and two dimensions respectively. In the tube method the rate at which the band appears to travel is proportional to the $\sqrt{\text{time}}$. If a series of tubes with identical concentrations of antibody is set up with a series of known antigen concentrations, the distance of the band from the starting point at a given time is proportional to log antigen concentration. This is also true in the slide method, which is much more rapid and convenient since a series of solutions of known antigen concentration may be placed in several of the wells and unknown solutions placed in the remaining wells. After a suitable interval the diameters of the rings of precipitation are measured and plotted against log antigen concentration. The unknown concentrations are estimated by interpolation from the best straight line obtained for the known solutions (Fig. 3.6). This method has come into widespread use for measuring concentrations of various proteins in biological fluids. In simple diffusion the band is formed by the reaction with antibody of the first molecules of antigen to diffuse to any given point. As diffusion continues the antigen concentration rises and the precipitate is dissolved in the excess of antigen. Meanwhile the front of diffusing antigen has arrived at a point further down the tube. The band thus *appears* to move.

2. **Double diffusion** In this type of design both antigen and antibody are allowed to diffuse toward each other in agar. Both simple and double diffusion methods are extremely powerful, since each antigen-antibody system may form a distinct band so that multiple bands are obtained if several antigens and their corresponding antibodies are present. In some instances bands may be concealed in other bands and the number of bands observed provides only a minimum estimate of the number of antigens present. In addition, double dif-

Fig. 3.5 Schematic representation of gel diffusion methods. (In simple and double diffusion in one dimension, the antigen concentration increases from left to right.)

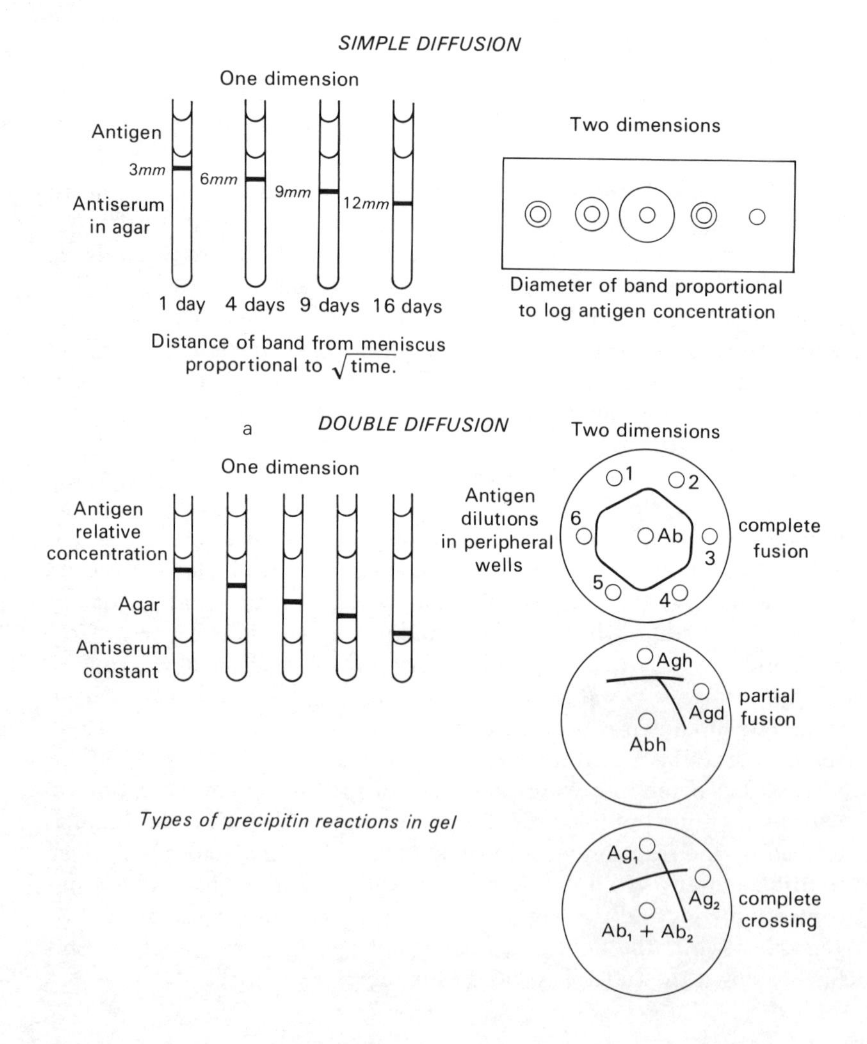

fusion permits the use of undiluted serum, and a large excess of antigen is not required. Double diffusion, also, may be carried out in one or in two dimensions (Fig. 3.5). In one dimension, the antiserum is placed at the bottom of a series of small capillary tubes; the antiserum may be in liquid form if undiluted antiserum is used, or it may be mixed with agar. A central layer of pure agar is layered over the antiserum and when this has hardened, antigen solution is placed over the agar layer; diffusion of antigen and antibody takes place with the formation of a precipitate in the central agar layer. The height of the agar layer is measured as is the distance of the band and the position (p) is expressed as percentage distance of the band from the antigen meniscus. Band position will vary with antigen or antibody concentration; a doubling of the concentration of either component will change the p by about 10 percent (Fig. 3.7).

When double diffusion is carried out in two dimensions an agar layer is generally poured in a Petri dish or glass plate, a series of wells is cut, and the agar is removed by suction. There are innumerable designs for the wells, but one very frequently used is a central well with six peripheral wells in a hexagonal arrangement (Fig. 3.5). Others will be seen in connection with subsequent presentation of experimental findings. The central well may be filled with antibody, and the peripheral wells may contain a variety of antigens or a series of dilutions of a single antigen or mixture of antigens. Diffusion takes

Fig. 3.6 Appearance of ring diffusion in an γG antibody-agar plate (immunoplate) after twenty-four hours. Seven dilutions of a standard serum of known γG concentration were placed along the top of the plate. Test samples were placed in the remainder of the antigen wells. (From Fahey J. L., and E. M. McKelvey, J. Immunol. **94**: 84 [1965]; reproduced by permission of the copyright owner, The Williams & Wilkins Company, Baltimore, Md.)

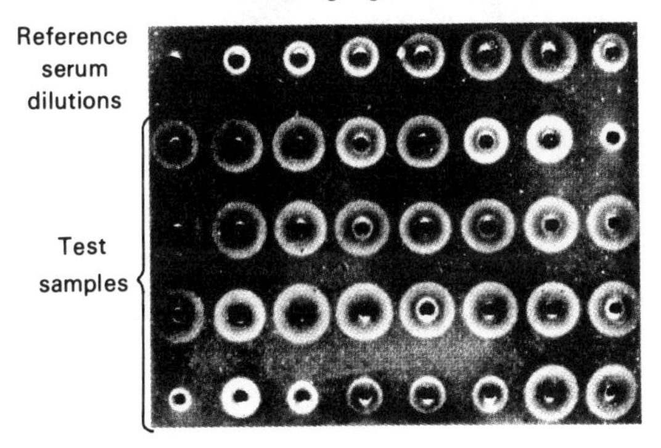

place concentrically from each well, and lines of precipitate are formed where antigen and antibody meet.

The tremendous advantage of this technique lies in the user's ability to identify antigens in mixtures, to recognize cross reactions, and to establish relationships between antigenic determinants and the original antigen. Much of this may also be accomplished by the other techniques, but not in so simple and direct a manner. For instance, if an antiserum containing antibodies to several antigens is placed in the central well and the mixture of antigens placed in a peripheral well, a series of bands will be formed. If one of these antigens is available in purified form and is placed in an adjacent peripheral well, it will form a single band that will fuse with the corresponding band observed with the mixture, thereby identifying it. When two antigen-antibody systems are totally unrelated their respective bands do not fuse, but cross one another as if the unrelated band was not present. If two purified antigens cross react, however, then placing them in adjacent peripheral wells with antibody to one in the central well will give a

Fig. 3.7 Double diffusion in one dimension. (Left) Two tubes: Reaction of paramecium brei with two rabbit antisera to paramecium brei; numerous bands are seen. (Right) Two tubes: Reaction of purified paramecium immobilization antigen with two rabbit antisera to paramecium brei; only a single band is present. Tubes have an inside diameter of about 1.8 to 2 mm. (Courtesy of Dr. Irving Finger, Haverford College, Pa.)

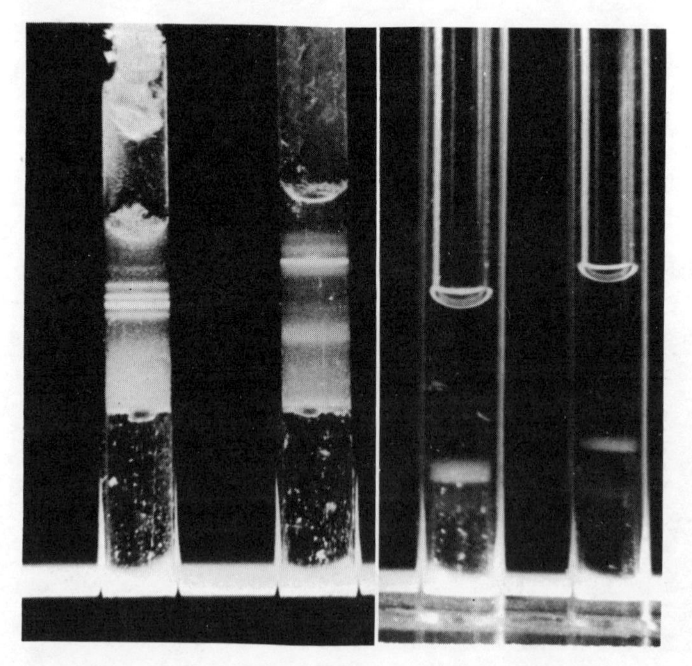

Fig. 3.8 Double diffusion in two dimensions. Center well: rabbit antiserum to human γG immunoglobulin. Peripheral wells (A) human γG immunoglobulin. (B) Multiple myeloma serum 29. (C) Myeloma globulin 28. (D) Myeloma globulin 1. (From Korngold, L., J. Immunol. **77**: 119 [1956]; reproduced by permission of the copyright owner, The Williams & Wilkins Company, Baltimore, Md.)

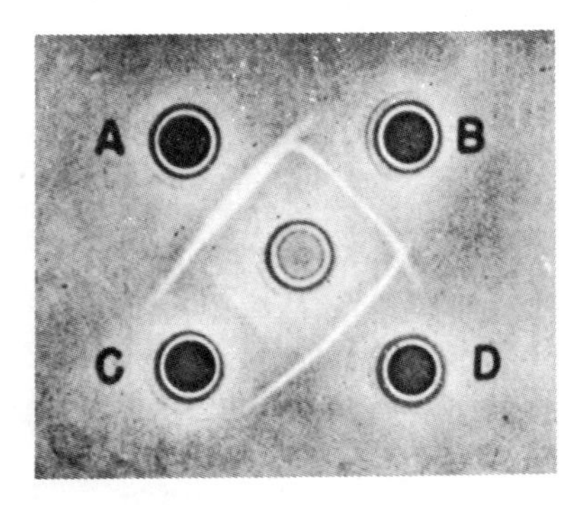

single band with the homologous and with the cross-reacting antigen. However, since the cross-reacting antigen lacks some of the antigenic determinants present in the homologous antigen and is therefore not able to precipitate all of the antibody, the remaining antibody will diffuse beyond the line of cross-reacting precipitate to react with the homologous antigen to produce a spur. Fig. 3.8 shows a gel diffusion pattern obtained after four days from reacting rabbit antiserum to normal human γG immunoglobulin (center) with whole human γG immunoglobulin (A), myeloma serum 29 (B), and two purified myeloma proteins 28 (C) and 1 (D). The band of the myeloma protein in (B) fuses with that of normal human γG immunoglobulin but lacks some of the determinants, since the latter forms a spur. The bands between wells (B) and (D) show some fusion, but two spurs are formed, showing that each myeloma protein has some determinants lacking in the other. The band in C is very weak.

Innumerable studies have been carried out by the gel diffusion techniques since they were introduced by Oudin and by Ouchterlony. They are applicable at all levels of immunochemical work – in the purification of antigens to establish when the investigator is dealing with a single antigen as well as in the study of fragments of a purified antigen to ascertain their relationship to the intact antigen. In testing whether a purified antigen is free from other contaminating proteins, one generally uses an antiserum containing antibody to as many of the antigens that could conceivably be present as it is possible to obtain. Thus, to establish that a preparation of crystalline human serum albumin is pure, one uses an antiserum prepared to whole human serum. Such an antiserum may contain antibodies to thirty or more distinct protein antigens. Failure to find more than a single band by the various gel diffusion methods, if properly carried out, would indicate the absence of these other antigens as contaminants in the serum albumin. Conversely, it is often necessary to determine whether an antiserum is monospecific—that is, contains antibody to only one antigen, for example anti-human serum albumin. In this instance, one sets up the antiserum by gel diffusion with a crude mixture of antigens such as whole human serum. If antibodies to more than one of the antigens in human serum are present, more than one band will be observed. A single band with the whole human serum which fused completely with the band formed by the purified albumin in an adjacent well would establish the absence of antibodies to other serum proteins in the antiserum used, within the sensitivity of the technique employed.

IMMUNOELECTROPHORESIS

In gel diffusion studies when one is dealing with complex mixtures of antigens, it often becomes very difficult to identify all the bands formed. Grabar and Williams introduced an extremely powerful tool that makes possible increased resolution of the bands and their identification by the additional parameter of their electrophoretic mobility. This procedure is termed IMMUNOELECTROPHORETIC ANALYSIS and has also come into almost universal use in immunology.

The principle of the method is very simple. The mixture of antigens, such as whole human serum, to be studied is placed in a small well in the center of a microscope slide on which has been placed a layer of agar about 2 to 3 mm in thickness prepared in a buffer solution of pH of about 8.5. Moistened strips of filter paper at each end connect with reservoirs of buffer containing electrodes, and a current is passed through the system. (Fig. 3.9). Under the influence of the current, the various proteins in the human serum travel at different

Fig. 3.9 Apparatus for immunoelectrophoretic analysis.

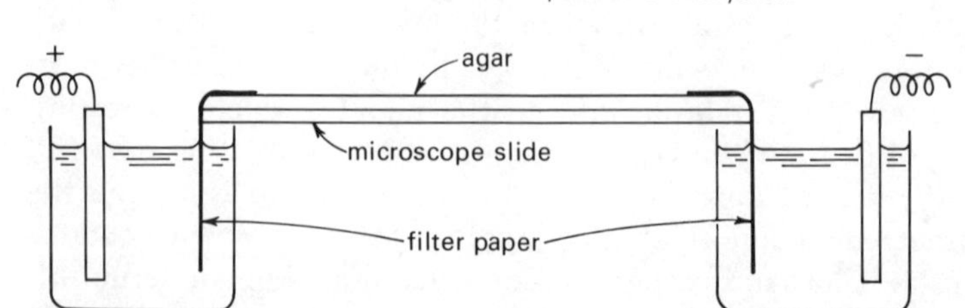

rates, that is, have different electrophoretic mobilities; in addition there is a backward flow of buffer through the slide which tends to move all the migrating proteins backward at a uniform rate (ENDOSMOTIC FLOW). After several hours the various proteins will have assumed different positions in the agar. The current is stopped, the filter paper strips are removed, and a long horizontal trough is cut at one side of the slide. Antiserum to whole human serum is placed in the trough, and double diffusion takes place. Each protein antigen forms an arc of precipitate as it interacts with its corresponding antibody, and these arcs are distributed at varying positions on the slide depending on the electrophoretic mobility of the antigen. Identification of the antigen is obtained from its position in the immunoelectrophoretic diagram or may be confirmed by cutting another trough on the other side of the slide and adding the purified antigen. As the antigen and antibody diffuse from their respective troughs, they will form a single band that will fuse completely with the arc formed by the antigen that had been electrophoresed. The various proteins apart from albumin have been named relative to their electrophoretic mobility in the Tiselius electrophoresis apparatus: α, β, and γ-globulins, the α-globulins moving the fastest behind the albumin peak.

A variety of other identification techniques have been developed. Thus, if an antigen has some enzymatic activity that is not neutralized by reaction with antibody, it may be located by staining procedures that demonstrate enzymatic activity in the antigen-antibody arc. Similarly, by using a radioactive antigen, a given arc may be shown to have become radioactive by the investigator's placing it in contact with photographic film. In addition the arcs may be stained and the patterns kept as a permanent record; these procedures may also be used with gel diffusion as well as with immunoelectrophoresis.

A major contribution of immunoelectrophoretic analysis was the demonstration that there were three families of immunoglobulins termed IgG, IgM, and IgA or, alternately, γG, γM and γA with which antibody activity is associated. Unlike the usual proteins, which tend to be fairly uniform or homogeneous in electrophoretic mobility, the immunoglobulins are heterogeneous, that is, show a wide range of electrophoretic mobilities. This is most clearly illustrated with respect to the γG line, which extends from the slow γ region all the way to the α_2 region. Fig. 3.10 shows an immunoelectrophoretic pattern of normal human serum developed with a horse antiserum to whole human serum and an antiserum containing antibody to the three immunoglobulins. A drawing with the various arcs labeled is also given.

A very convenient immunoelectrophoretic technique that is carried out in two dimensions and permits quantitative estimation of proteins has recently been developed. It is called CROSSED IMMUNOELECTROPHORESIS. The first electrophoresis is carried out as previously

Fig. 3.10 Immunoelectrophoretic pattern of human serum. (Above) Schematic diagram of bands (Below) Actual photograph of immunoelectrophoretic bands. (Courtesy of Dr. Pierre Grabar and Mlle Janine Courcon, Institut Pasteur, Paris.)

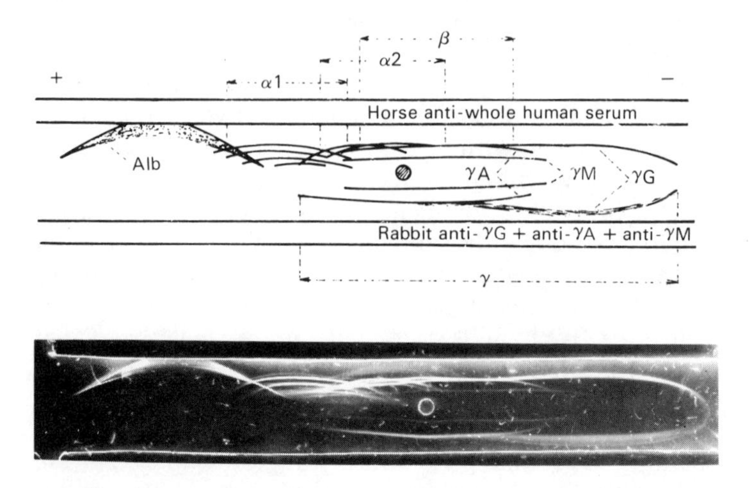

described. A strip of agar containing the separated bands is cut out and placed on a larger glass plate onto which a layer of agar containing antiserum has been placed. The second electrophoresis is carried out at right angles to the initial direction of travel. Arcs of antigen-antibody precipitate appear (Fig. 3.11) as the antigens move through and react with the antiserum under the influence of the electric field. The two-dimensional patterns give a much better indication of the relative concentrations of the different components. The height of each peak is roughly proportional to the logarithm of antigen concentration at any given concentration of antibody.

For quantitative estimation of any protein antigen in serum, antiserum to that protein is mixed with agar and layered on a plate. The unknown serum and a series of known concentrations of the protein are placed in a series of holes in the agar, and a current is passed through the agar. The migrating antigens react with the antiserum to form a series of sharp peaks, the height of the peak being proportional to the antigen concentration; the unknown value is obtained by interpolation.

DETECTION OF SOLUBLE ANTIGEN-ANTIBODY COMPLEXES

With certain antigens such as insulin, one may not see visible antigen-antibody precipitation, and in many other systems the quan-

Fig. 3.11 (Top) Precipitation pattern obtained when analyzing human serum with antigen-antibody crossed electrophoresis using a goat anti-human serum. (Center) Contact drawing of contours of precipitation figures; arrows indicate (1) serum albumin, (2) α_1-antitrypsin, (3) haptoglobin [1 : 2], (4) transferrin, (5) γA, and (6) γG. (Bottom) Contact drawing of precipitation pattern when running conventional immunoelectrophoresis with the same antiserum and identical migratory distance of the electrophoretic run. (From Laurell, C. B. Anal. Biochem. **10**: 358 [1965]; by permission of the copyright owner, Academic Press, New York.)

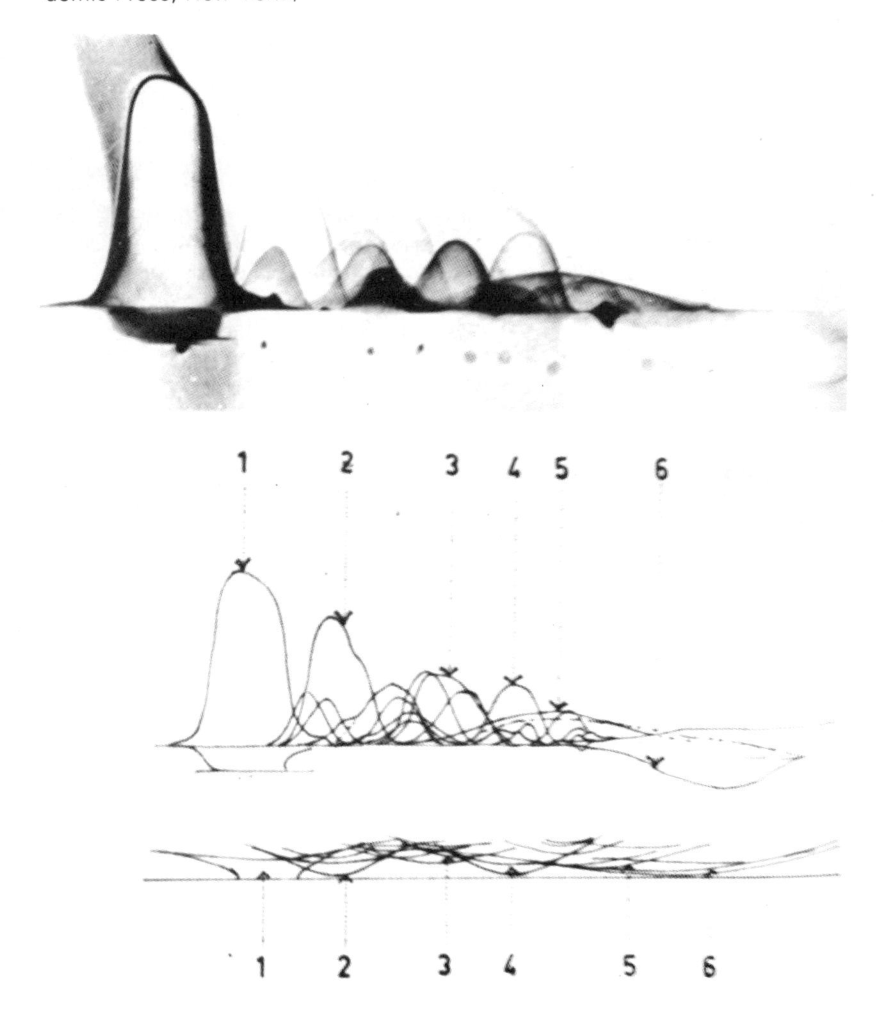

tities of antigen-antibody complex may be insufficient for precipitation to take place. However, the presence of antibody may be detected by using a radioactive antigen because of the effect of the antibody in changing the electrophoretic mobility of the antigen when it forms a complex with it. Thus in electrophoresis on paper, I^{131} insulin is adsorbed and remains at the point of application; if mixed with antibody, however, the insulin is no longer adsorbed but migrates with the antibody. From assays of radioactivity at the origin and in the migrating peak, the proportions of bound to free insulin may be determined. In other media such as starch, the insulin migrates but travels less rapidly than the insulin-antibody complex so that the bound and free insulin may also be computed from assays of radioactivity. If a mixture of radioactive insulin and antibody is prepared and the ratio of bound to free insulin by electrophoresis on paper is

Fig. 3.12 Chromatoelectrophoresis of insulin-I^{131}-antiserum mixtures containing known concentrations of human insulin (left) and unknown plasma (right). At the bottom of each set is a control mixture to which no antiserum had been added; migrating activity in control tubes respresents damaged fractions. The standard curve (middle) is obtained from measurement of areas under each of the two peaks in the complete series of chromatograms, of which eight are shown. The insulin concentration in the 1-hr post-glucose specimen of patient RA is calculated as shown. (From Yalow, R. S. and S. Berson. Methods of Biochem. Anal., Interscience Press **12**: 69 [1964]; by permission of the copyright owner, Wiley, New York.)

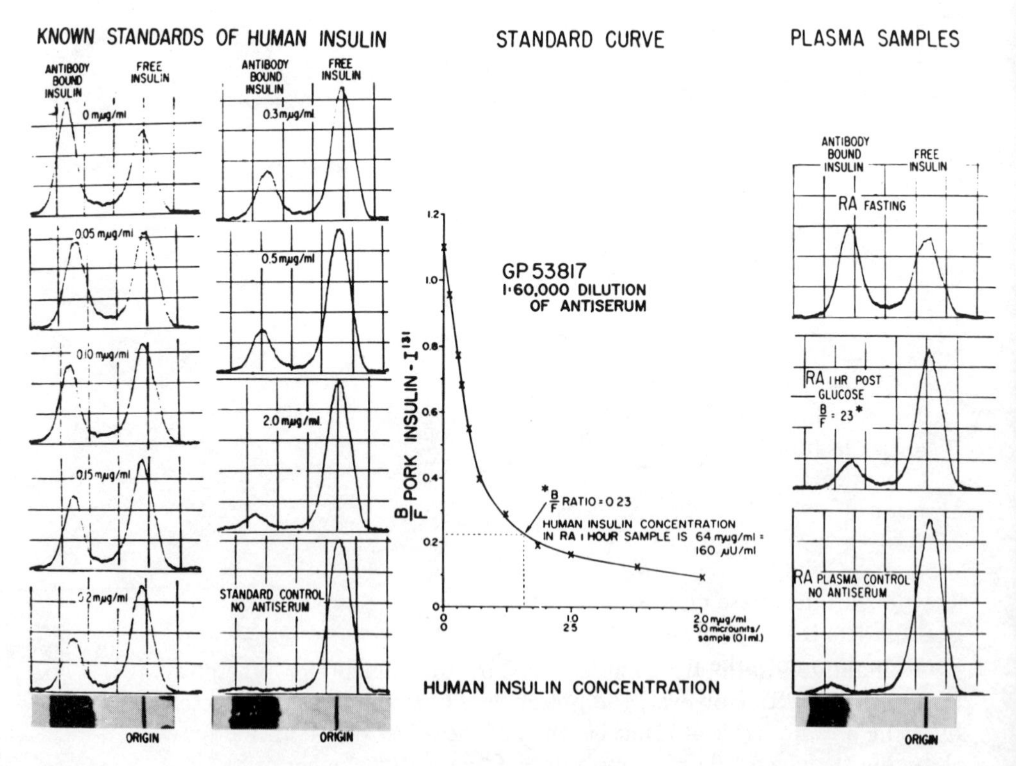

measured, the addition of nonradioactive insulin will displace some of the radioactive bound insulin. If the system is calibrated with known quantities of insulin, the curve of bound I^{131}/free I^{131} insulin at various concentrations of unlabeled insulin may be used to assay for insulin in plasma (Fig. 3.12). This principle may be used to assay for many substances.

ANTIGEN-ANTIBODY INTERACTIONS INVOLVING MORE THAN TWO COMPONENTS

Inhibition Reactions

The direct methods of demonstrating antigen-antibody combination such as precipitation and agglutination, since they are truly reversible reactions in the thermodynamic sense, readily lend themselves to the detection of substances that compete with antigen for the antibody combining site. Thus, a low molecular weight hapten in suitable concentration will displace its homologous antigenic determinant from the antibody combining site and dissolve an antigen-antibody precipitate. Similarly, agglutination by antibody of bacteria or erythrocytes can be reversed by the addition of soluble antigen, which causes disaggregation of the bacteria or erythrocytes by displacing their antigenic determinants and forming soluble antigen-antibody complexes.

Inhibition of precipitation, first introduced by Landsteiner, has proved extremely valuable for establishing the relative degree of complementarity or specificity of small fragments of an antigenic determinant for the antibody combining site. If a known quantity of antigen and antibody is used, the relative effectiveness of a series of haptenic substances may be assayed, since the relative molar concentration of each, causing a given degree of inhibition of precipitation, is inversely proportional to the degree of complementarity for the antibody combining site—for example, a hapten making up a larger portion of the site or fitting better into the site will inhibit at a lower molar concentration. Inhibition of agglutination may be employed in a similar fashion.

A special case of hemagglutination and inhibition of hemagglutination in which the role of the components is reversed occurs with certain viruses that possess an intrinsic property of combining with certain receptors on the surface of the red cells to cause hemagglutination. Under these circumstances antibody reacts with the virus and renders it incapable of attaching to the red cell so that hemagglutination does not take place. Such tests are widely used for diagnosis of viral infections. Since little or no antibody is present in the acute stage of the infection and only appears during convalescence, demonstration of a fourfold rise in titer to a given virus in direct comparisons with serum samples taken during the acute and convalescent phases of the disease provides a retrospective diagnosis. However, inhibition of hemagglutination by viruses occurs not only with antibody but also with substances that have a structure similar to that of the receptor site on the red cell with which the virus combines. These materials are usually mucoprotein in nature and their presence must be excluded, or they must be destroyed, before any inhibition of hemagglutination is attributed to antibody.

Reactions Involving Complement

Other substances may play an important auxiliary role in antigen-antibody interaction. One complex of substances, which goes under the name of COMPLEMENT and is abbreviated as C′, is present in fresh serum of vertebrates and may be bound by antigen-antibody aggregates. Thus far, complement has been shown to consist of nine components that react in a known sequence when antigen and antibody combine. The mechanism will be considered in more detail in Chapter 11. C′ reacts at the sites of antigen-antibody combination on erythrocytes to cause the release of hemoglobin into solution; electron microscopic studies have clearly shown that holes are formed through which the hemoglobin is released; this effect is called HEMOLYSIS. With certain Gram-negative bacteria, antibody and C′ kill the organisms; this is termed a BACTERICIDAL EFFECT.

Complement is readily inactivated by heating serum to 56°C for 30 min; it deteriorates if kept at refrigerator temperatures, but is stable when kept frozen at −60°C. Fresh guinea pig serum is most widely used as a source of complement, and human complement has also been extensively studied.

Complement, or at least some of its components, are taken up when antigen and antibody interact even when no visible reaction may be seen. Thus a precipitate of egg albumin and rabbit antibody to egg albumin will combine with, and is said to FIX, C′. This is the basis of a very sensitive test for antibody, or for antigen, called the COMPLEMENT FIXATION TEST.

The test uses as an indicator system sheep erythrocytes coated with a suitable amount of rabbit antibody to sheep erythrocytes, that is, an amount insufficient to cause hemagglutination. These coated red cells are called "sensitized red cells." They will hemolyze in the presence of C′ as follows:

1. $$\text{RBC} + \text{Ab} + \text{C}' \longrightarrow \text{hemolysis}$$

and thus can serve as a test for free complement. Similarly, an unrelated antigen-antibody system under suitable conditions may fix C′

with egg albumin (Ea) and a rabbit antiserum to egg albumin (anti-Ea); the reaction would be:

2. Ea + anti-Ea + C′ ⟶ (EaAbC′)
complement fixed;
no longer free.

Thus, if the sensitized sheep erythrocytes were added to the system after Reaction 2 had occurred, hemolysis would not take place since the C′ was no longer available.

If no antibody were present or if antibody were present in insufficient quantity to fix all of the C′, some C′ would remain free to hemolyse the sensitized sheep cells:

3. Ag + normal serum + C′ ⟶ no reaction;
C′ remains free

and when the indicator system is added hemolysis takes place.

Failure to obtain hemolysis of the sensitized sheep cell system is thus an indication that antibody was present in reaction 2, while hemolysis shows that no antibody was present in reaction 3. The method requires several controls that must be set up with each experiment to demonstrate that the antigen alone and the antiserum alone do not react with, inactivate, or destroy the C′. Obviously, if either antigen or antiserum alone inactivates the C′, that reagent is said to be ANTICOMPLEMENTARY and a valid indication that an antigen-antibody reaction took place cannot be obtained. Animal and human sera are often anticomplementary at high concentration and must be diluted until they no longer show any inactivating effect on the added C′. Tissue extracts used as antigen may also be anticomplementary and require similar dilution. The quantities of reagents used must be carefully standardized, and the antisera are generally heated at 56°C to inactivate any C′ that they may contain so that the amount of C′ added is under control.

C′ is generally measured in terms of 50 percent hemolytic units ($C'H_{50}$), since in the region of 50 percent hemolysis small changes in C′ concentration are most readily seen. This is carried out with a standard suspension of sensitized sheep erythrocytes by the addition of varying dilutions of guinea pig serum as the source of complement (fresh guinea pig serum stored at −60°C retains its complement activity for long periods). The degree of hemolysis is determined spectrophotometrically. A sigmoid curve is obtained by plotting the percent of hemolysis against the volume of C′ added, and the volume giving 50 percent hemolysis is read off. For C′ fixation tests five $C'H_{50}$ units are used, that is, five times the volume of guinea pig serum giving the 50 percent hemolytic end point. The sensitivity of the test varies with the amount of C′ used. If too much C′ is employed small amounts of antibody will not fix all the C′ added and will be missed. If too little C′ is added, false positive nonspecific results will be obtained. (Further details may be found in *Experimental Immunochemistry*.)

A low molecular weight hapten combining with antibody which prevents the antigen from reacting will also inhibit the fixation of C′. This also serves as a very useful method of studying hapten inhibition reactions. It is called the COMPLEMENT FIXATION INHIBITION TEST. Antibodies formed in some animal species–such as the horse, chicken, and duck–do not fix guinea pig complement well, but can bind antigen and prevent it from reacting with antibody (rabbit antibody) to the same antigen that does fix C′. Such antibodies may also be assayed by the complement fixation inhibition test.

γG immunoglobulin that has been aggregated by heat has been shown to fix C′ in a manner that is indistinguishable from that in antigen-antibody interaction.

When bacteria, protozoa, or other particulate antigenic materials are agglutinated by antibody in the presence of C′, they exhibit a tendency to adhere to normal blood platelets, erythrocytes, silica, or starch granules, and so forth. This reaction has been termed SEROLOGICAL ADHESION and more recently the term IMMUNE ADHERENCE, has been used in a restricted sense to describe the attachment of Ag-Ab-C′ complexes to primate erythrocytes and nonprimate platelets. Immune adherence may also be used to detect antibody to bacterial or protozoal antigens.

Gram-negative bacteria that have taken up antibody and C′ are engulfed more rapidly by the phagocytic cells of the body – the polymorphonuclear leucocytes and macrophages (PHAGOCYTOSIS). With many types of microorganisms, this is followed by digestion and destruction of the bacteria; but other microorganisms, notably the tubercle bacillus, multiply very effectively inside phagocytic cells. Organisms with polysaccharide capsules, such as the pneumococcus, are protected against phagocytosis but when coated with the homologous horse antibody are rapidly taken up; the role of C′ in this system is not clear.

LOCALIZATION OF ANTIGEN AND ANTIBODY IN CELLS AND TISSUES

It is evident that specific antibodies are reagents for the detection and precise localization of their corresponding antigens. Thus, by attaching some characteristic colored or fluorescent label, the sites of uptake of the labeled antibody in tissue sections may be observed under the microscope. Coons first introduced this principle, using fluorescein-tagged antibodies (see Chapter 2), it has since come into widespread use. The antigen detected may be of exogenous origin (such as a microorganism) and the uptake of a specific fluorescent antibody frequently serves to make a definite diagnosis, or the antigen may be an intrinsic part of the tissue or cell and its exact location or time of appearance in the cell can be established. A variety of procedures are used which permit detection of antibody as well as antigen and these are of great importance in efforts to determine which cells can form antibody. These procedures are summarized in Fig. 3.13. In (A) antigen may be demonstrated by the use of its specific antibody labeled with fluorescein. In (B), the most convenient and most widely used method, the antibody specific for the antigen is not labeled, but after it has attached to the antigen, the tissue section is washed and treated with a fluorescent antibody against the γG globulin of the species used. It is thus possible in working with rabbit antibodies that are specific for a large variety of antigens to use only a single fluorescein-

Fig. 3.13 Block diagram showing the various modifications of the fluorescent-antibody method. (A) Direct method for demonstrating antigen by the use of a single layer of fluorescein-labeled specific antibody. (B) Indirect or double-layer technique: unlabeled specific antibody is used first, and the material is subsequently treated with fluorescent antibody against γ-globulin. Thus if the first layer employed rabbit antibody, fluorescent antibody against rabbit γ-globulin would be used in the second layer. (C) Sandwich technique for the detection of antibody. The section is first treated with a dilute solution of antigen. After a wash to get rid of the excess antigen, the section is exposed to fluorescent antibody. (D) Indirect method for detection of antigen employing complement (fresh guinea-pig serum) and rabbit antibody to guinea-pig complement (From Humphrey, J. H. and R. G. White. Immunology for students of medicine. Davis, Philadelphia [1963].)

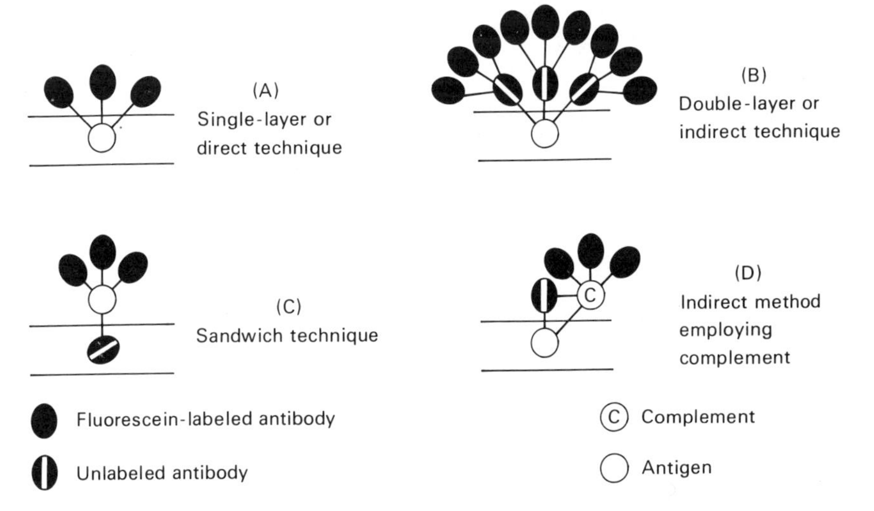

labeled reagent—for example, goat antibody to rabbit γG immunoglobulin. Method (C), the so-called sandwich technique, is used to demonstrate the presence of antibody in tissue sections. Antigen is first placed on the section and is taken up by the antibody. After washing, fluorescein-labeled antibody is then added and serves to locate the antigen and, hence, the site at which antibody was present in the original cell. Finally, in (D), the ability of antigen and complement to be bound to the antibody in the tissue cell is utilized, and

Fig. 3.14 Mucosa (Upper) From body of stomach (Group A secretor) stained with rabbit anti-A fluorescein isothiocyanate conjugate; direct method. Surface and foveolar epithelium positive for (water-soluble) group A mucoid. Parietal cells also positive in unfixed tissue, but would have been negative if section had been fixed in alcohol. (Lower) From a Group A nonsecretor. Surface epithelium negative for A substance, but specific A mucoid present in neck cells of gastric glands. The negative surface of epithelium would have given positive staining with anti-Lewis[a] conjugate. (From E. J. Holborow *in* Immunological Methods. J. F. Ackroyd [ed.], Blackwell, Oxford, p. 155 [1964].)

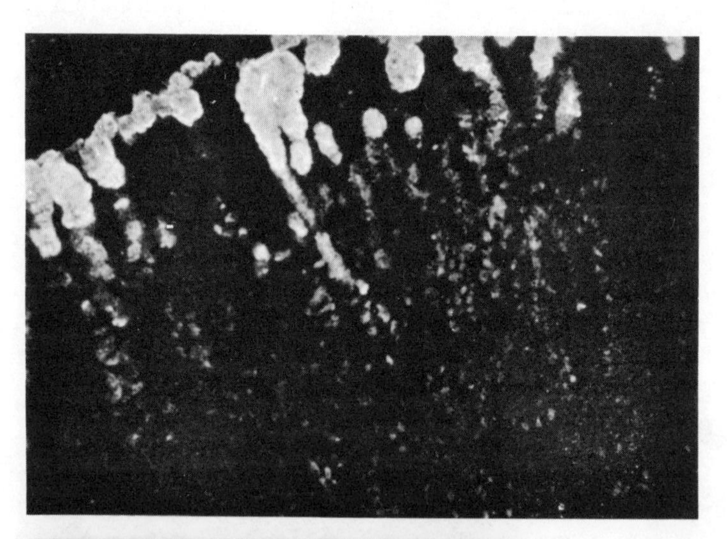

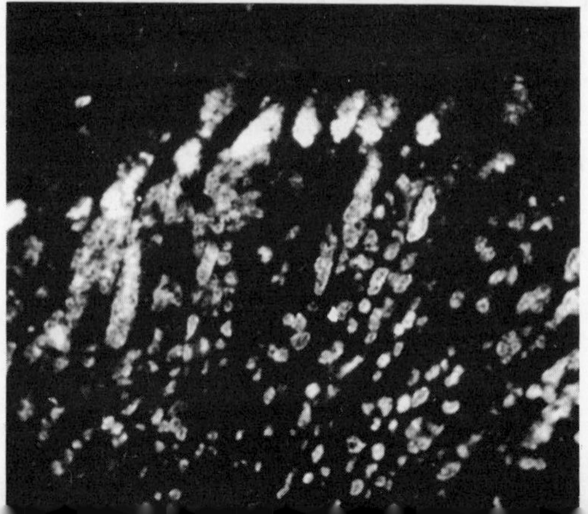

the guinea pig C′, is located with fluorescein-labeled antibody to guinea pig complement.

The use of fluorescent antibody to human blood group A substance to localize A substance in tissues is seen in Fig. 3.14. In the upper section in the figure large amounts of A substance are seen in mucosal glands that secrete water-soluble A substance. In both upper and lower sections in the figure, the presence of A substance in other nonsecreting cells may be seen.

For electron microscopic localization, antibody is labeled with ferritin, an iron-containing, x-ray opaque protein, by means of a diazotization reaction. Ferritin has a very characteristic pattern under the electron microscope and readily localizes the structures with which the antibody has combined. It is especially useful for studies with viruses.

Fig. 3.15 shows ferritin conjugated antibody to vaccinia virus reacting with intracellular virus particles.

Fig. 3.15 Reaction of ferritin-labeled rabbit antibody to vaccinia virus with intracellular particles of virus × 180,300. (From Morgan C., R. A. Rifkind, K. C. Hsu, M. Holden, B. C. Seegal, and H. M. Rose. Virology **14**: 292 [1961].)

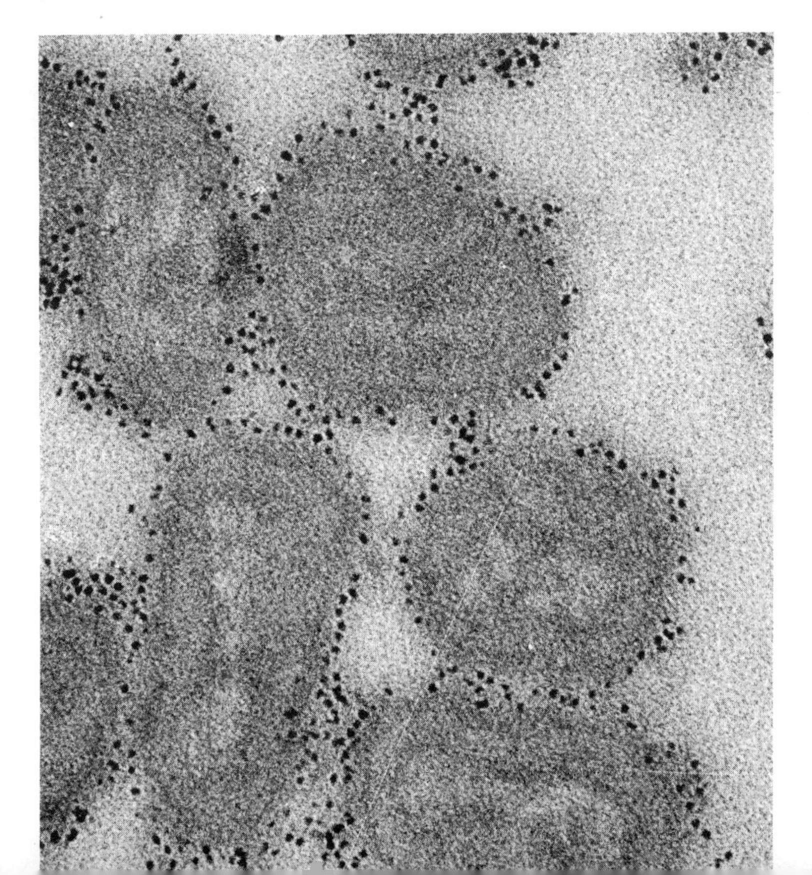

SUGGESTED READINGS

Kabat, E. A. Kabat and Mayer's Experimental immunochemistry.(2d ed.; 1961) Charles C. Thomas, Publisher, Springfield, Ill.

Ackroyd, J. F Immunological methods, (1964) Blackwell, Oxford.

Campbell, D. H., J. S. Garvey, N. E. Cremer, and D. Sussdorf. Methods in immunology. (1963) W. A. Benjamin, Inc., New York.

Oudin, J. Specific precipitation in gels and its application to immunochemical analysis, Methods in Medical Research, Yearbook **5**: 335 (1952).

Ouchterlony, O. Diffusion in gel methods for immunological analysis I, II. *In* Progress in Allergy **5**: 1 (1958); **6**, 30 (1962). [S. Karger Basel.]

Crowle, A. J. Immunodiffusion. Academic Press, New York (1961).

Grabar, P. and P. Burtin. Immunoelectrophoretic analysis. (1964) Elsevier Publishing Company, Amsterdam [English translation].

Chase, M. W. and C. A. Williams, Jr. Methods in immunology and immunochemistry. (1967) Academic Press, New York, vol. **1**.

Munoz, J. Effect of bacteria and bacterial products on antibody response. Advances in Immunology **4**: 397 (1964). [Academic Press, New York].

Coons, A. H. Fluorescent antibody methods. *In* General cytochemical methods. (1958) (J. F. Danielli ed.). Academic Press, New York, p. 400.

4

Precise Measurement of Antigen-Antibody Interaction

The era of modern immunochemistry began in 1929 with the introduction of the precise methods of quantitative analytical chemistry for the measurement of antibodies and antigens by Michael Heidelberger and his school. Prior to this it had not been possible to develop a comprehensive picture of antigen-antibody interaction or to understand its mechanism.

QUANTITATIVE PRECIPITIN REACTION

An understanding of quantitative immunochemistry is best obtained by considering the course of the precipitin reaction as a function of the addition of increasing quantities of antigen to a constant volume of antiserum. Measurements are made with analytical pipettes and, with careful attention to technique, a precision of ±2 to 5 percent or less may be obtained, depending upon the quantities of antigen and antibody measured. Since antibodies are proteins and most proteins contain about 16 percent nitrogen (N), analyses were originally carried out by the micro-Kjeldahl method, but more recently a variety of other analytical methods have been used, including ultraviolet absorption, biuret, the Folin-Ciocalteu reaction, Nessler's reagent, and the ninhydrin reaction. Many of these procedures can be carried out on samples of 5 to 20 μg total N and thus permit the use of small quantities of reagents. It should be emphasized that quantitative precipitin reactions should be set up in the smallest convenient volume, since antigen-antibody precipitates have appreciable solubility. With very small quantities of antibody N, the tubes are allowed to remain in the refrigerator for from five to seven days to ensure maximum precipitation. Because of the high degree of complementarity or specificity of antigen-antibody reactions and if complement is absent or removed, precipitates consist entirely of antigen and antibody. After a suitable period in the refrigerator to ensure equilibrium, the precipitates are centrifuged off in a refrigerated centrifuge, washed twice with chilled saline, and then analyzed.

A typical set of quantitative precipitin data is given in Fig. 4.1 and Table 4.1 (taken from the original publication of Heidelberger and Kendall in 1935). These data were obtained with 1 ml of antiserum diluted one half in a total volume of 3 ml, and the washed precipitates were analyzed for N by the micro-Kjeldahl method. Were they to be obtained today, about 10 to 50 μl of antiserum would be used, the quantities of antigen being reduced proportionately and the total volume kept to about 100 to 150 μl with analyses being carried out by the Folin-Ciocalteu or ninhydrin techniques, illustrating the improvement in microanalytical methods during the past thirty years. In carrying out quantitative precipitin assays, it is of great importance to study the supernatant serum to determine whether antibody or antigen is present. This is usually accomplished by dividing each supernatant in half after decanting it from the centrifuged precipitate. To one half, one adds a small quantity of antigen and to the other a small amount of antiserum, the former giving a precipitate if antibody is still present and the latter precipitating if antigen is present. The use of supernatant tests permits definition of the region of the precipitin curve and gives useful information as to the purity of the system under study; it may provide some indication that the antigen is degraded. Supernatant tests are often set up in gels using double diffusion in two dimensions.

Fig. 4.1 and Table 4.1 show that with the addition of increasing quantities of antigen the amount of specific precipitate (antigen + antibody) rises until it reaches a maximum and then declines. From the tests on the supernatant, several regions or zones are recognized: the ZONE OF ANTIBODY EXCESS corresponding to the first six points; a region called the EQUIVALENCE ZONE in which neither antigen nor antibody may be detected in the supernatant; and, finally, a ZONE OF ANTIGEN EXCESS. That portion of the antigen excess zone in which the quantity of antigen-antibody precipitate decreases is called the INHIBITION ZONE.

TABLE 4.1

Addition of Increasing Amounts of Egg Albumin to 1.0 ml of a 1 : 2 Dilution of Rabbit Antiserum to Egg Albumin at 0°C

EaN Added (μg)	EaN_{pptd} (μg)	Total N_{pptd} (μg)	Antibody N by Difference (μg)	Ratio AbN : EaN in Precipitate	Antibody N_{pptd} Calculated from Equation (μg)	Tests on Supernatant
9.1	Total	156	147	16.2	137	Excess Ab
15.5	Total	236	220	14.2	225	Excess Ab
25	Total	374	349	14.0	343	Excess Ab
40	Total	526	486	12.2	499	Excess Ab
50	Total	632	582	11.6	582	Excess Ab
65	Total	740	675	10.4	677	Excess Ab
74	Total	794	720	9.7	714	No Ab or Ea
82	Total	830	748	9.1	738	No Ab, 1 μg of EaN
90	87	826	739	8.5	746	Excess Ea
98	89	820	731	8.2		Excess Ea
124	87	730	643	7.4		Excess Ea
135	[72] [a]	610	[538]	7.5		Excess Ea
195	[48]	414	[366]	[7.6]		Excess Ea
307	[4]	106				Excess Ea
490		42				Excess Ea

Data from M. Heidelberger and F. E. Kendall. J. Exp. Med. **62**: 697 (1935).

[a] Values in brackets are considered uncertain.

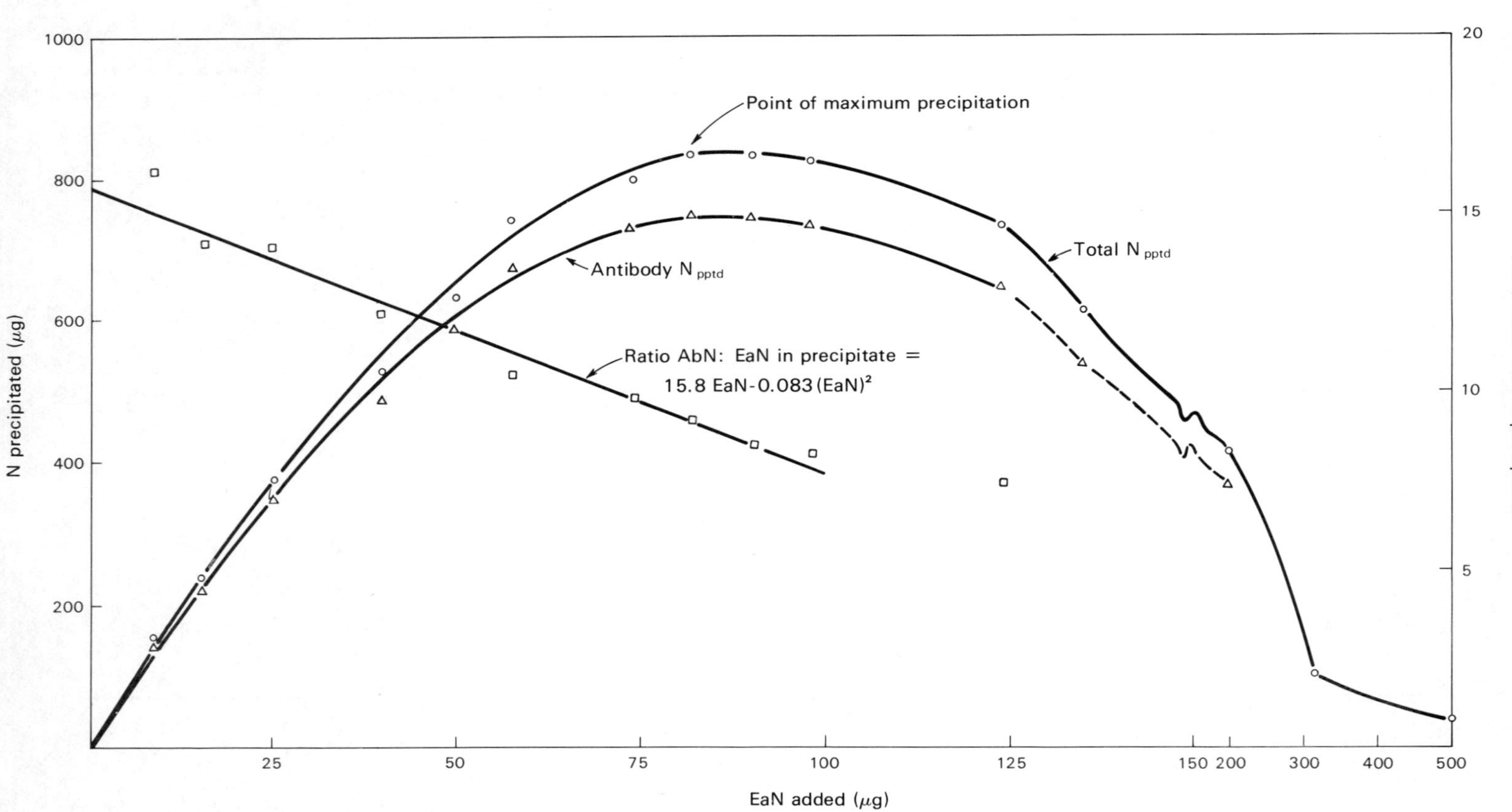

Fig. 4.1 Quantitative precipitin reaction between crystalline hen egg albumin and rabbit antibody to crystalline hen egg albumin. (From Heidelberger, M., and F. E. Kendall. J. Exp. Med. **62**: 697 [1935]; by permission of The Rockefeller University Press.)

In the zone of antibody excess all the antigen is contained in the precipitate and so the quantity of antigen N added (column 1) is subtracted from the total N precipitated (column 3) to give the amount of antibody N (AbN) precipitated (column 4). That this subtraction is valid has been verified with colored antigens, with radioactive antigens, and with antigens containing some distinctive constituent so that direct analyses for both antigen N and total N could be performed on the precipitates. Of course, with polysaccharide antigens that do not contain nitrogen, one obtains the AbN content directly from analyses on the washed precipitates. In the region of antigen excess one must determine the quantity in the supernatant and subtract the value from the total amount of antigen N added.

Inspection of the values in column 4 shows that the maximum quantity of antibody N is precipitated at the point at which antigen first definitely appears in the supernatant. This is termed the point of maximum precipitation; conceptually it coincides with the practice in analytical chemistry of adding a small excess of reagent to assure complete precipitation of the constituent to be analyzed. The data for total N and for AbN precipitated against egg albumin nitrogen (EaN) added are plotted in Fig. 4.1.

Knowing the values for AbN and EaN in the precipitate, it is possible to calculate the composition of the precipitate with respect to antigen and antibody. This is expressed as the ratio AbN : EaN in column 5 and is plotted in Fig. 4.1. This is seen to give a straight line following the equation:

$$\frac{\mathrm{AbN}_{\mathrm{pptd}}}{x} = a - bx \tag{4-1}$$

in which x is the amount of antigen N added. The constants a and b represent the intercept of the line on the y axis and the slope respectively.

In Fig. 4.1 the values for a and b are 15.8 and 0.083, and substituting EaN for x, Eq. (4-1) becomes

$$\frac{\mathrm{AbN}_{\mathrm{pptd}}}{\mathrm{EaN}} = 15.8 - 0.083\ \mathrm{EaN} \tag{4-2}$$

multiplying both sides by EaN gives

$$\mathrm{AbN}_{\mathrm{pptd}} = 15.8\,\mathrm{EaN} - 0.083\ (\mathrm{EaN})^2 \tag{4-3}$$

the equation representing the curve for antibody N precipitated in Fig. 4.1. Column 6 of Table 4.1 gives results at each point calculated from the equation which agree fairly well with the experimental values in column 4.

If one differentiates Eq. (4-1) with respect to x and sets the derivative equal to zero

$$\frac{d\,\text{AbN}_{\text{pptd}}}{dx} = a - 2bx = 0$$

then

$$x_{\text{max}} = \frac{a}{2b} \qquad (4\text{-}4)$$

Substituting the values for a of 15.8 and b of 0.083 gives

$$\text{EaN}_{\text{max}} = \frac{15.8}{0.166} = 95.2\ \mu\text{g N}$$

Substituting this value in Eq. (4-3) gives $\text{AbN}_{\text{max}} = 750\ \mu\text{g}$ N in good agreement with the experimental value of 748 μg AbN in Table 4.1.

Equation (4-1) was found empirically, but was given a certain degree of theoretical foundation when it was derived from the law of mass action involving the reaction of multivalent antigen and bi- or multivalent antibody. With many sera the equation does not fit the data too closely and other empirical equations have been used. While it offers a convenient way of looking at the data, recent developments showing the extreme heterogeneity of the antibodies formed even to a single antigen tend to limit its usefulness. The lack of a completely satisfactory theory for the course of the precipitin reaction does not seriously hamper the use of quantitative methods for the measurement of antigen and antibody.

The ratio of AbN : EaN in the precipitate changes continuously over the entire course of the reaction. Converting these ratios to molecular ratios shows an average molecular composition of Ab_5Ea in extreme antibody excess and of Ab_3Ea to Ab_5Ea_2 in the equivalence zone. The precipitate in moderate antigen excess is about Ab_2Ea and the soluble complex is $AbEa_2$ and perhaps Ab_2Ea_3. These molecular ratios vary for each antigen-antibody system depending upon molecular weight and combining proportions.

USE OF THE QUANTITATIVE PRECIPITIN CURVE TO MEASURE ANTIGEN IN UNKNOWN SOLUTIONS

In Fig. 4.1 the curve for total N precipitated defines the relationship between quantity of EaN added and the amount of antigen-antibody precipitate for the particular serum. It thus may serve as a CALIBRATION CURVE for the analysis of unknown solutions for their content of egg albumin. Thus, if a dilute solution of egg white that contains many proteins is added to the same quantity of antiserum used to obtain the points on the curve, only the egg albumin in the egg white will precipitate the anti-Ea, the amount of precipitate depending on the quantity of Ea present in the volume of solution added. The precipitate formed is then centrifuged, washed with saline, and analyzed in the usual manner. The total N obtained is interpolated on the curve and the corresponding amount of EaN read off.

In the estimation of antigen, supernatant tests are of utmost importance, for valid results are obtained only in the antibody excess region. Thus, if the total N obtained on adding the egg white to the antiserum were 500 μg, from Fig. 4.1, this could correspond to two concentrations of egg albumin—36 μg N or 138 μg N, the former being obtained if there was an excess of antibody while the latter would be observed in the region of antigen excess. Examination of the supernatant would readily establish whether there was an excess of antibody or of antigen. In the latter instance the analysis would have to be repeated with the use of a smaller quantity of the egg white solution. Obviously, in the use of an antiserum to assay mixtures of antigens for any given constituent one must be sure that the antiserum contains only antibodies to the antigen to be assayed and not to other antigens. This is best established by gel diffusion studies as outlined in the previous chapter.

Quantitative precipitin assays have been carried out for determining the quantities of many different proteins in biological fluids and have proved especially useful for the determination of γG immunoglobulin in human cerebrospinal fluid. Using the more micro methods in a small volume, they permit the measurement of quantities as low as 0.5 to 2 μg of antigen N. For most purposes, however, the immunoplate method (see Fig. 3.6) is much more rapid and is capable of almost as great precision, but as yet cannot be used at quite so low levels of antigen concentration.

ANALYSES OF ANTISERA FOR TOTAL ANTIBODY CONTENT

It is generally unnecessary to make an entire precipitin curve to find out the total antibody N content of an antiserum. With a few preliminary tests one can locate the point of maximum precipitation and set up a quantitative analysis at that point.

FLOCCULATION CURVES

A special type of precipitation curve was observed many years ago in studies with horse antisera to diphtheria and tetanus toxins and for many years was known as the toxin-antitoxin type of curve. It has now been encountered with antigens other than toxins and has also been found in certain human sera from patients with a disease called Hashimoto's thyroiditis who are known to have autoantibodies to human thyroglobulin; most individuals form antithyroglobulin which gives a typical precipitin curve, but several giving the flocculation type of response have been found.

Essentially the flocculation curve differs from the precipitin curve in that a soluble complex of antigen and antibody can form in the antibody excess region as well as in the antigen excess region, while in the precipitin type of curve a precipitate forms with small amounts of antigen so that the curve appears to go through the origin. (It should be borne in mind that every antigen-antibody precipitate has some solubility and that minute amounts of antigen will not precipitate until the quantity of antigen-antibody aggregate exceeds its solubility.)

The precipitin- and flocculation-type curves with two human antisera to thyroglobulin are shown in Figs. 4.2 and 4.3 respectively; the curves are plotted as extinction (optical density) at 280 mμ against amount of thyroglobulin added. The latter figure shows that no significant precipitation occurred until more than 0.6 mg thyroglobulin was added, while in the former 0.1 mg gave a significant precipitate and the curve passed through the origin.

At present there is no theoretically satisfying mechanism to account for the flocculation type of curve; an ultimate explanation will have to be in terms of antibody heterogeneity, of the relative binding affinities of these antibodies as compared to precipitating antibodies, as well as whether they involve the same antigenic determinants. In the region in which flocculation occurs, the ratio of Ab : Ag in the precipitate varies over about a twofold range.

Fig. 4.2 Amount of precipitate formed on addition of increasing weights of human thyroglobulin to 0.10 ml of Hashimoto serum (R.S.). The washed precipitates were dissolved in 2.0 ml of 0.1 M Na_2CO_3, and the protein content estimated by measuring the extinction coefficient at 280 mμ. (From Roitt, I. M., P. N. Campbell, and D. Doniach. Biochem. J., **69**: 248 [1958].)

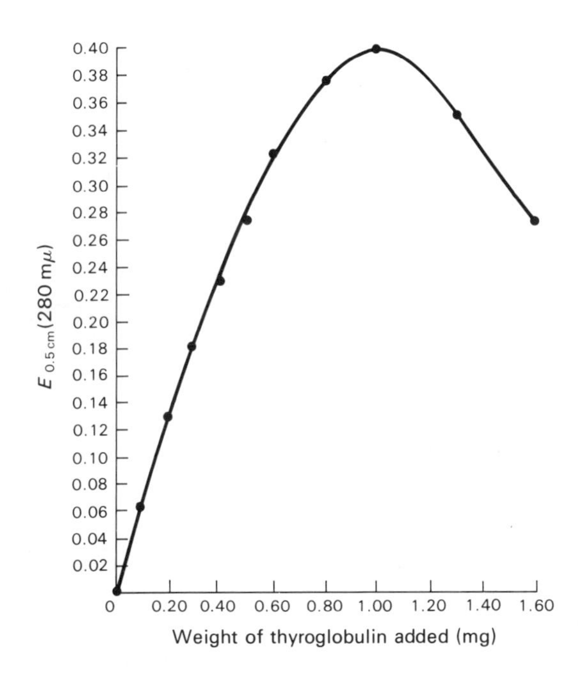

QUANTITATIVE DETERMINATION OF AGGLUTININ

The antibody content of an antiserum containing antibacterial agglutinins can be determined by adding a suspension of killed bacteria which has been repeatedly washed until soluble materials have been removed. A known quantity of bacterial suspension is added to a given volume of antiserum, and after a suitable interval the agglutinated bacteria are centrifuged off, washed with saline, and analyzed for N. The antibody N as agglutinin is obtained by subtracting the quantity of bacterial N added from the total N found for the washed agglutinated bacteria. Care must be taken to ensure that the amount of bacterial suspension was sufficient to remove all the antibody. The course of the agglutination reaction for Type I pneumococci and horse antibody to the Type I capsular polysaccharide was studied and found to be essentially similar to the quantitative precipitin reaction between

Fig. 4.3 Amount of precipitate formed on addition of increasing weights of human thyroglobulin to 0.10 ml of Hashimoto serum (W. A.). The precipitates were treated as described in Fig. 4.2. (From Roitt, I. M., P. N. Campbell, and D. Doniach. Biochem. J. **69**: 248 [1958].)

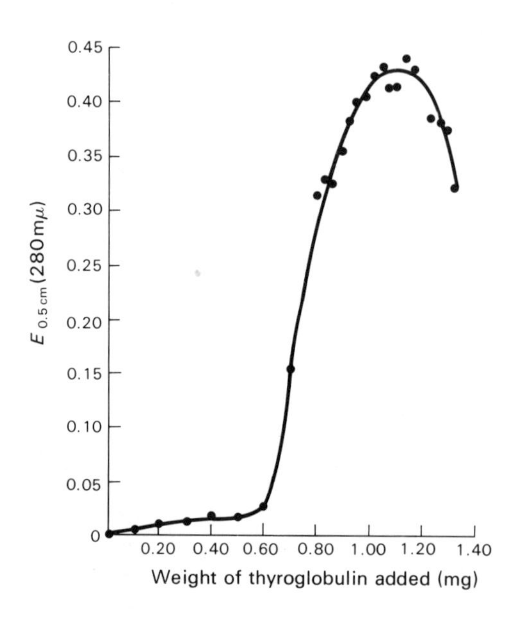

Type I pneumococcal polysaccharide and its homologous antibody except that the cell walls of the bacteria reduced the amount of antibody which could be taken up by the polysaccharide at its surface as compared with the amount in solution. Suspensions of washed red cell stromata may be similarly used to measure amounts of antibody to red cell antigens.

The principle of the quantitative agglutinin method has been extended to the use of washed antigen-antibody precipitates to measure amounts of antibody formed in another species toward the immunoglobulin portion of the specific precipitate. Thus, for example, well-washed precipitates of dextran and human antidextran may be added to a rabbit antiserum to human γG immunoglobulin, and the amount of AbN removed from the serum determined.

The components of C′ which combine with antigen-antibody precipitates have also been measured by the formation of antigen-antibody precipitates in fresh guinea pig or human serum and in the same volume of serum from which the C′ has been inactivated. The differences are about 40 to 60 μg of N per ml of fresh guinea pig serum and about 30 to 50 μg of N per ml for fresh human serum.

MEASUREMENT OF ANTIBODY CONTENT BY THE USE OF ANTIGENS COUPLED TO INSOLUBLE SUPPORTS

A variety of protein antigens have been rendered insoluble by attaching them covalently to materials such as cellulose. These insoluble antigens may be added to antiserum to react with the corresponding antibody. The insoluble antigen complexed with antibody is then washed to remove extraneous proteins, and the antibody determined either by measuring its capacity to take up a dye such as amido black or by extracting with alkali and measuring the quantity of antibody protein extracted. A blank with normal serum is set up to evaluate nonspecific absorption. The antigen coupled to cellulose may be used batchwise or may be made into a paper and the antiserum applied to the paper disc that is then washed and the antibody extracted. With the antigen-cellulose made into a paper, antibody levels of 100-300 μg of protein per ml are required for assays; but with a powdered antigen-cellulose, values as low as 5 to 10 μg of protein per ml have been measured.

MEASUREMENT OF ANTIGEN-BINDING CAPACITY

From a consideration of the precipitin curve in Fig. 4.1, it is evident that the amount of antigen bound at any comparable point such as the point of maximum precipitation should be generally proportional to the amount of antibody present in the serum. This is not strictly true, since the ratios of AbN : AgN at the point of maximum precipitation and at other comparable points vary from one antiserum to another and also with serum samples obtained from the same animal after successive courses of immunization. This variation is another manifestation of the heterogeneity of antibodies. Thus, during three successive courses of immunization the maximum amount of EaN needed to precipitate 1 mg of anti-EaN was 127, 99, and 82 μg of N, respectively. However, several methods have been used which measure antibody in terms of the amount of antigen bound per ml of antiserum. These methods generally make use of I^{131}- (or I^{125}-) labeled antigen. A known amount of labeled antigen is added to varying dilutions of antiserum made in normal rabbit serum. The precipitates are allowed to come to equilibrium in the refrigerator. They are then centrifuged off and washed, and the I^{131} in the precipitate is counted. The volume of antiserum at which 80 percent of the added I^{131}-labeled antigen is precipitated is taken as the end point, and the binding capacity per ml antiserum is calculated. This is termed the P-80 method. Another variant that is used expecially with soluble antigen-antibody complexes and farther out in the inhibition zone is set up in a similar manner, but after reaction has taken place the antigen-antibody complexes are precipitated by adding $(NH_4)_2SO_4$ to one-half saturation. The precipitates are centrifuged and washed with half-saturated $(NH_4)_2SO_4$ and the I^{131} in the precipitate is counted. The amount of antiserum binding 33 percent of the added antigen is determined, and the quantity of antigen bound per ml antiserum computed. The method can be used only with antigens that are not precipitated at 50 percent saturation with $(NH_4)_2SO_4$, and controls are always set up with normal serum to evaluate any nonspecific precipitation of antigen. The specificity of the antigen-antibody complexes may be tested by carrying out the assay in the presence of a large quantity of unlabeled antigen that competitively reduces the amount of labeled antigen bound. The choice of the 80 percent and 33 percent is arbitrary, but is essentially designed to give a reasonable degree of precision in counting the radioactive iodine. The method does not yield accurate analyses for total antibody because of the variation in binding affinity of the different antibody molecules. This would be especially marked in mixtures of bivalent γG and pentavalent γM molecules.

QUANTITATIVE COMPLEMENT FIXATION TESTS

Another procedure for measuring the amount of C′ fixed by antigen-antibody combination involves adding a relatively large amount of C′ (50 or more $C'H_{50}$ units) to the system and measuring the amount of free C′ by a precise spectrophotometric reaction. This type of measurement, using a constant volume of antiserum and varying quantities of antigen, gives curves for $C'H_{50}$ units fixed which resemble quantitative precipitin curves. Three C′ fixation curves are shown in Fig. 4.4. They were obtained through the use of different quantities of rabbit antiserum to the Type III pneumococcus (anti-S III). The $C'H_{50}$ units fixed are plotted against the amount of antibody to the Type III polysaccharide (S III) added. They have been used for estimation of antigen in the antibody excess region of the curve as was done with the quantitative precipitin curves. Complement-fixation inhibition curves also may be obtained by this technique with the use of various low molecular weight haptens; a very close parallelism between findings in the same system by inhibition of complement fixation and inhibition of precipitation has been obtained.

Fig. 4.4 Fixation of C' (guinea pig complement) by constant amounts of S III and varying quantities of rabbit antipneumococcal Type 3 serum C-28. Δ = 0.125 μg of S III; □ = 0.23 μg of S III; ○ = 0.50 μg of S III. (From Osler, A. G., M. M. Mayer, and M. Heidelberger. J. Immunol. **60**: 205[1948]; by permission of the copyright owner, the Williams & Wilkins Company, Baltimore, Md.)

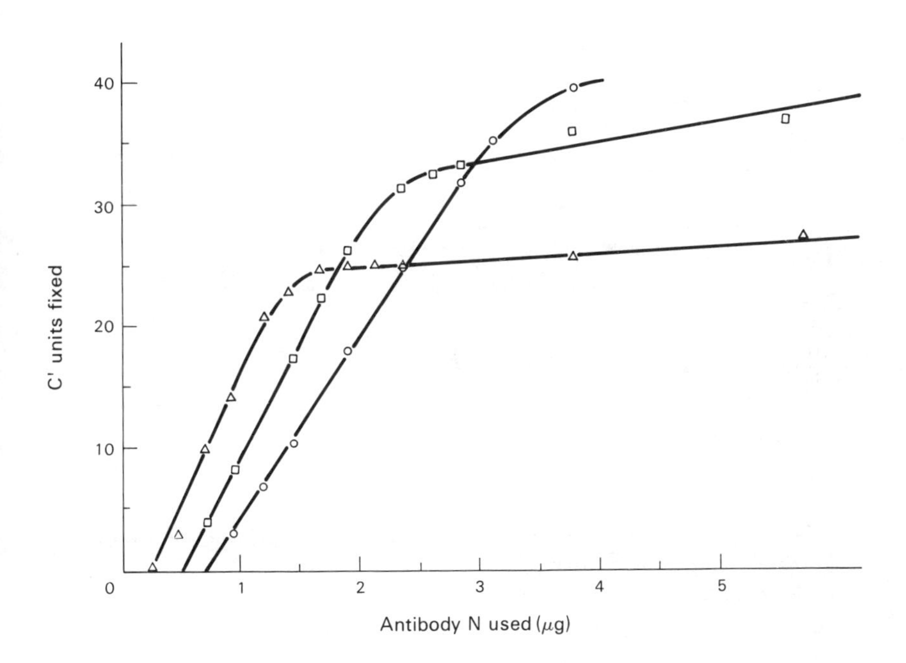

SUGGESTED READINGS

Heidelberger, M. Quantitative absolute methods in the study of antigen-antibody reactions. Bacteriological Reviews **3**: 49 (1949).

Heidelberger, M. Lectures in immunochemistry. (1956) Academic Press, New York.

Kabat, E. A. Kabat and Mayer's Experimental immunochemistry. (2d ed.; 1961) Charles C. Thomas, Publisher, Springfield, Ill.

Campbell, D. H., J. S. Garvey, N. E. Cremer, and D. Sussdorf. Methods in immunology. (1963) W. A. Benjamin, Inc., New York.

The last four references outline quantitative immunochemical methods and their applications.

Raynaud, M. Heterogeneity of diphtheria antitoxin *in* Antibodies to biologically active molecules. (1966) Pergamon Press, Oxford, **1**: 197; *for theories to explain the flocculation reaction.*

5

Precise Measurement of Hapten-Antibody Interaction

To obtain real insight into the nature of the reaction of an antibody combining site with an antigenic determinant, the biochemist and molecular biologist must have available precise methods for measuring the strength of the bond formed. A variety of methods have been developed which not only permit such data to be obtained but have also served to establish the bivalence of γG antibody and provide additional indications of antibody heterogeneity.

EQUILIBRIUM DIALYSIS

This is a very important procedure for measuring the interaction of small molecules with macromolecules such as proteins, nucleic acids, etc. It provides a thermodynamically sound method for obtaining association constants, since measurements are carried out at equilibrium. Dissociation constants have traditionally been used because of the theory of ionization with its emphasis on dissociation in solution to form ions; but in immunochemistry it is the complexing of antigen or hapten with antibody which is important, and association constants are more appropriate. The interaction of a low molecular weight hapten with an antibody combining site may be expressed by the following equation:

$$H + B \rightleftarrows HB \tag{5-1}$$

in which H represents the hapten and B the antibody combining site. The equilibrium constant for this reaction expressed as an association constant is

$$\frac{[HB]}{[H][B]} = K \tag{5-2}$$

To evaluate K it is necessary to know the molar quantities of antibody and of free and bound hapten. Since known amounts of antibody and of hapten can be used, equilibrium dialysis is essentially a method for determining free and bound hapten. In principle, the antibody and hapten are placed on one side of a dialysis membrane in a given volume and buffer on the other side, or antibody may be placed on one side and hapten on the other. Equilibrium is achieved by rocking in a bath at constant temperature. The membrane is freely permeable to the hapten, but does not permit the antibody to pass through. When equilibrium has been reached the free hapten concentration is measured on the side that does not contain the antibody. This is most readily accomplished with colored or radioactive haptens. The free hapten concentrations on both sides of the membrane are equal at equilibrium, and if the volumes on both sides are the same the bound hapten equals the total hapten minus twice the free hapten. Expressed on a molar basis it is possible to calculate r, the ratio of the number of moles of hapten bound per mole of antibody at the concentration of free hapten measured (c). In practice, a series of such measurements is made over a wide range of hapten concentrations. If no antibody is present or if normal γG immunoglobulin is used as a control, the total hapten will be equally distributed on both sides of the membrane. Indeed, such controls are always included to establish that equilibrium has been reached. It is also necessary to measure and correct for a small amount of adsorption of the hapten to the membrane. This is done by adding a known amount of hapten to one side and buffer to the other. At equilibrium the concentration on both sides is measured, and the difference between the amount added and the amount recovered is taken as the quantity adsorbed by the membrane. Whenever possible, as with radioactive haptens, increased precision may be obtained by measuring hapten concentration on both sides of the membrane. This eliminates the correction for adsorption by the membrane. It cannot be used with colored haptens because of shifts in the spectral absorption of the bound hapten.

Equilibrium dialysis measurements may be carried out very adequately in small screw cap vials and one-quarter inch cellophane tubing; volumes of 1 or 2 ml are convenient for inside and outside compartments. The cellulose tubing is soaked in several changes of distilled water, knotted at one end, dried lightly to remove droplets, and filled with the desired volume of solution with an analytical pipette. A small air bubble is left in the top, and the membrane is then knotted. The cellulose sac is then placed in the vial containing the outer liquid; and the vial is capped, sealed with parafilm, and rocked at the desired temperature to equilibrium. About 3 to 4 mg of antibody protein per ml per tube is suitable if equilibrium constants are in the range of 10^5; for each tenfold increase in anticipated value of K, the antibody concentration may be reduced tenfold.

If the reaction of hapten at one site does not influence the reaction at another site and if all sites are assumed to have the same association constant, the following equation may be derived (see Klotz in the Suggested Readings) which serves as a very convenient way of evaluating the data:

$$r/c = n\mathrm{K} - r\mathrm{K} \tag{5-3}$$

in which K is the association constant and n the valence of antibody. The data are generally plotted as r/c against r. This equation is a straight line with the intercept on the abscissa ($r/c = 0$) equal to n and whose intercept on the ordinate is equal to nK. An alternate form of the equation identical with the Langmuir adsorption isotherm is

$$\frac{1}{r} = \frac{1}{nk}\frac{1}{c} + \frac{1}{n} \tag{5-4}$$

in which a plot of $1/r$ against $1/c$ would give a straight line for a homogeneous antibody.

A straight line is not obtained if the antibody molecules do not all have the same association constants, for example, if the antibody is heterogeneous or if the interaction of hapten with one antibody site influences another site.

With antibody solutions a straight line is generally not obtained. A representative set of equilibrium dialysis data was obtained by Karush for the binding of an azo dye containing lactose by antibody to a lactosyl-azoprotein. The haptenic group *p*-azo-phenyllactoside had been coupled to protein and used to immunize rabbits and had been coupled to dimethylaniline to obtain the hapten for equilibrium dialysis. The dimethylaniline was to provide an additional ring somewhat similar to the tyrosine onto which the lactosyl-azo group was coupled in the protein.

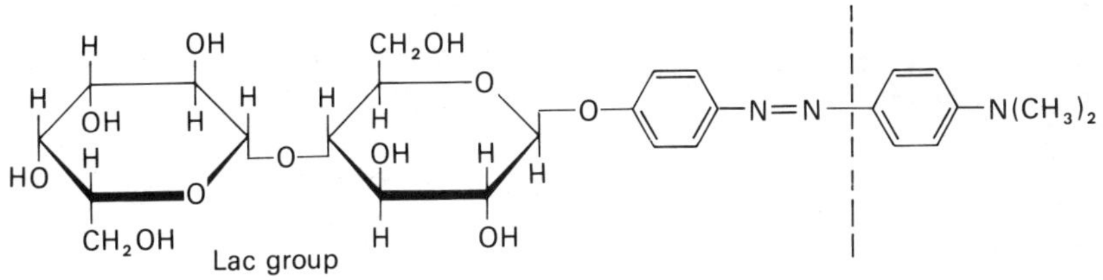

Lac group

Figure 5.1 shows the actual plot for r/c against r for this system. The valence of n by extrapolation to the abscissa which is equivalent to infinite excess of free hapten is seen to be 2.0 both at 25°C and at 7.1°C. The shape of the curve is an indication that the antibody combining sites have varying association constants. The average association constant Ko is taken as equal to the reciprocal of the concentration c at $r = 1$ and is obtained by reading from the curve the value of r/c at $r = 1.0$ This is the concentration of free hapten which maintains half of the antibody sites in combination with hapten.

From the association constant the standard free energy $\Delta F°$ may be calculated in the usual manner

$$\Delta F° = -RT \ln \text{Ko} \tag{5-5}$$

in which R is the gas constant and T the absolute temperature.

When measurements of K at two temperatures are made the enthalpy, $\Delta H°$ may be calculated

$$\frac{d \ln \text{Ko}}{dT} = \frac{\Delta H°}{RT^2} \tag{5-6}$$

using the integrated form

$$\log_{10} \frac{K_2}{K_1} = \frac{\Delta H°(T_2 - T_1)}{2.303 RT_2 \cdot T_1} \tag{5-7}$$

and the entropy $\Delta S°$

$$\Delta F° = \Delta H° - T\Delta S°. \tag{5-8}$$

For the data in Fig. 5.1, the values are as follows:

$$\begin{aligned} \text{Ko} &= 1.57 \times 10^5 \text{ liters per mole at } 25°C \\ &= 4.48 \times 10^5 \text{ liters per mole at } 7.1°C \\ -\Delta F° &= 7.09 \text{ kcal per mole at } 25°C \\ &= 6.85 \text{ kcal per mole at } 7.1°C \\ -\Delta H° &= 9.7 \text{ kcal per mole} \\ \Delta S° &= -8.8 \text{ entropy units per mole} \end{aligned}$$

Fig. 5.1 Binding results at 25° and 7.1°C for the reaction between Lac dye and purified anti-Lac antibody (#2). The points are experimental, and the curves are theoretical. (From Karush, F. J. Amer. Chem. Soc. **79**: 3380. Copyright 1957 by the Amer. Chem. Soc. Reprinted by permission of the copyright owner.)

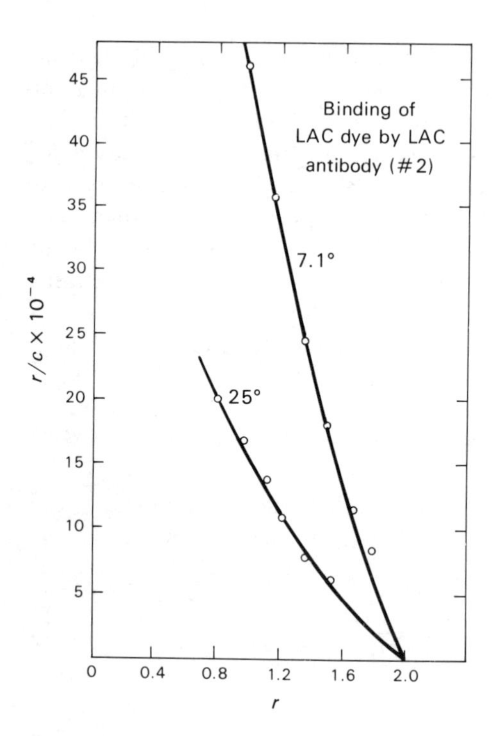

Since with very rare exception measurements of hapten-antibody interaction by equilibrium dialysis all show substantial deviation from linearity, it is desirable to have some way of expressing the range and distribution of association constants or binding affinities of antibody for hapten. This is generally assumed to be a random distribution around Ko so that it may be represented by an error function such as the Gaussian distribution. Evaluation of the degree of spread in association constants must be carried out empirically. A more convenient type of representation, which is now in widespread use, is the Sips distribution which closely approximates the Gauss error function but which can be integrated exactly to:

$$r/n = \frac{(\mathrm{Ko}\ c)^{a}}{1 + (\mathrm{Ko}\ c)^{a}} \tag{5-9}$$

in which a is the index of heterogeneity and ranges from 0 to 1. A value of $a = 1$ indicates a homogeneous antibody.

Equation (5-9) can be written as

$$\log (r/n - r) = a \log c + a \log \text{Ko} \tag{5-10}$$

Plotting $\log (r/n - r)$ versus $\log c$ over a sufficiently wide range of concentration gives a straight line, the slope of which is a and the X intercept may be used to obtain Ko. An a value of 0.5 indicates that 75 percent of the antibody sites have K values between one fortieth and 40 times that of Ko; for 0.7 they range from one sixteenth to 16 times that of Ko; and for 0.8 from about 0.27 to 3.7 times Ko. Applications of these plots will be seen subsequently.

Equilibrium dialysis may also be used to measure the affinity of structurally related colorless or unlabeled haptens for the antibody combining site. To do this the inhibitor hapten is added to an equilibrium dialysis in which a known amount of binding of labeled hapten will occur and the extent of displacement of the labeled hapten from the site measured. The association constant of the inhibitor is calculated in a region in which comparable amounts of inhibitor and labeled hapten are bound to antibody. Haptens of smaller size than the lactose containing azo dye used for studies in Fig. 5.1 such as p-nitrophenyl-β-lactoside and lactose gave Ko values of 6.75 and 2.02×10^4 as compared with a value for the colored hapten used of 13.4×10^4 in the same experiment. With haptens that do not bind to other serum protein constituents it is possible to carry out measurements in whole serum or with concentrated globulin fractions of antiserum.

A very ingenious use of equilibrium dialysis was in detection and as a guide in the purification of the Lac repressor protein from *E. coli* by its property of binding specifically to radioactive isopropylthiogalactoside.

FLUORESCENCE QUENCHING

This technique, which was introduced only recently, has come into extensive use with certain systems for studying the binding of purified antibody to hapten. Unlike equilibrium dialysis, it is essentially an empirical method and may have to be standardized by carrying out equilibrium dialysis measurements on the same solution. In principle, proteins irradiated with ultraviolet light at a wavelength corresponding to their absorption maxima, 280 mμ, will fluoresce and emit light of wavelength 330–350 mμ as a way of partially dissipating the absorbed energy. Of the two chromophores absorbing in this region, tyrosine and tryptophane, the fluorescence spectrum for antibody has been shown to correspond to that of the latter. In the interaction of a hapten with an antibody combining site, some of the energy that would ordinarily be emitted as fluorescence from the tryptophane is transferred to the bound hapten and dissipated, for example, the fluorescence obtained by a molecule of antibody combined with hapten is less than that of free antibody. This quenching of fluorescence tends to be most effective when the hapten absorbs in the region of the emitted fluorescent light. However, the extent of quenching to be expected is not predictable from one hapten to the other, and some quenching has been obtained with haptens that do not absorb in the region of fluorescence.

In spite of the above complications, fluorescence quenching has the very great advantages that binding constants higher than those measurable by equilibrium dialysis can be obtained, that very small amounts of antibody are needed, and that it may be carried out very rapidly. Sequential addition of 10 to 20 μl of hapten may be made to 1 or 2 ml of a suitably buffered solution containing about 40 to 100 μg of antibody protein in a cuvette in the spectrophotofluorometer. The cell should be maintained at constant temperature. After such addition the solution is stirred and the fluorescence read. As additions are made fluorescence decreases and generally reaches a constant value. The fluorescence of a solvent blank is subtracted from all values, and the values are corrected for the dilution occurring on adding hapten. The proportion of sites bound is taken as the degree of quenching observed (Q_i) relative to the maximum quenching (Q_{max}) obtained for the hapten-antibody system under study when all sites are occupied. Q_i/Q_{max} multiplied by the total moles of antibody titrated, multiplied by the valence of antibody—which is taken as 2—gives the number of moles of bound hapten. This is subtracted from total hapten to give free hapten; Ko may be obtained at 50 percent maximum quenching. In some instances with DNP antibody, plots of quenching against moles of hapten added are linear and become sharply horizontal at the point of which the antibody is completely saturated with hapten Q_{max}. The intersection of the two lines gives the moles of hapten bound per mole of antibody and establishes the valence of antibody as 2 (Fig. 5.2).

The determination of Q_{max} often poses considerable difficulty when the quenching does not reach a clearly constant level (Fig. 5.3) as often occurs with low affinity antibodies. Several investigators recommend carrying out a parallel equilibrium dialysis on the same solutions to obtain an independent value for Ko. The fluorescence quenching data is then used to calculate Ko for various values of Q_{max}, and the Q_{max} is selected which gives best agreement with the equilibrium dialysis method. A representative set of such data is given in

Fig. 5.2 The titration of 0.02 mg of anti-DNP antibody with ϵ-DNP-lysine as measured by fluorescence quenching. (From Velick, S. F., C. W. Parker, and H. N. Eisen. Proc. Nat. Acad. Sci. **46**: 1170 [1960].)

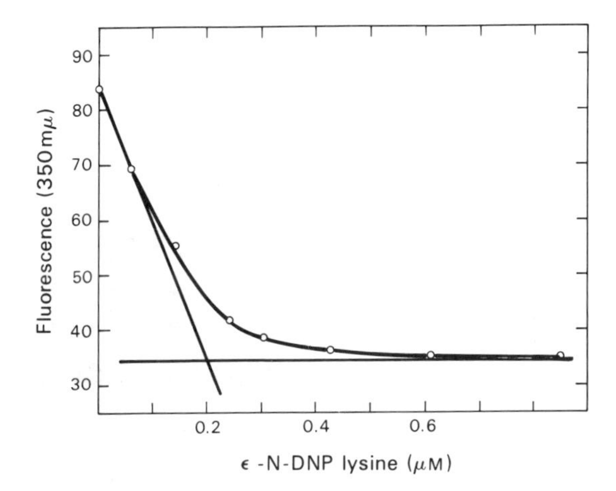

Fig. 5.3 for the binding of 2,4-dinitroaniline by two preparations of rabbit DNP antibody. (A) shows the fluorescence quenching data, (B) the equilibrium dialysis data, and (C) is a Sips plot of the two sets of data when Q_{max} was taken as 0.72 by equating Ko by the two methods. It is clear that the heterogeneity distribution is the same by both methods when the Ko values have been equated. In another study, however, using guinea pig antibody to dinitrophenyl proteins, even a value of 100 percent for Q_{max} did not give a Ko equal to that found by equilibrium dialysis on the same solution, but was about 2 to 3 times higher. Under these circumstances the values by fluorescence quenching become only relative to one another within a given hapten-antibody system. With rabbit antibody to other conjugated proteins, values for Q_{max} of 64, 30, and 32 percent were calculated for the same antibody with hapten of different sizes; surprisingly, Q_{max} was lower for a more strongly bound hapten than for a more weakly bound one lacking a small portion of its structure.

Much remains to be learned about fluorescence quenching. Many of the difficulties encountered may be resolved when one understands the role of antibody heterogeneity in the quenching of fluorescence. Although it is assumed that all sites would quench to the same extent, there are some instances in which the first small additions of hapten cause more quenching than would be expected from the number of sites with which they combine; this would indicate the binding causes more quenching of fluorescence on some antibody molecules than on others. In studies to date, such points have been ignored in the calculations.

Fig. 5.3 Binding of 2,4-dinitroaniline by antibody preparations 2A and 5 at 31°C. (A) Fluorescence quenching; antibody preparations were 95 μg per ml for 2A and 90 μg per ml for 5. The solvent was 0.1 M Tris-Cl, pH 7.6. Titrations were the same in this solvent and in 0.1 M KCl-0.1 M Tris-Cl, pH 7.6. (B) Equilibrium dialysis with [1-^{14}C]-2,4-dinitroaniline; antibody concentrations were 225 μg per ml for 2A and 825-865 μg per ml for 5. The solvent was 0.1 M KCl-0.1 M Tris-Cl, pH 7.6. (C) Combined data of (A) and (B) plotted according to Eq. (5-10). Fluorescence-quenching data are calculated from $Q_{max} = 0.72$. The Ko values for 2A and 5 were $3.5 \pm 0.7 \times 10^6$ and $1.3 \pm 0.3 \times 10^5$ by equilibrium dialysis (●) and $2.3 \pm 0.7 \times 10^6$ and $1.4 \pm 0.4 \times 10^5$ by fluorescence quenching (○), respectively. In the case of 2A, 10 to 85 percent of the binding sites were occupied; in the case of 5, 2 to 80 percent of the binding sites were occupied. (From Eisen, H. N., and G. W. Siskind. Biochemistry **3**: 996. Copyright 1964 by the Amer. Chem. Soc. Reprinted by permission of the copyright owner.)

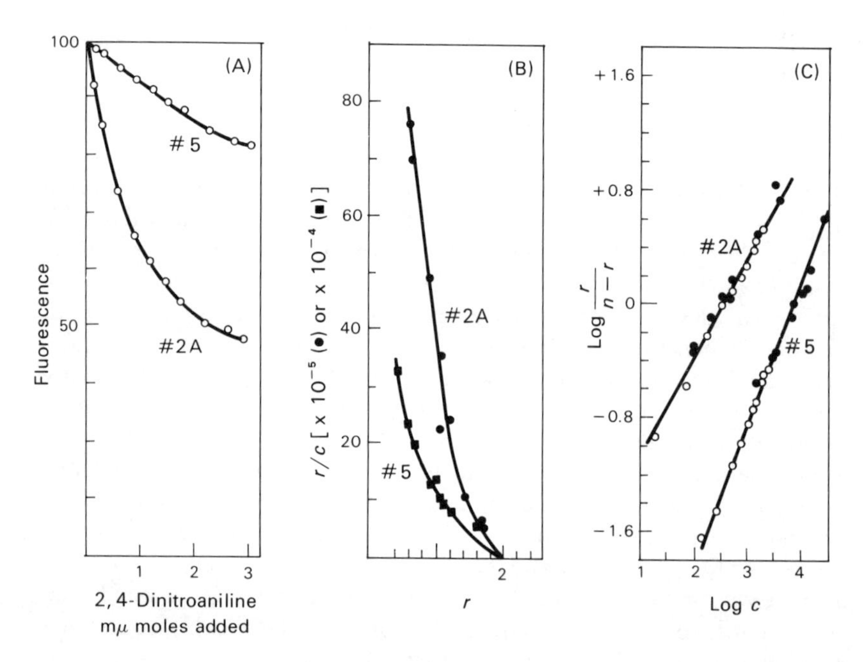

ULTRACENTRIFUGE MEASUREMENTS

The method of ultracentrifuge measurement will probably come into much more widespread use, since the Spinco ultracentrifuge can now provide automatic integration of light absorption measurements throughout the cell, together with simultaneous measurements of protein concentration by refractive index methods. In principle, if a solution of a hapten-antibody complex is centrifuged, the bound hapten will centrifuge with the antibody while the free hapten will sediment at a much slower rate. The hapten-antibody mixture is placed at the bottom of a synthetic boundary cell, and buffer is placed in the upper well. As the rotor accelerates, a boundary of buffer forms; and as sedimentation of the antibody-hapten complex takes place the free hapten concentration at the boundary can be measured. By knowing the initial hapten concentration and measuring the free hapten, bound hapten can be calculated. For this method to be used, the hapten must absorb strongly in the visible or ultraviolet. If runs are carried out at varying hapten concentrations, data comparable to those of equilibrium dialysis may be obtained. The binding of hapten to antibody frequently involves a small shift in the absorption spectrum of the hapten, so that bound hapten is generally not directly measured. As the hapten-antibody complex sediments, its concentration increases relative to the stabilizing free hapten, so that shifts in the equilibrium could occur. Whether these take place rapidly enough to affect the equilibrium constants has not been determined. Fig. 5.4 shows a typical experiment with antibody and with normal γG immunoglobulin. The coincidence in the ultracentrifuge cell of the antibody peak by refractive index with a large portion of the absorption of the dye hapten and the smaller peak resulting from the free hapten is evident. With the nonantibody immunoglobulin there is no evidence of increased light absorption at the sedimenting protein boundary.

A binding curve by this method requires several milligrams of antibody protein, but the antibody can be recovered after each run.

ELECTRON-SPIN RESONANCE (ESR)

ESR is another technique which has recently been employed to study hapten-antibody binding and which may have many potential applications. Electron-spin resonance spectra provide a measure of tumbling motion in solution of a free radical with an unpaired electron. The magnitude of the spin is dependent on the size of the molecule to which the free radical is bound, a larger molecule showing much less tumbling motion than a smaller one. Similarly, the tumbling motion of the small free radical is reduced by immobilizing it in a glass at −196°C. In studies of hapten-antibody interaction, anti-dinitrophenyl antibody was used and the hapten was dinitrophenylnitroxide,

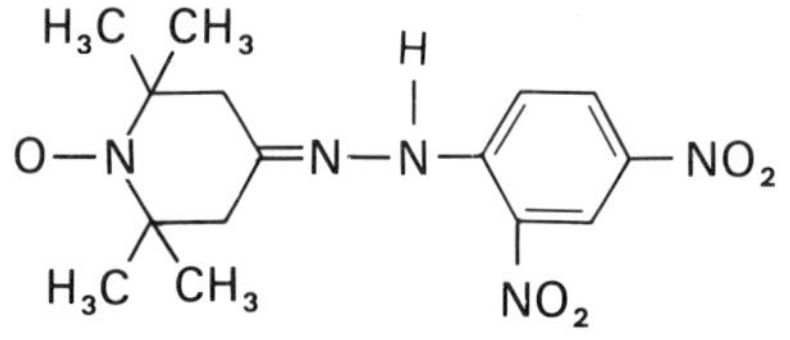

H_3C CH_3 H
O—N =N—N— —NO_2
H_3C CH_3 NO_2

the nitroxide radical providing the unpaired electron spin and the dinitrophenyl residue the haptenic group. The free radical hapten was

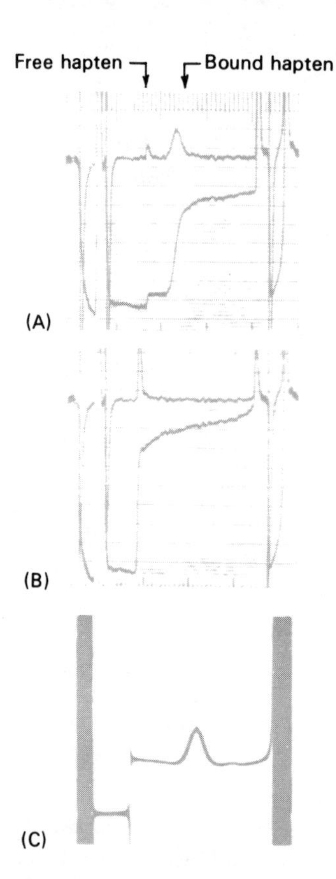

Fig. 5.4 Binding of ε-DNP-lysine by purified rabbit anti-DNP antibody as seen from ultracentrifugal light absorption diagrams at 3654 A. (A) 5.6×10^{-5} M ε-DNP-lysine plus 2.75×10^{-5} M rabbit anti-DNP antibody. (B) 5.6×10^{-5} M ε-DNP-lysine plus 2.75×10^{-5} M normal rabbit γG immunoglobulin. (C) Schileren photograph of (B) taken simultaneously. In (A) the two absorption peaks in integrated and derivative form represent the small amount of excess free hapten and hapten bound to antibody. (B) shows only a free hapten peak, the position of the sedimenting normal γG immunoglobulin being shown in (C). (From Schachman, H. K., L. Gropper, S. Hanlon, and F. Putney. Arch. Biochem. Biophys. **93**: 175 [1963]; by permission of the copyright owner, Academic Press, New York.)

Fig. 5.5 ESR spectra of dinitrophenyl nitroxide. (A) In aqueous solution containing anti-dinitrophenyl antibody. (B) and (D) In aqueous solution without antibody. (C) In a glass at −196°C. Spectrometer sensitivity is the same for (A) and (B), but is tenfold lower for (D). The sensitivity of (C) is not quantitatively related to the others. The free radical concentrations of (A), (B), and (D) are 10^{-4} M, while that of (C) is 10^{-3} M. The antibody concentration in (A) is 0.77×10^{-4}. Acqueous solutions were in 0.1-M phosphate buffer, pH 6.8 at 23°C. (From Stryer, L., and O. H. Griffith. Proc. Nat. Acad. Sci. **54**: 1785 [1965].)

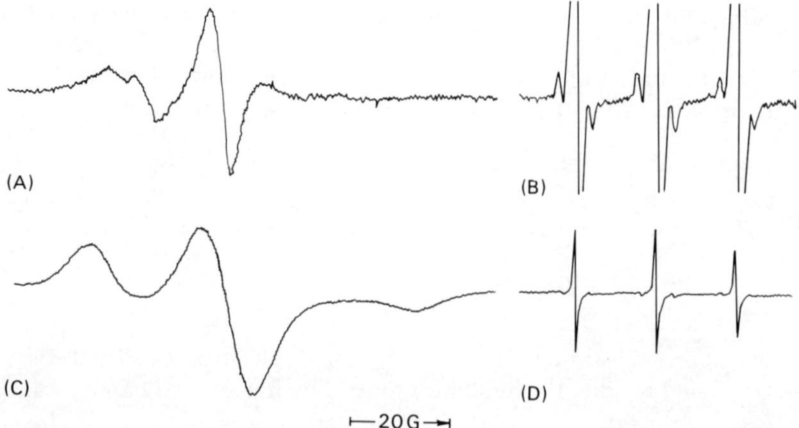

Fig. 5.6 ESR titration of the binding of dinitrophenyl nitroxide to antibody. (A) Antibody in excess (1.80 haptens per antibody molecule). (B) Hapten in excess (2.28 haptens per antibody molecule). (C) is a tenfold reduction in spectrometer sensitivity for solution (B). The antibody concentration was 0.77×10^{-4} M. (From Stryer, L., and O. H. Griffith. Proc. Nat. Acad. Sci. **54**: 1785 [1965].)

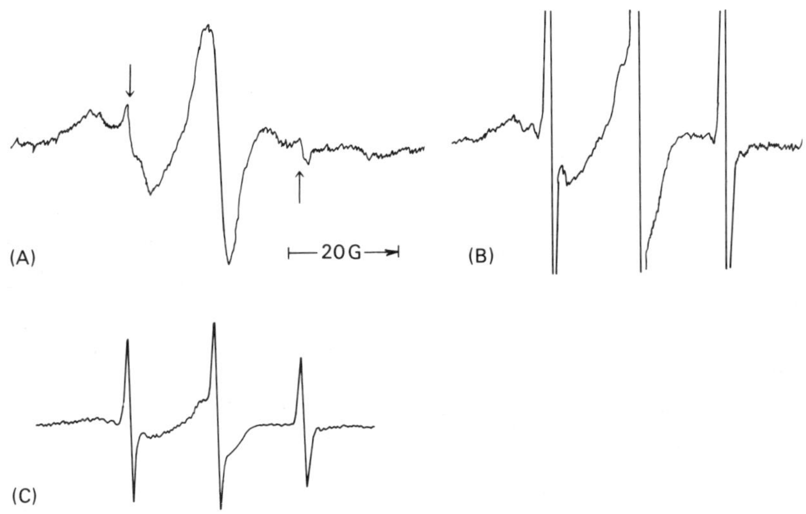

bound to antibody about as strongly as ϵ-dinitrophenyl lysine; the Ko of the antibody used was somewhat less than 10^8. Fig. 5.5 shows the ESR spectra of the free radical hapten in aqueous solution at two different sensitivities [(B) and (D)] and in the presence of antibody (A). The broad spectrum in the presence of antibody indicates that the free radical hapten is restricted in its ability to rotate by combination with antibody. An even greater broadening in the spectrum for the hapten alone is seen when it is kept in a glass at −196°C in glycerol-water [Fig. 5.5(C)]. The curves at the ratio of hapten to antibody of 1.3 in Fig. 5.5(A) gave no evidence of free hapten, but a trace of free hapten could be seen with a hapten-antibody ratio of 1.8 [Fig. 5.6(A)]; with a ratio of 2.28 the spectrum of unbound hapten partially masked the spectrum of the antibody-hapten complex [Fig. 5.6(B) and 5.6(C)]. Thus an estimate of two binding sites per antibody molecule was obtained.

OTHER METHODS

Another potentially useful technique for studying hapten-antibody interaction is by measuring polarization of fluorescence of the hapten-antibody complex as compared with the hapten alone—but this has not yet been applied.

While the binding of hapten to antibody usually produces just a small spectral shift, with anti-DNP antibody and the hapten 2(2,4-dinitrophenylazo)-1-naphthol-3,6-disulfonate

at pH near neutrality a shift from blue to pink occurs when antibody is added to the hapten. This shift is so great as to permit direct measurement of the association constant and the determination of the Sips heterogeneity constant. Unusual systems of this type may be of substantial value. The smaller spectral shift produced by interaction of ε-DNP-L-lysine with rabbit anti-DNP antibody is seen in Fig. 5.7; no spectral shift occurred with nonantibody rabbit γG globulin. Dinitrotoluene gave an even smaller spectral shift. The ε-DNP-lysine has been shown to undergo a spectral shift on interaction with tryptophan as the free amino acid in solution; other amino acids show no such effect. This interaction is thought to result from the formation of a complex be-

Fig. 5.7 Spectral shifts produced by binding of ε-DNP-lysine and dinitrotoluene by anti-DNP antibody. Key: ○ = free ligand; ● = bound ligand. (Adapted from Eisen, H. N., and G. W. Siskind. Biochemistry **3**: 996. Copyright 1964 by the Amer. Chem. Soc. Adapted with permission of the copyright owner.)

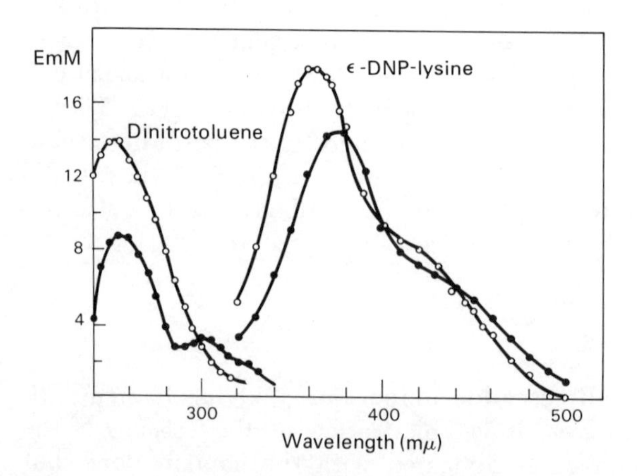

tween the tryptophan acting as an electron donor and the dinitrophenyl groups as an electron acceptor (charge-transfer complex). On this basis the spectral shift that occurs when ϵ-DNP-lysine binds to anti-DNP has been attributed to a charge-transfer complex of the hapten with tryptophan in the antibody combining site. Rabbit, guinea pig, goat, and horse antibodies with specificity for DNP or trinitrophenyl (TNP) determinants showed similar spectral changes in reacting with haptens containing either DNP or TNP groupings.

SIGNIFICANCE OF THERMODYNAMIC DATA FOR ANTIGEN-ANTIBODY INTERACTION

The use of the methods described to give values for Ko, ΔF, ΔH, and ΔS does not yet permit one to define precisely the relative contributions of the various types of weak interactions to the hapten-antibody bond. This is essentially because Eq. (5-1) is a great oversimplification of the true reaction that takes place in an aqueous environment in that water molecules held around the hapten and in the antibody combining site may be released in the formation of the hapten-antibody bond so that the reaction probably is as follows:

$$H_{(x+n)H_2O} + B_{(y+m)H_2O} \rightleftharpoons H_{nH_2O}\,B_{mH_2O} + (x+y)H_2O \quad (5\text{-}11)$$

x and y represent only molecules of bound water released as a result of the reaction, while n and m represent any remaining water. Apart from actual release of water, changes in the structure of the water atmosphere around the hapten or antibody site could also affect the thermodynamic parameters.

Thus the ΔF and ΔS values involve changes due to the release or change of state of water resulting from hapten-antibody combination. The values for Ko for rabbit antibodies to ϵ-DNP-bovine γG immunoglobulin have varied over a 10,000-fold range so that the ΔF° would range over 5 kcal per mole. This indeed is not much smaller than the spread in ΔF° values of from -5 to -12 kcal per mole for all of the hapten-antibody interactions studied to date. ΔS° for the different systems vary from $+22$ to -30 entropy units per mole. While the release of bound water and the consequent interaction of an apolar group on the hapten with an apolar region in the antibody site would yield an increase in entropy, actual antibody-hapten binding would have a substantial negative ΔS° by reducing the freedom in the system. The great spread in values suggests that the contributions of the various weak interactions differ sharply for haptens of varying structure and that among the heterogeneous populations of antibody molecules, even to a small hapten,the various types of weak bonds involved may make different over-all contributions. Part of this difficulty may be a consequence of the use of systems in which the population of antigenic determinants is very heterogeneous (for further details see Karush in the Suggested Readings).

SUGGESTED READINGS

Klotz, I. M. Protein interactions. *In* the Proteins **1** B: 727 (1953). (H. Neurath and K. Bailey, eds.). [Academic Press, New York]; *for a detailed discussion of the interaction of small molecules with proteins.*

Karush, F. Immunological specificity and molecular structure. Advances in Immunology **2**, 1 (1962). [Academic Press, New York]; *for hapten-antibody interactions, the significance of thermodynamic measurements and the relative importance of hydrophobic and other bonds.*

Eisen, H. N. Equilibrium dialysis for measurement of antibody-hapten affinities. Methods in Medical Research, Yearbook **10**: 106 (1964). Chicago.

Eisen, H. N. Determination of antibody affinity for haptens and antigens by means of fluorescence quenching. Methods in Medical Research, Yearbook **10**: 115 (1964); [Chicago].

For operational details of equilibrium dialysis and fluorescence quenching.

Eisen, H. N. and G. W. Siskind. Variations in affinity of antibodies during the immune response. Biochemistry **3**: 996 (1964).

Siskind, G. W., W. E Paul, and B. Benacerraf. Studies on the effect of the carrier molecule on anti-hapten antibody synthesis I. Effect of carrier on the nature of the antibody synthesized. Journal of Experimental Medicine **123**: 673 (1966).

Saha, A., F. Karush, and R. Marks. Antibody affinity. I. Studies with a large haptenic group. Immunochemistry **3**: 279 (1966);

The last three papers show some of the problems in standardizing fluorescence quenching relative to equilibrium dialysis.

Gilbert, W. and B. Müller-Hill. Isolation of the Lac repressor. Proceedings of the National Academy of Sciences **56**: 1891 (1966); *an important application of equilibrium dialysis in molecular biology.*

Schachman, H. K., L. Gropper, S. Hanlon, and F. Putney. Ultracentrifuge studies with absorption optics. II. Incorporation of a monochromator and its application to the study of proteins and interacting systems. Archives of Biochemistry and Biophysics **99**: 175 (1963); *the use of ultracentrifugation to determine hapten-antibody binding constants.*

Stryer, L. and O. H. Griffith. A spin labelled hapten. Proceedings of the National Academy of Sciences **54**: 1785 (1965); *the first application of electron spin resonance to hapten-antibody interaction.*

Isenberg, I. Free radicals in tissue. Physiological Reviews. **44**: 487 (1964); *for an introduction to electron spin resonance.*

Metzger, H., L. Wofsy, and S. J. Singer. A specific antibody-hapten reaction with novel spectral properties. Archives of Biochemistry and Biophysics **103**: 206 (1963); *reaction of an unusual DNP hapten with antibody produces a large spectral shift.*

Little, J. R. and H. N. Eisen. Evidence for tryptophan in the active sites of antibodies to polynitrobenzenes. Biochemistry **6**: 3119 (1967).

6

Antigenic Determinants and the Size of the Antibody Combining Site

Having outlined the methods that are used to obtain information about antigen-antibody and hapten-antibody interaction, we shall now attempt to consider the nature of an antigenic determinant and the structural features and dimensions of the antibody combining sites that recognize it. It is evident that these are aspects of the same question and that the problem is a very important one in immunochemistry.

HOW BIG IS IT?

If we ask ourselves how large an antibody combining site is, one answer would be that it is as large as the antigenic determinant that fills it. This is not so ridiculous as it seems at first glance, since if one could determine the size of an antigenic determinant of known structure one would have a measure of the size of the antibody combining site.

For this purpose the interaction of dextran and human antibody to dextran serves as an ideal molecular probe. We may reasonably assume that the antidextran, in reacting with dextran, combines optimally, so that the entire antibody combining site is filled. Since the dextran consists of long chains of glucose units and since the oligosaccharides of glucose of the dextran structure from the disaccharide (isomaltose) to the heptasaccharide (isomaltoheptaose) are available (see Figs. 2.2 and 2.3), one may use them competitively to displace the dextran from its combination with antibody. In practice this is done by determining their relative capacity to inhibit the precipitation of antidextran by dextran. Since we are interested in their relative inhibiting power molecule for molecule, these comparisons are generally made on a molar basis. Small oligosaccharides that do not completely occupy the combining site would be expected to be relatively weak and, as oligosaccharide size increases, inhibiting power should increase, reaching a maximum when the site is completely filled by an oligosaccharide of the proper size. Larger oligosaccharides should be equal in potency to the oligosaccharide of the proper size, since in the antigen itself the chains are generally longer than the portion reacting with the site.

This assumption is borne out in practice. Figure 6.1 shows a series of hapten-inhibition curves with the antidextran of six individuals. The same quantities of dextran and antidextran were used, and oligosaccharides from the trisaccharide to the hexasaccharide were assayed. In all cases one sees not only that inhibiting power per molecule increases in going from the trisaccharide to the hexasaccharide, but also that the increment in inhibiting power decreases as the size of the oligosaccharide inhibitor increases, the latter indicating that a limit in inhibiting power is being attained. Figure 6.2 shows a comparison of the hexa- and heptasaccharides and indicates that, within experimental error, the two are equal.

Figure 6.1 also yields important evidence indicating the heterogeneity of the antidextran combining sites, in that the ratio of the inhibiting power of the smaller oligosaccharides to isomaltohexaose (IM6) is not the same for all six antisera but varies from one to the other. In antiserum $30D_4$ it requires only 2.5 times as much trisaccharide (IM3) as hexasaccharide for 50 percent inhibition, while with antiserum $20D_3$ about 30 times as much IM3 is needed. The other antisera show intermediate values. Were all antidextran molecules uniform with respect to their combining sites, the ratio of inhibiting power of the various oligosaccharides to IM6 would be expected to be the same. Figure 6.3 shows inhibition curves for a seventh individual who produced antidextran in which the heptasaccharide (IM7) can be seen to be slightly but significantly better than IM6. One may think of each individual as having produced a population of antibody molecules with combining sites of various sizes, the upper limit being that of a hexasaccharide or heptasaccharide and the lower limit not being deter-

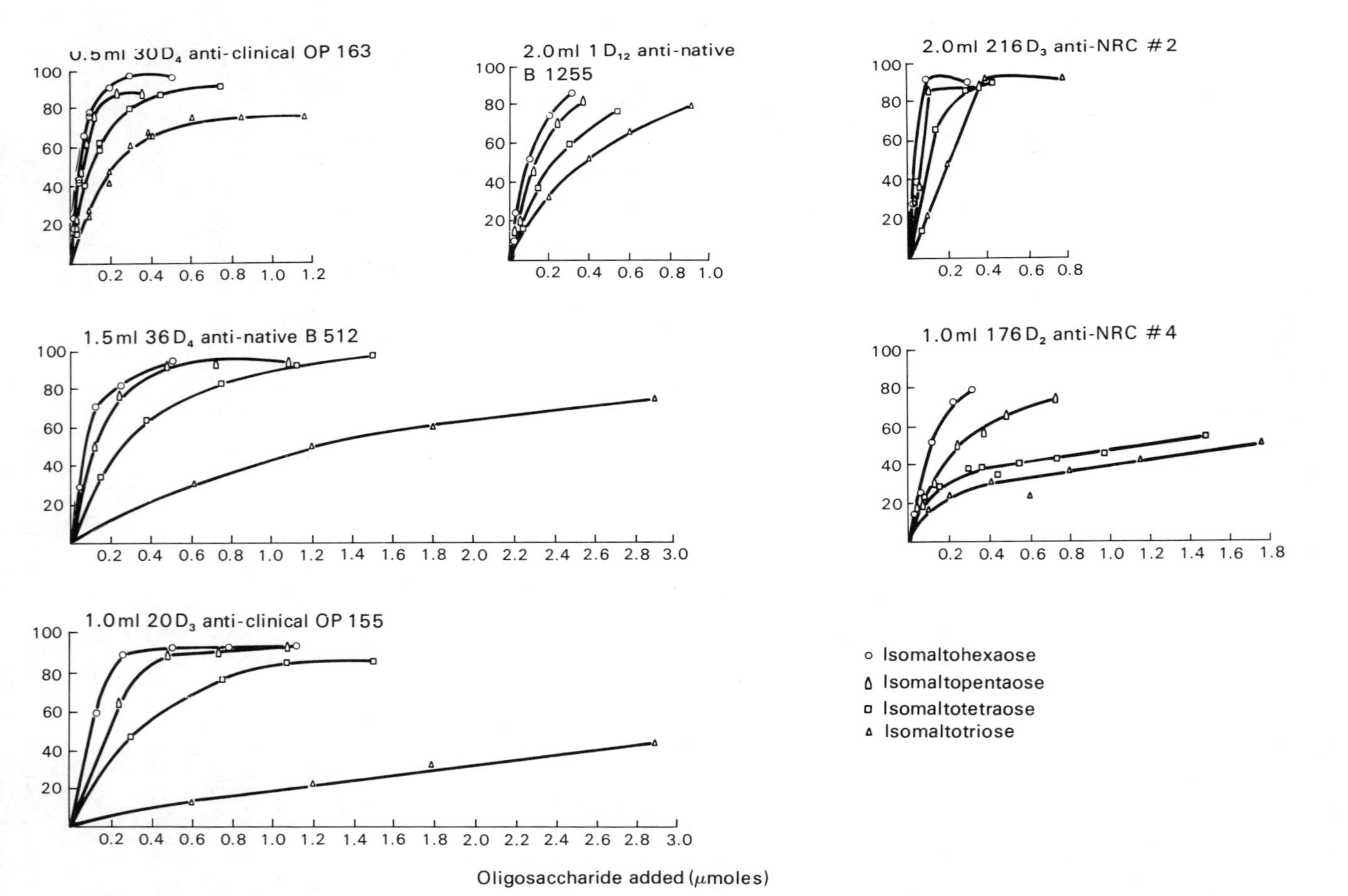

Fig. 6.1 Inhibition by isomaltose oligosaccharides of precipitation by dextran of the antidextran in six human antisera. (From Kabat and Mayer's Experimental immunochemistry. [2d ed.; 1961] Charles, C. Thomas, Publisher, Springfield, Ill.)

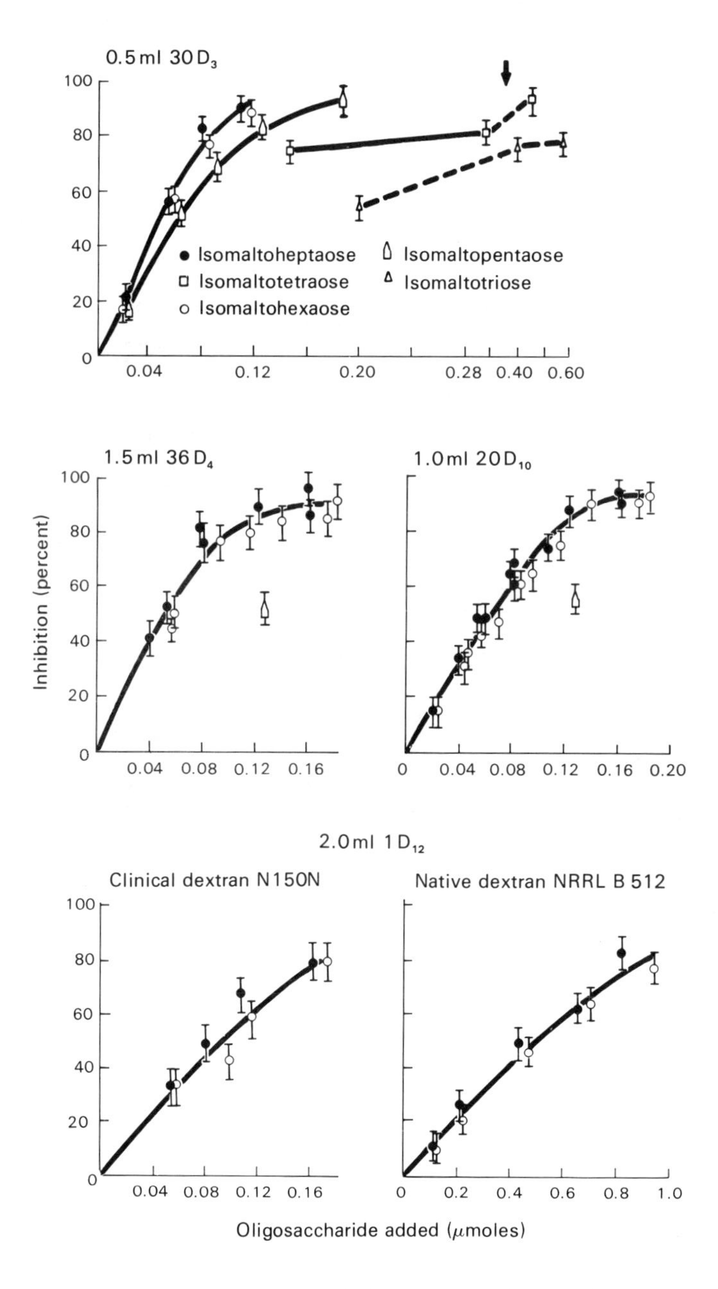

Fig. 6.2 Comparison of isomaltoheptaose and isomaltohexaose as inhibitors of precipitation by dextran of human antidextran. (From J. Immunol. **84**: 82 [1960]; by permission of the copyright owner, The Williams & Wilkins Company, Baltimore, Md.)

Fig. 6.3 Comparisons of isomaltoheptaose with isomaltohexaose and isomaltopentaose as inhibitors of precipitation by dextran of human antidextran. (From J. Immunol. **84**: 82 [1960]; by permission of the copyright owner, The Williams & Wilkins Company, Baltimore, Md.)

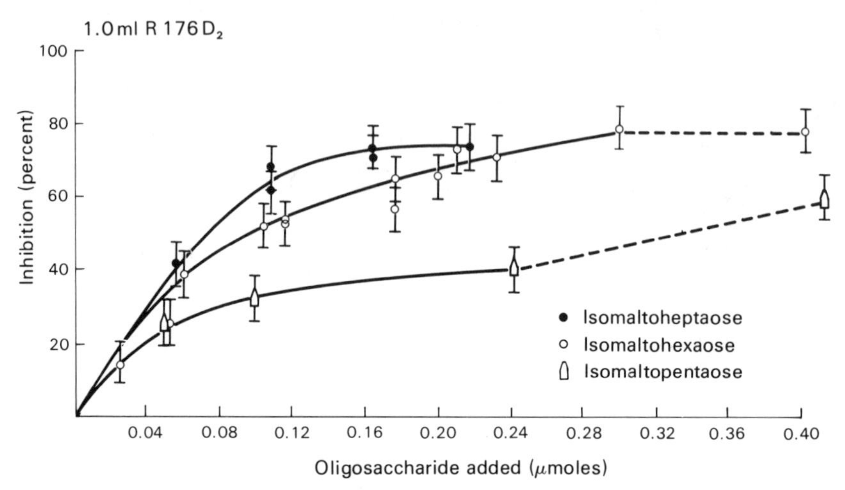

minable from these data. The proportion of molecules with combining sites of a given size would vary from one antiserum to another. Antiserum $30D_4$ can be thought to have a smaller proportion of molecules with larger sized sites than antiserum $20D_3$.

A molecule of isomaltohexaose is seen in Fig. 6.4 in its most extended form. Its dimensions are about $34 \times 12 \times 7$ Angstrom units ($1A = 10^{-8}$ cm). While this gives some idea of the size of an antigenic determinant, one must not necessarily consider that the antibody combining site has a shape corresponding to this stretched-out form. The hexasaccharide may fold over into some more compact form. Moreover, it has a substantial degree of freedom to assume many conformations in solution. There is relatively free rotation of each ring around carbon 6, so that the planes of the six rings are theoretically free to assume any angle relative to one another. In solution some conformations may well be more stable, so that most of the molecules may exist in these forms. There is no information as to whether antibodies may be formed to all possible conformations or to only one or a few of the more stable conformations; but it is clear that this offers another dimension for antibody heterogeneity. With oligosaccharides containing acetylated amino sugars, evidence from optical rotatory dispersion studies indicate that preferred conformations actually exist in solution.

Since the inhibition data are obtained under equilibrium conditions, one may assume that at any given comparable point on the curves, for example, at 50 percent inhibition, the relative inhibiting

Fig. 6.4 The extended form of isomaltohexaose. (From Kabat, E. A. J. Cell. Comp. Physiol. **50** [suppl 1]:79 [1957]; by permission.)

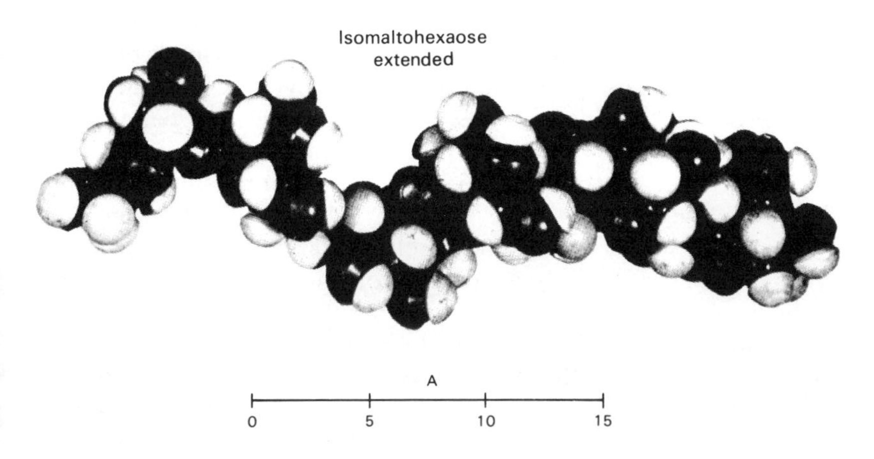

power of the isomaltose oligosaccharides is proportional to their ΔF°. Assuming the ΔF° for the hexasaccharide to have a value of −7500 calories, which was close to that found by equilibrium dialysis for the *p*(*p*-dimethylaminobenzeneazo-)phenyl-β-lactoside (see Chapter 4), the relative decrease in binding energy Δ(ΔF°) with decreasing oligosaccharide chain length may be calculated. These data are given in Table 6.1 for the two antidextran sera in Fig. 6.1 showing the greatest

TABLE 6.1

Decrease in Free Energy (−ΔF°) of Binding of the Oligosaccharides with Decreasing Degree of Polymerization

Oligosaccharide	Δ(ΔF°) (Isomaltohexaose[a] −Other Oligosaccharide)			
	Antiserum $30D_4$ (*cal*)	*Estimated Contribution to Total Binding* (*percent*)	*Antiserum* $20D_2$ $3 \rightarrow 4$ (*cal*)	*Estimated Contribution to Total Binding* (*percent*)
Isomaltohexaose	—	100	—	100
Isomaltopentaose	160	98	240	97
Isomaltotetraose	330	95	650	91
Isomaltotriose	730	90	1900	75
Isomaltose	3000	60		
Glucose	(4600)[b]	39		

[a]Assuming ΔF° for hexasaccharide = −7500 cal

[b]( ) = 50-percent inhibition estimated to occur at 300 μM.

From J. Immunol. **77**: 377 (1956); by permission of the copyright owner, The Williams & Wilkins Company, Baltimore, Md.

differences in inhibiting power. It is evident that the first glucose contributes most to the ΔF°, with each succeeding glucose contributing a smaller increment. Similar data were obtained by equilibrium dialysis for the lactosyl hapten and various smaller compounds of related structure; the values for Ko and for ΔF° are given in Table 6.2. Thus methyl-β-D-lactoside contributes 5.88 of the 7.00 kcal found for the lactosyl hapten—or 84 percent of the total binding energy—and methyl-β-D-galactoside contributes 2.56 or 37 percent of the binding energy. These relationships have been found to hold for all antigen-antibody systems studied, including linear polysaccharides and polypeptides. They suggest that there is a primary point of attachment of an antigenic determinant to an antibody combining site and that this involves the grouping that contributes the highest proportion of the binding energy. This is called the IMMUNODOMINANT group. In branched polysaccharides the terminal nonreducing sugar is readily recognized as immunodominant, but in linear polymers or with antibody directed toward determinants not involving the ends of chains, the principle is equally applicable. That the amino acid at the end of a polypeptide chain or a terminal nonreducing sugar residue makes a proportionally larger contribution to binding energy than the other portions of an antigenic determinant was shown with azoproteins many years ago by Landsteiner and by Goebel.

The estimate of the hexasaccharide or heptasaccharide as the upper limit for the size of an antibody combining site has been extensively verified with a number of other antigen-antibody systems.

TABLE 6.2

The Inhibition of Lac Dye Binding by Structurally Related Molecules at 25° C
[*p*-(*p*-dimethylaminobenzeneazo)-phenyl-β-lactoside]

Anti-Lac Antibody + Lac Dye, $K_o = 13.4 \times 10^4$, $-\Delta F° = 7.00$ kcal/mole		
Inhibitor	$K_o \times 10^{-4}$	$-\Delta F°$
p-Nitrophenyl-β-lactoside	6.75	6.60
Methyl-β- lactoside	2.02	5.88
Lactose (64% β)	1.10	5.52
Cellobiose (66% β)	0.00275	1.96
Methyl-β-D-galactoside	0.00747	2.56
Methyl-α-D-galactoside	0.00134	1.54
Methyl-β-D-glucoside	0.00054	0.97

From Karush. F. J. Amer.Chem. Soc. **79**: 3380.

TABLE 6.3
Sizes of Various Antigenic Determinants

Antigen	Determinant	Size in Most Extended Form (A)	Molecular Weight
Dextran	Isomaltohexaose	34 × 12 × 7	990
Silk fibroin	Gly [gly_3ala_3] Tyr	27	632
	Dodecapeptide mixture	44	1000
$G_{60}A_{40}$, $G_{60}A_{30}T_{10}$, and $G_{42}L_{28}A_{30}$	Hexaglutamic acid	36 × 10 × 6	792
Polyalanyl bovine serum albumin	Pentaalanine	25 × 11 × 6.5	373
Polylysyl rabbit serum albumin	Penta-(or hexa-) lysine	27 × 17 × 6.5	659
Polylysine + phosphoryl bovine serum albumin	Pentalysine	27 × 17 × 6.5	659
α-DNP-heptalysine	α-DNP-heptalysine	30 × 17 × 6.5	1080

From J. Immunol. **97**: 1 (1966): by permission of the copyright owner, The Williams and Wilkins Company, Baltimore, Md.

In this connection the synthetic polypeptides have proved especially valuable, polyalanine, polylysine and polyglutamic acid having been used. Table 6.3 summarizes the data obtained. With silk fibroin, an octapeptide was less active than a mixture of dodecapeptides, probably placing the upper limit as somewhere between the two.

Fig. 6.5 shows data with antisera to poly-D-lysine of molecular weight 90–100,000 on the capacity of oligolysines to inhibit C′ fixation (see Chapter 3) by the poly-D-lysine. Inhibiting potency increased with chain length and reached a maximum with a penta-D-lysine; larger oligopeptides up to an oligomer with 13 lysines were as potent on a molar basis as the penta-D-lysine.

In another study using a polylysyl rabbit serum albumin with an average chain length of 5.5 lysines, antisera showed a somewhat different type of behavior. Inhibiting power increased rapidly and uniformly with size for the first few residues, and the rate of increase diminished sharply above the pentalysine with some increment up to the nona-lysine; nona-and decalysines were equally potent (Fig. 6.6). The data from the initial portion of the curve extrapolated to a penta- or hexapeptide as the upper limit for the determinant, but the basis for the two different types of result is not clearly understood.

In a similar series of polylysines in which the terminal α-amino of lysine was substituted by the immunodominant DNP group and antibody produced to α-DNP-$(Lys)_{11}$ or α-DNP-$(Lys)_9$, an upper

Fig. 6.5 Amounts of D-lysine oligopeptides required for 50 percent inhibition of complement fixation by anti-poly-D-lysine with 0.06 μg poly-D-lysine. The four symbols represent different antisera. (From Van Vunakis, H., J. Kaplan, H. Lehrer, and L. Levine. Immunochemistry **3**: 393 [1966]; by permission of the copyright owner, Pergamon, Oxford.)

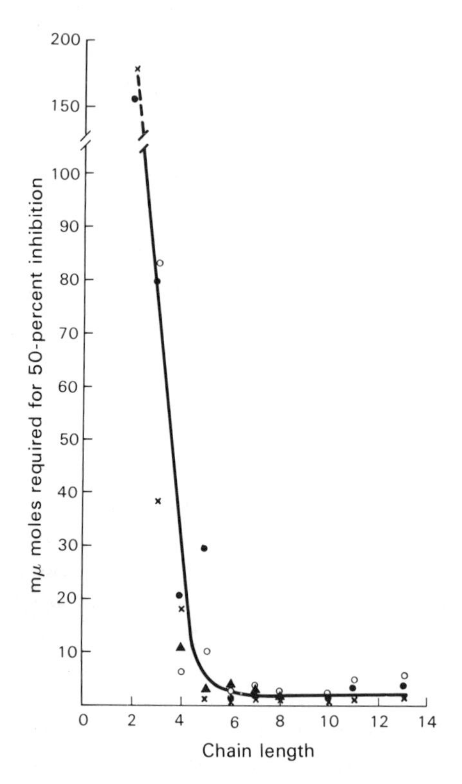

limit in inhibition was reached with α-DNP-heptalysine, the hepta-, octa-, and nona-DNP-lysines being of equal potency. This would be about the largest polypeptide antigenic determinant thus far encountered, being close to isomaltohexaose. It is of especial interest that the α-DNP-heptalysine is itself antigenic and gives rise to the antibodies, although they precipitate only with a multivalent antigen formed by coupling the α-DNP- heptalysine to succinylated bovine serum albumin using carbodiimide. Whether the size observed is truly that of the extended molecule or whether specificity is directed toward some more compact form is not clear. (For other studies with this system, see Chapter 13).

From studies of the action of carboxypeptidase A on oligopeptides of L-alanine containing one or more D-alanines at various positions, the active site of this enzyme was inferred to be complementary to a tetra- or pentapeptide quite close to that for combining sites of antibodies to synthetic polypeptides. As previously noted (see Chapter 1), the active site of lysozyme accommodates a hexasaccharide, being therefore quite comparable to the larger antidextran combining sites.

Returning to the dextran-antidextran system, one may reasonably ask whether the contribution of all six glucoses is truly specific and represents part of the antigen-antibody interaction or whether the small increment in $\Delta F°$ for the penta- and hexasaccharides is merely a nonspecific contribution resulting from some binding outside of the true antibody combining site. Evidence for the specificity of binding for the first four glucoses is very strong, since a small change in oligosaccharide structure – such as the change of the linkage between the third and fourth glucose from the nonreducing end from α-(1⟶6) in isomaltotetraose to α-(1⟶4) to give 4-O-α-isomaltotriosyl-D-glucose– caused a significant loss of inhibiting power to below that of isomaltotriose itself. Moreover, if the isomaltose oligosaccharides have a single glucose branch on the third or fourth sugar from the reducing end, their activity as inhibitors is reduced, a glucosyl substituted isomaltohexaose becoming less potent than isomaltotetraose; glucosyl substituted penta- and tetrasaccharides were correspondingly less active than the glucosyl substituted hexasaccharide. In another polysaccharide-

Fig. 6.6 The molar ratio of oligolysine required for 30 percent (left) or 40 percent (right) inhibition to the homologous antigen at the equivalence point, as a function of the inhibitory peptide. (From Arnon, R., M. Sela, A. Yaron, and H. A. Sober. Biochemistry **4**: 948. Copyright 1965 by the Amer. Chem. Soc.; reproduced by permission of the copyright owner.)

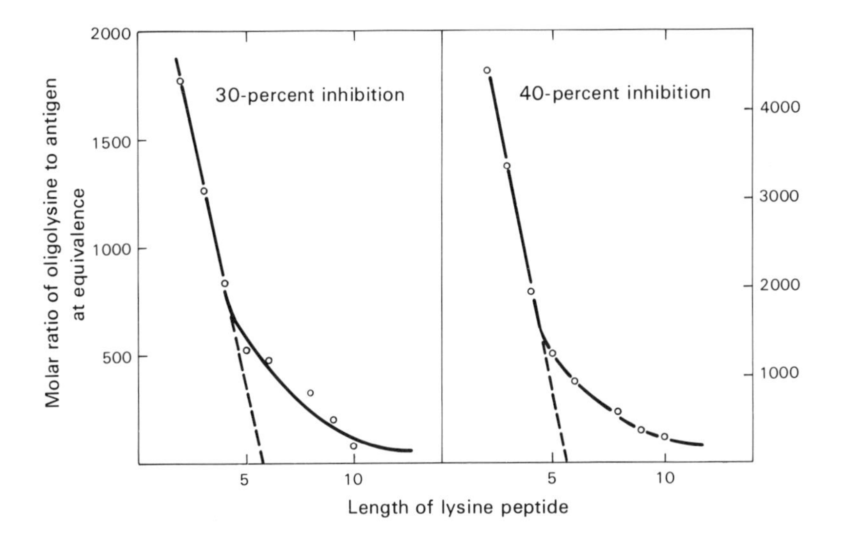

antipolysaccharide system, the specific polysaccharide of pneumococcus Type III, which is a linear polymer of glucose linked β-(1→3) to glucuronic acid which is in turn linked β-(1→4) to the next glucose, a hexasaccharide was also found to be the best inhibitor. If the reducing end was converted to the alcohol by sodium borohydride, the inhibiting power was reduced to about that of the pentasaccharide. Corresponding losses in inhibiting activity occurred on reduction of the smaller oligomers. These data, too, would tend to implicate the entire hexasaccharide as specific to the antibody combining site.

Perhaps the most striking evidence that the antigenic determinant is composed of a series of amino acids each of which makes a specific contribution to binding energy comes from work with a dinitrophenyltetrapeptide, Val-ε-DNP-Lys-Leu-Phe-OEt, linked by carbodiimide to human serum albumin by means of the α-amino group of the valine. Rabbit antisera were of two types, LT-A and LT-B, as seen in Table 6.4. For comparison, an antiserum to DNP bovine gamma globulin is included, in which the antigenic determinants are heterogeneous since each lysine onto which a DNP residue is attached is linked to different sequences of amino acids.

With antiserum LT-A, Ko was greatest for the homologous DNP-tetrapeptide and indeed the substitution of a glycine for leucine as

TABLE 6.4

Contribution of Various Amino Acids to Ko of the Antigenic Determinant -Val-ε-DNP-Lys-Leu-Phe-OEt in Reacting with Purified Rabbit Antibodies as Measured by Fluorescence Quenching

Hapten	K_o l/mole × 10^{-6}		
	Anti-DNP-tetrapeptide		Anti-DNP-bovine -γG
	LT-A	LT-B	
1. Val-ε-DNP-Lys-Leu-Phe-OEt	110	50	80
2. Val-ε-DNP-Lys-Gly-Phe-OEt	100	150	200
3. Val-ε-DNP-Lys-Gly-Gly-OEt	12	180	300
4. Val-ε-DNP-Lys-OMe	10	230	300
5. ε-DNP-L-Lys	5	160	320
6. ε-DNP-aminocaproate	7	180	350
7. ε-DNP-Lys-OMe	5	160	300
Val-ε-DNP-Lys-Val-Tyr-Leu-OMe	20	50	60
D-Val-ε-DNP-D-Lys-D-Leu-D-Phe-OMe	80		70
ε-DNP-D-Lys	4.5	150	300

Data from Parker, C. W., S. M. Gott and M. C. Johnson. Biochemistry **5**: 2314 (1966).

the subterminal amino acid produced a slight reduction in Ko. The two end amino acids were important, as seen by the replacement of the Leu-Phe by Gly-Gly which reduced Ko almost to one-tenth, as did the removal of these two residues. ϵ-DNP-L- or D-lysine and the L-methyl ester had but one twentieth the Ko of the entire haptenic grouping; this still represents the major portion of the total $\Delta F°$. It is of interest that if the DNP-tetrapeptide were made up entirely of D-amino acids a diminution in Ko from 110 to 80 occurred, while the substitution of a valine-tyrosine and leucine for the leucine and phenylalanine in the L-peptide also gave a Ko of only 20.

Antiserum LT-B showed a different type of specificity in which the best inhibitor was Val-ϵ-DNP-Lys-OMe with a Ko of 230, while ϵ-DNP-L-Lys and its methyl ester showed a Ko of 160, which indicated that the ϵ-DNP-lysine was the immunodominant group of the antigenic determinant to which this rabbit formed antibody. Indeed, further substitution on the lysine, as in the tetrapeptide, gave lower Ko values; larger peptides containing the site of attachment of the valine might have proved even better inhibitors. The ϵ-DNP-D-lysine had a Ko only slightly less than the L-isomer.

The antibody to DNP bovine γG immunoglobulin also behaved similarly to antiserum LT-B in that the predominant specificity was for the ϵ-DNP group and the carbon chain of lysine, since ϵ-DNP-aminocaproate was the best inhibitor followed closely by ϵ-DNP-L-lysine with its methyl ester and ϵ-DNP-D-lysine having only slightly lower Ko values. Val-ϵ-DNP-Lys-OMe and Val-ϵ-DNP-Lys-Gly-Gly-OEt were about equal to ϵ-DNP-Lys-OMe, but the addition of any peptide with larger side chains to the carboxyl of lysine to replace the glycines caused a sharp reduction in Ko. The heterogeneity of the determinants of the DNP-bovine-γG immunoglobulin did not permit probing into the sites beyond the common ϵ-DNP-lysine residue.

In insulin in which only a single lysine is present, it is possible to introduce only a single DNP group per molecule. Antibody to DNP insulin shows the DNP to be the immunodominant group with the antigenic determinant extending to the adjacent amino acids.

Studies on certain anti-pneumococcal sera which cross react with dextran also give comparable estimates for the sizes of the antibody combining sites. Thus dextran cross reacts with Type II anti-pneumococcal horse serum. The type II specific polysaccharide has an entirely different composition, being made up of the methylpentose rhamnose as well as of glucose and glucuronic acid. Yet dextran precipitates a considerable fraction of the antibody, and this cross reaction is best inhibited by isomaltopentaose, indicating that a pentassaccharide of the isomaltose series can fit into those Type II antibody sites that cross react with dextran.

Much other evidence in various systems using human, horse, and rabbit antibodies has been consistent with these estimates of the upper limit for the size of an antibody combining site. The horse anti-pneumococcal antibodies were largely γM immunoglobulins, while the human and rabbit antibodies were predominantly or almost exclusively γG immunoglobulins. (Details may be found in the Suggested Readings.)

In studies of the specificity of linear polypeptides containing glutamic acid and lysine as well as alanine, phenylalanine, or tyrosine, the amino groups were found to be important in specificity. Substances such as 1,5-pentanediamine-$H_2N-CH_2-CH_2-CH_2-CH_2-CH_2-NH_2$ and 1,6-hexanediamine-$H_2N-CH_2-CH_2-CH_2-CH_2-CH_2-CH_2-NH_2$ of lengths 7.5 and 9 A were the best inhibitors, while compounds in which the NH_2 groups were replaced by OH to give the analogous alcohols did not inhibit. The value of 7 to 9A corresponds to the spacing between the side chains on an extended polypeptide chain.

COMBINING SITES OF ANTIBODIES TO PROTEIN ANTIGENS

Another major approach to the study of antigenic determinants and the dimensions of antibody combining sites of protein antigens is the degradative one. Such degradative studies have shown that proteins contain many different antigenic determinants that can be ascribed to different portions of the molecule. Obviously, if one could isolate a polypeptide fragment from a protein antigen that contained a single antigenic determinant and know its structure and conformation in solution, one would have a measure of the size of the antibody combining site. The initial approach with a protein such as serum albumin was by enzymatic degradation. If human serum albumin is treated with enzymes from rabbit spleen three fragments are formed, each of which contains different antigenic determinants in that three bands are obtained in gel diffusion with anti-human serum albumin, although the orginal antigen gave only a single band. This is readily seen in Fig. 6.7, in which the samples of the albumin are set up in gel diffusion after varying times of digestion. The three bands fuse with the single band formed to the original albumin. A similar type of degradation has been carried out with other antigens. The findings with digested diphtheria toxin illustrate the complexities of the problem and the important role that antibody heterogeneity plays. Figure 6.8 shows the reaction of four horse diphtheria antitoxic sera with native toxin (T) and with digested toxin (TD) in gel diffusion. In each instance the original toxin gave a single precipitin line. Three of the antitoxins, 441, 1451, and 341, gave two lines with digested toxin,

Fig. 6.7 Gel diffusion studies of the reaction of rabbit anti-human serum albumin with serum albumin digested for various times from 0 to 48 hours (T = native albumin). (From Lapresle, C. Ann. Inst. Pasteur **89**:654 [1955]; by permission.)

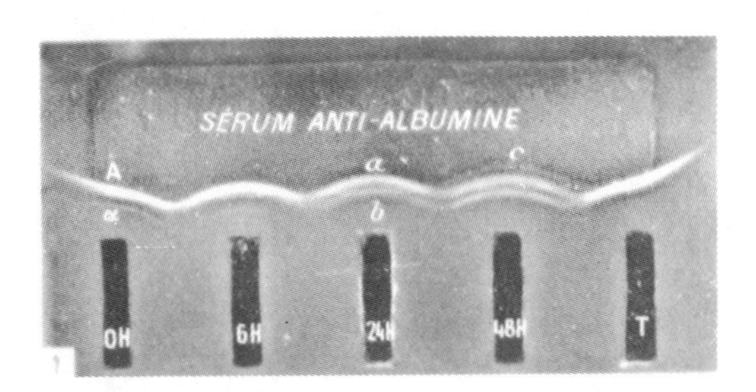

Fig. 6.8 Evidence for multiple antigenic determinants in diphtheria toxin from comparisons of digested and native diphtheria toxins with four horse antitoxins. Three of the antisera, 341, 441, and 1451 each gave two bands with digested toxin, the fourth 825 gave but a single band indicating that this horse had not responded to certain determinants on the toxin. With all four antitoxins native toxin formed a substantial spur over the lines with digested toxin indicating destruction of a third set of antigenic determinants. (From Raynaud, M., and E. H. Relyveld. Ann. Inst. Pasteur **97**: 636 [1959]; by permission.)

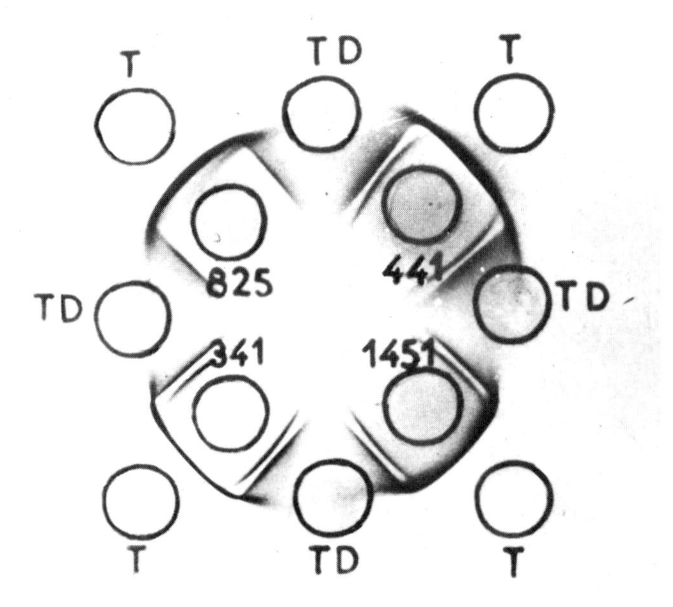

both of which fused completely with the line formed with the original toxin. Unlike the findings with serum albumin, these two fragments did not comprise all of the antigenic determinants, since a substantial spur was formed by the toxin, indicating that some determinants had been destroyed by the digestion. Horse 825 was of special interest in that it gave only a single line with digested toxin and a large spur is also seen with native toxin; this horse had evidently formed antibody to only the antigenic determinants contained in one of the two digested fragments.

Considering once again the case of serum albumin, on prolonged digestion the three bands seen in gel diffusion disappear and smaller fragments are formed which partially inhibit the precipitation; only partial inhibition is obtained, since many of the antigenic determinants are probably destroyed and the fragments that inhibit are complementary to antibodies that comprise only a small proportion of the total anti-serum albumin. One fragment with a molecular weight of 11,000 had two distinct antigenic sites. From this, another fragment of molecular weight 6600 having only one of these two antigenic sites was obtained. This fragment was coupled to an insoluble adsorbent and was found to remove from 1 to 7 percent of the antibody to rabbit serum albumin, indicating that a small proportion of the total antibody was directed to this determinant.

The elucidation of the complete primary structure of various proteins—for example, the sequence of amino acids—makes available as a by-product the peptides obtained by tryptic and chymotryptic digestion, and these should facilitate the study of antigenic specificity and the structure of the antigenic determinants of the proteins. Insulin, ribonuclease, myoglobin, and tobacco mosaic virus protein have all been studied to various degrees. As yet, ascribing any portion of the amino acid sequence in peptides that inhibit as interacting directly with the antibody combining site or as stabilizing a more favorable conformation of the other amino acids so that inhibiting power is increased has not been clearly accomplished, but substantial progress is being made.

In sperm whale myoglobin for which not only the primary sequence but also the exact three-dimensional structure is known (from the studies of Kendrew), six chymotryptic peptides have been studied (Table 6.5) for their capacity to inhibit precipitation. Antisera to metmyoglobin and to apomyoglobin were used. In no instance was more that 15 percent inhibition obtained, which indicates that there are many more antigenic determinants present in other portions of the molecule, or that the peptides obtained could not assume the proper conformation to inhibit maximally, or that the peptides did not repre-

Fig. 6.9 Model of myoglobulin chain from 2-A x-ray analysis showing helical regions with amino acids sequentially numbered. The position of the antigenic determinants may be located by referring to Table 6.5. Key: P = propionic acid; V = vinyl; M = methyl; the five membered rings at residues 93 and 64 represent histidines associated with the heme group. (From Dickerson, R. E. *In* The Proteins, H. Neurath [ed.] Academic Press, New York, vol. 2, p. 634 [1964] with numbering of Kendrew replaced by amino acids numbered in sequence from the data of Edmundson, A. B. Nature **205**: 883 [1965].)

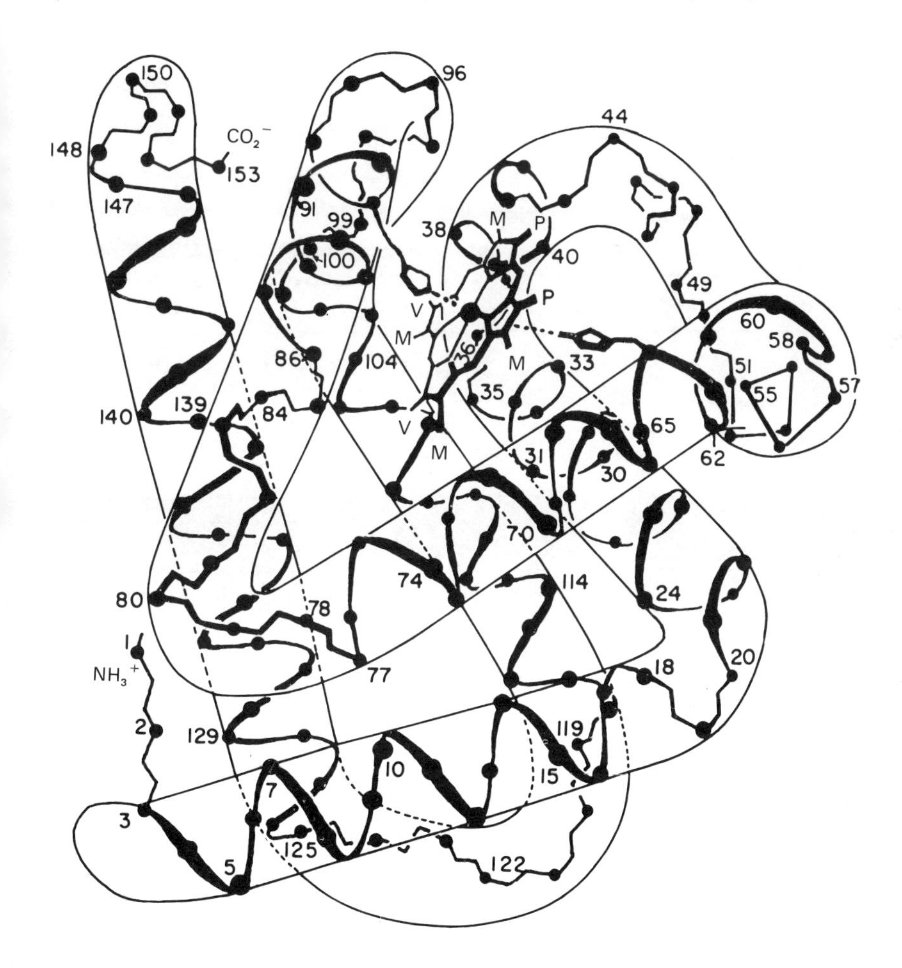

sent the complete sequence of any single determinant; indeed, all three circumstances could well be the case.

Of especial interest are peptides A_2 and A_4. Both of these peptides gave a maximum of 12 percent inhibition and a mixture of the two was no better, indicating that both were reacting with the same fraction of the antibody. Moreover, the larger peptide A_2 reached maximum inhibition with a mole ratio of 12, while for the smaller A_4, a mole ratio of 50 was needed. These two peptides were identical in structure except that the larger contained four additional amino acids at the carboxy terminal end. These four amino acids are known to be in the interior of the myoglobin molecule (Fig. 6.9), and one may reasonably infer that the increase in inhibiting capacity of A_2 over A_4 is caused by a more favorable conformation of the 15 identical amino acids stabilized by the four additional ones; the strong hydrophobic character of these four amino acids is undoubtedly of considerable importance.

Peptide B_1 inhibited the reaction of antiserum with metmyoglobin,

TABLE 6.5

Structures of Six Chymotryptic Peptides from Sperm Whale Myoglobin and Their Activities in Inhibiting Precipitation of Antimyoglobin by Metmyoglobin and Apomyoglobin

Peptide	H_2N Structure COOH
A_2	15 ... 33 Ala-Lys-Val-Glu-Ala-Asp-Val-Ala-Gly-His-Gly-Glu[b] -Asp-Ile-Leu-Ile-Arg-Leu-Phe
A_4	15 ... 29 Ala-Lys-Val-Glu-Ala-Asp-Val-Ala-Gly-His-Gly-Glu[b]-Asp-Ile-Leu
B_1	56 ... 69 Lys-Ala-Ser-Glu-Asp-Leu-Lys-Lys-His-Gly-Val-Thr-Val-Leu
C_1a	77 ... 89 Lys-Lys-Lys-Gly-His-His-Glu-Ala-Glu-Leu-Lys-Pro-Leu
C_2	70 ... 76 Thr-Ala-Leu-Gly-Ala-Ile-Leu
D_1b	139 ... 146 Arg-Lys-Asp-Ile-Ala-Ala-Lys-Tyr
D_2	147 ... 153 Lys-Glu-Leu-Gly-Tyr-[Gln, Gly]
D_3	1 ... 7 Val-Leu-Ser-Glu-Gly-Glu-Trp

Data from Crumpton, M. J. and J. M. Wilkinson. Biochem. J. **94**; 545 (1965).

[a] Ratio of moles hapten: moles myoglobin to give indicated percent inhibition.

[b] This is given as Gln in the complete structure by A. B. Edmundson. Nature **205**: 883 (1965).

but not with apomyoglobin. The histidine in this peptide forms a hydrogen bond with a molecule of water which is coordinated to the iron atom of the heme group. This bond might stabilize a conformation in metmyoglobin which differs from that of apomyoglobin.

Peptide D_3, which was inactive, contains the *N*-terminal sequence and is from a helical region while active peptide D_2 was from the C-terminus, the last four residues of which were nonhelical. It is of special significance that all peptides except D_2 and D_3 were adjacent to, or included, corners of the molecule. Except for the mixture of A_2 and A_4, mixtures of the other peptides gave additive inhibition, indicating that they represented different determinants. The location of the various peptides in Table 6.5 may be seen in Fig. 6.9, which shows the peptide chain of myoglobin.

Molecular Weight	Inhibiting Power					
	Antiserum WF				*Antiserum WH*	
	with Metmyoglobin		with Apomyoglobin		with Apomyoglobin	
	inhibition (percent)	*mole ratio*[a]	*inhibition (percent)*	*mole ratio*[a]	*inhibition (percent)*	*mole ratio*[a]
2051	12	12				
1522	12	50	8	60	9	65
1523	0		8	145	0	
1513	0				9	150
657	0				>7	> 290
963	5	70				
793	15	80	7	70	>6	> 300
818	0		0		0	

Another protein whose primary structure is known is the protein subunit of tobacco mosaic virus, which contains 158 amino acids. Tryptic peptide 8, which represents residues 93-112 was found to show substantial immunological activity and either was itself or contained an important determinant of specificity of the protein, since substantial inhibition of C′ fixation by TMV protein with anti-TMV protein was obtained and the binding constant of peptide 8 was over 10^9 l per mole. The structure of tryptic peptide 8 is as follows:

93
(H_2N end) Ile-Ile-Glu-Val-Glu-Asn-Gln-Ala-Asn-Pro-
112
Thr-Thr-Ala-Glu-Thr-Leu-Asp-Ala-Thr-Arg (COOH end)

In trying to evaluate the role of the various amino acid residues in the antigenic specificity the following observations were made:

1. Treatment with subtilisin or pepsin destroyed all activity.
2. The five amino acids at the N-terminal end could be removed without changing the capacity to inhibit C′ fixation and reducing by only about 50 percent the capacity relative to unlabeled peptide 8 to displace C^{14}-labeled peptide 8 from a complex with antibody.
3. Removal of the C-terminal arginine did not affect potency in C′ fixation, but did diminish by 85 percent the potency relative to peptide 8 in displacing the labeled peptide.
4. Only a slight additional decrease in activity was found on removing C-terminal threonine from the peptide lacking the C-terminal arginine.
5. Even removal of the five N-terminal and the two C-terminal amino acids left a fragment of 13 amino acids with substantial activity that was not much lower than that due to peptide 8 lacking the two C-terminal amino acids.

It is very difficult at present to ascribe the contribution of any of the amino acids to the determinant proper or to stabilization of other portions of the chain in the proper configuration.

The C-terminal decapeptide was synthesized by the solid-phase procedure and was shown to be very active as measured by competition with peptide 8 for antibody; by direct binding it was somewhat less active than peptide 8.

Individual sera vary in the relative binding contributions of the C-terminal decapeptide and the N-terminal pentapeptide in their binding relative to peptide 8, which indicates a heterogeneity of response involving various regions of peptide 8.

HOW SMALL MIGHT IT BE?

Turning once again to polysaccharide determinants and accepting a hexa- or heptasaccharide as the upper limit as well as the evidence for heterogeneity in the size of antibody combining sites, the question now arises as to how small an antibody combining site might be. Evidence on this point is much harder to obtain, and we are just beginning to get some information. It is very difficult to design an antigen that will give an unequivocal answer to the problem.

One piece of evidence which indicates that some antibodies may have a combining site as small as a monosaccharide is the following: Human antibodies to blood group A substance were absorbed on an insoluble polyleucyl A substance prepared by adding polyleucyl side chains on the amino groups of the A substance. After washing to remove nonspecific protein, a portion of the antibody was eluted with *N*-acetyl-D-galactosamine, the immunodominant group of the blood group A substance. After removal of the *N*-acetyl-D-galactosamine this eluate contained anti-A antibodies of the three immunoglobulin classes γG, γM, and γA. The γM antibodies were separated from the γG antibodies by density gradient ultracentrifugation in sucrose. This procedure involves preparing a gradient in a plastic centrifuge tube ranging from 10 percent sucrose at the top to 40 percent at the bottom. The antibody is layered on top, and after a suitable period in the ultracentrifuge the heavy γM antibody will be at the bottom while the lighter γG will be located as a narrow band about two thirds of the way down the tube. A minute hole is made in the bottom of the tube, and a series of ten small fractions carefully collected. The first fractions have the γM antibody; there is then a region free of antibody or it may contain γA antibody, and the succeeding few tubes have the γG antibody and any 7S γA antibody that may be present.

The capacity of various oligosaccharides to inhibit the precipitation of the γM and γG anti-A by A substance was assayed. Three sugars were available:

1. *N*-acetyl-D-galactosamine
2. a trisaccharide of structure

   α-D-GalNAc-(1 $\longrightarrow$ 3)-β-D-Gal-(1 $\longrightarrow$ 3)-D-GNAc
3. a reduced pentasaccharide of structure

$$\begin{array}{c} \alpha\text{-L-Fuc} \\ \downarrow {\scriptstyle 1 \atop 2} \\ \alpha\text{-D-GalNAc-}(1 \longrightarrow 3)\text{-}\beta\text{-D-Gal-}(1 \longrightarrow 4)\text{-}\beta\text{-D-GNAc-R} \end{array}$$

in which GalNAc = *N*-acetyl-D-galactosamine, Fuc = fucose, Gal = galactose, and GNAc = *N*-acetyl-D-glucosamine. R is a reduced unsaturated degradation product of galactose. The oligosaccharides had been isolated by acid and alkaline degradation of A substance.

It was found with the γG anti-A that the pentasaccharide was the best inhibitor, the trisaccharide next, and *N*-acetyl-D-galactosamine the poorest—the usual type of finding for antibody combining sites. However, with the γM-anti-A, all three sugars gave the same degree of inhibition on a molar basis, which indicated that the γM molecules that had been eluted by the N-acetyl-D-galactosamine had a complementary area that extended only to N-acetylgalactosamine itself and did not involve a larger portion of the molecule. Thus some γM antibody molecules may have combining sites as small as a monosaccharide.

Another line of evidence derives from studies with the isomaltose oligosaccharides. Isomaltose and isomaltotriose were oxidized with bromine to give isomaltonic and isomaltotrionic acids, and these were coupled to bovine serum albumin (BSa) by the mixed anhydride technique (see Chapter 2). The structure of the antigens is seen in Fig. 6.10. On immunization of rabbits, none of six animals injected with the isomaltonic acid-BSa cross reacted with dextran although they had

Fig. 6.10 Formulas of conjugated oligosaccharide-protein antigens.

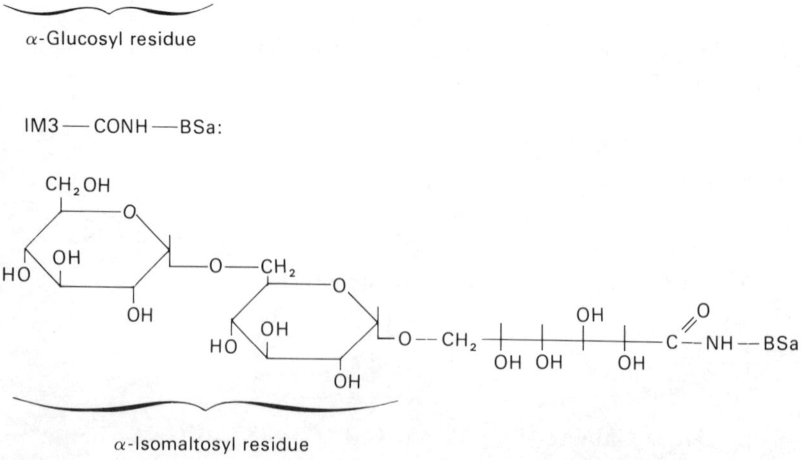

IM2—CONH—BSa:

CH_2OH, O, OH, HO, OH — O—CH_2—, OH OH, OH, OH, C(=O)—NH—BSa

α-Glucosyl residue

IM3—CONH—BSa:

CH_2OH, O, OH, HO, OH — O—CH_2, O, OH, HO, OH — O—CH_2—, OH OH, OH, OH, C(=O)—NH—BSa

α-Isomaltosyl residue

considerable amounts of antibody showing specificity for the terminal α-D-glucosyl residue, while all of six animals injected with the isomaltotrionic acid-BSa cross reacted extensively with dextran. Thus a terminal sequence of a single α-D-glucosyl residue is insufficient for cross reactivity with dextran, while a terminal sequence of two α-D-glucosyl units gives cross reactivity. Although in each case much of the antibody formed may well have been directed toward larger segments of the antigenic determinant than the sugar moiety, on the hypothesis that populations of sites of various sizes were present, complementarity involving more than a single α-linked glucose, and perhaps as much as two α-linked glucoses, is needed for precipitation with dextran. An observation consistent with this interpretation was made with Salmonella in which it was found that two polysaccharide antigens, one with a terminal α-D-glucosyl-(1 ⟶ 4)-D-Gal and the other with a terminal α-D-glucosyl-(1 ⟶ 6)-D-Gal, showed no cross reactivity.

It is evident that we are just beginning to learn about the lower limits of antibody combining sites.

WHAT SHAPES CAN IT HAVE?

On the subject of antibody shapes our knowledge is even more limited. Many years ago Landsteiner and van der Scheer attached two types of groups to the same benzene ring such as an arsanilic and a succinanilic acid or a glycine and a leucine (Fig. 6.11). These were then diazotized and coupled to protein. Antibodies were formed either to one haptenic group or to the other, but not to both. It is dif-

Fig. 6.11 Haptens containing two groups attached to same benzene ring.

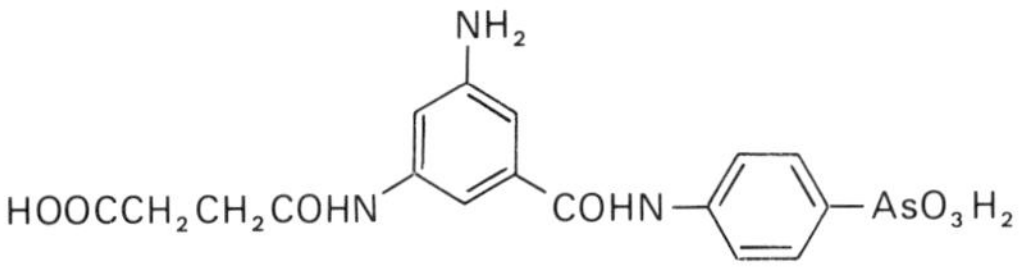

NH_2

$HOOCCH_2CH_2COHN$ — $COHN$ — AsO_3H_2

"(3-amino-5-succinylaminobenzoyl)-*p*-aminophenylarsonic acid (SA)"

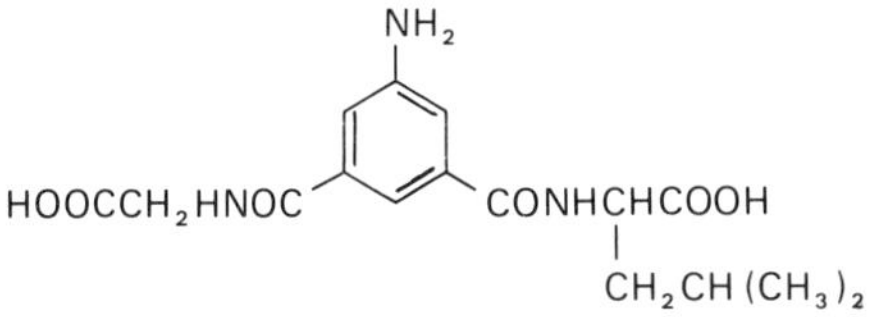

NH_2

$HOOCCH_2HNOC$ — $CONHCHCOOH$

$CH_2CH(CH_3)_2$

"Sym. aminoisophthalyl glycine-leucine (GIL)"

ficult to evaluate this observation as unequivocally related to shape or to size or to the inability to form an antibody site with two immunodominant groups.

In other studies with antibodies to haptens such as *p*-azobenzoate, $-N{=}N-C_6H_4-COOH$, some antibody molecules were found to be able to accomodate an ortho substituent on the hapten while others could not. There would thus appear to be a heterogeneity with respect to the complementary region even around a single benzene ring. Part of the enormous range in binding constants for anti-dinitrophenyl antibodies already mentioned could be attributable to such heterogeneity as well as to heterogeneity in size. Data to demonstrate this are not available as yet for carbohydrate antigens. Tertiary structure of the antigen is also important in providing the antibody forming cells with a multiplicity of forms toward which they can respond.

An interesting example was recently observed with the antisera to apomyoglobin and metmyoglobin mentioned above. When metmyoglobin was added to antisera to apomyoglobin, the ferriheme was released from the antigen and the antigen-antibody precipitate contained no ferriheme; in the metmyoglobin-antimetmyoglobin reaction, however, the ferriheme of the metmyoglobin was contained in the antigen-antibody precipitates. Thus a conformational change in the metmyoglobin had been induced by the interaction with antiapomyoglobin, which disrupted the region that binds the ferriheme. Whether this effect will prove to be a direct one on an antigenic determinant involved in heme binding or is an allosteric one resulting from reaction with a determinant at a site remote from the heme is of considerable interest.

Optical rotatory dispersion and circular dichroism studies have shown that the change from metmyoglobin to apomyoglobin by removal of heme reduces the α-helix content; metmyoglobin contains 15 more residues in helical arrangement than does apomyoglobin. Addition of heme restores helix content.

More and more instances are being noted in which tertiary structure may be important in the specificity of carbohydrate antigens. In a study of the glycerol-teichoic acid of the streptococcus

$$\cdots\!-O-\overset{\overset{\displaystyle O}{\|}}{\underset{\underset{\displaystyle O^-}{|}}{P}}-O-CH_2-\overset{\overset{\displaystyle H}{|}}{\underset{\underset{\displaystyle OH}{|}}{C}}-CH_2-O-\overset{\overset{\displaystyle O}{\|}}{\underset{\underset{\displaystyle O^-}{|}}{P}}-O-CH_2-\overset{\overset{\displaystyle H}{|}}{\underset{\underset{\displaystyle OH}{|}}{C}}-CH_2\cdots$$

which is a repeating polymer of glycerol phosphate and which may have alanine esterified on about half of the secondary hydroxyls of carbon 2, three types of antibody to the teichoic acid were found in various rabbit antisera to the streptococcus. These types may be described as follows:

1. Gives good precipitin curve with alanylated teichoic acid but fails to react with polymer lacking alanine—therefore, the antigenic determinant involves complementarity to alanine.

2. Precipitates well with teichoic acid lacking alanine, but reacts only slightly with alanylated teichoic acid—indicating that the antibody is complementary to the conformation of teichoic acid involving secondary hydroxyl and alanine sterically blocks approach to the antibody combining site. This antibody may have been formed to teichoic acid from which the alanine had been cleaved *in vivo* during immunization.

3. Both alanylated and non-alanylated polymers gave identical quantitative precipitin curves. This is best explained by antibody complementarity directed toward the —C—H aspect of carbon 2 and not involving the more hydrophilic side of the molecule.

In all instances the antibody combining sites are probably directed against more than a single glycerolphosphate unit. This system presents another type of antibody heterogeneity.

TYPES OF BONDS INVOLVED

It has been pointed out in Chapter 5 that it is extremely difficult to evaluate thermodynamic data on hapten-antibody interaction in terms of the various types of bonds involved in the interaction because of the participation of water molecules in the reaction.

However, in several instances in which unexpected cross reactivities were noted, studies of molecular models showed a complementarity involving hydrophobic groups. That this occurred with carbohydrates was even more surprising, since carbohydrate chemistry has been studying reactions of the hydrophilic hydroxyl groups and has generally not been concerned with the relatively hydrophobic hydrogens. Antigen-antibody interactions involving carbohydrates were almost automatically attributed to hydrogen bonding.

One very astonishing set of cross reactions was noted by Springer while he was studying the blood group H specificity of eel serum, which contains a cross-reacting antibody preferentially agglutinating O and A_2 erythrocytes, and with extracts of the seeds of *Lotus tetra-*

Fig. 6.12 Mirror image forms A, D- and L-fucose; C, 2-*O*-Methyl-D-fucose and 2-*O*-Methyl-L-fucose; E, 3-*O*-Methyl-D-fucose and 3-*O*-Methyl-L-fucose. In B, D and F, the L derivatives of A, C and E have been rotated about 180° to show the D and L derivatives in the position in which they would react with an antibody or Lotus combining site on the left-hand side of the molecules. The oxygen atoms on C-1 are marked with a piece of white tape. (From Biochem. J. **85**: 291 [1962]; by permission of the copyright owner.)

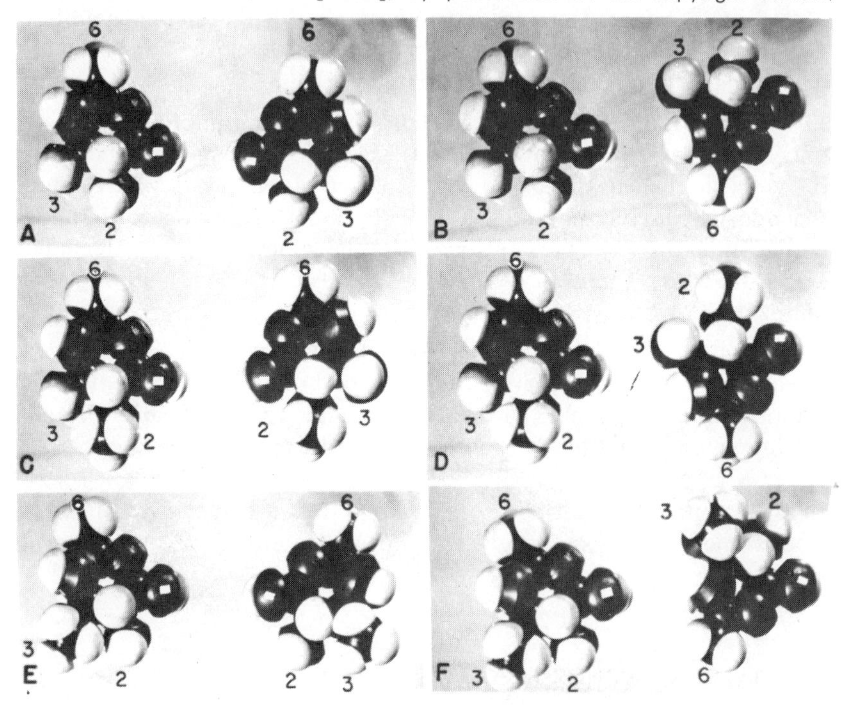

gonolobus, which contains a protein that hemagglutinates O and A_2 cells and reacts with blood group H substance. The methylpentose, L-fucose, has been shown to be involved in H specificity, since in low concentration it inhibited hemagglutination of human group O red cells by eel serum or by the Lotus hemagglutinin; D-fucose was entirely inactive. This was the traditional result obtained with optical isomers. However, when the monomethyl fucoses were studied in the Lotus system and in the eel system very surprising results were obtained. With the eel anti-H, 3-*O*-methyl-L-fucose was considerably more active than L-fucose itself but 3-*O*-methyl-D-fucose was just as active as 3-*O*-methyl-L-fucose. Indeed the D- and L- compounds were equal as inhibitors when assayed by quantitative precipitin tests. With the Lotus hemagglutinin, 2-*O*-methyl-L-fucose was just as active as L-fucose and 2-*O*-methyl-D-fucose showed considerable activity although not as much as the L-isomer. This apparent conflict with well-established principles of stereospecificity was resolved by examination of three-dimensional models (Fig. 6.12). The mirror image forms of D- and L-fucose of their 2-*O*-methyl and 3-*O*-methyl derivatives are seen (A), (C), and (E) of this Figure; in (B), (D), and (F), the L-isomers have been rotated through 180 degrees so that the hydroxyls of carbon 1 with a small white patch occupy the same relative positions for reacting with the antibody combining site on the left. The lack of similarity in profile of the D- and L-fucoses and the striking similarity of their 2-*O*-methyl and 3-*O*-methyl derivatives is evident. Moreover, the replacement of the hydrophilic hydroxyl group by the hydrophobic methoxyl group with its lower tendency to form hydrogen bonds would make for even greater complementarity of the methylated derivatives in which the hydrophobic CH_3 of carbon 6 has its analogous hydrophobic OCH_3 on carbon 2 or 3.

Additional insight into the importance of hydrophobicity was provided in this system when a monomethyl galactose was reported to show H activity. By use of the models in Fig. 6.12 it was predicted that this would turn out to be 3-*O*-methyl-D-galactose without knowledge that this structure had actually been established for the compound. When models of L-fucose and 3-*O*-methyl-D-galactose were superimposed (Fig. 6.13) it became obvious that there was a hydro-

Fig. 6.13 Molecular model of 3-*O*-Methyl-D-galactose superimposed on L-fucose. The OH of C-1 in both models is at the bottom center and the two hydrogens of C-4 are at the top center. The arrows indicate correspondence of hydrophobic groups.

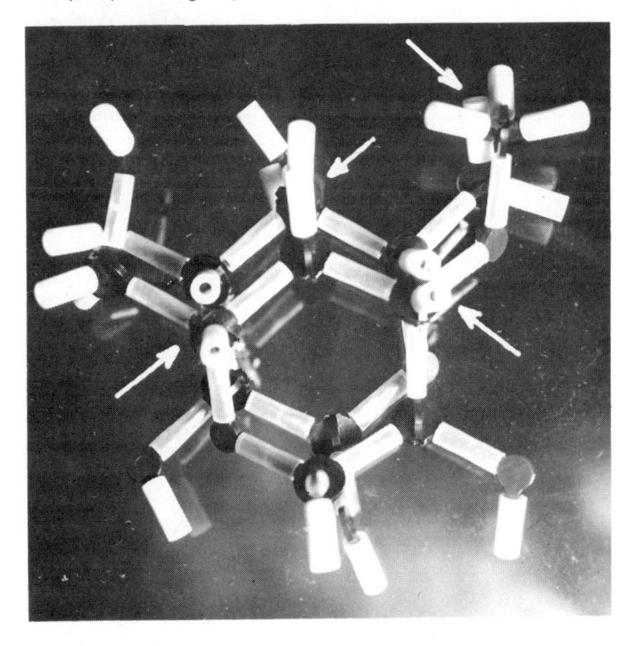

phobic patch that was practically the same on both molecules involving the following atoms or groups in each

Atom or Group involved	L-fucose	3-*O*-methyl-D-galactose
H	C4	C4
H	C3	C5
H	C5	C3
CH_3 or OCH_3	C6	C3

The only hydrophilic groups that would correspond except for the hydroxyls of carbon 1 which would be linked glycosidically to other sugars in an antigen are the hydroxyls on carbon 4, since both have the galactose configuration. It would seem reasonable therefore to infer that a substantial portion of the binding energy was derived from complementarity of an apolar nature.

The other instance involves antibodies that reacted with denatured DNA. The antigen was prepared by reacting 6-trichloromethyl purine with bovine serum albumin so that the reaction took place by addition to the amino groups of lysine as follows:

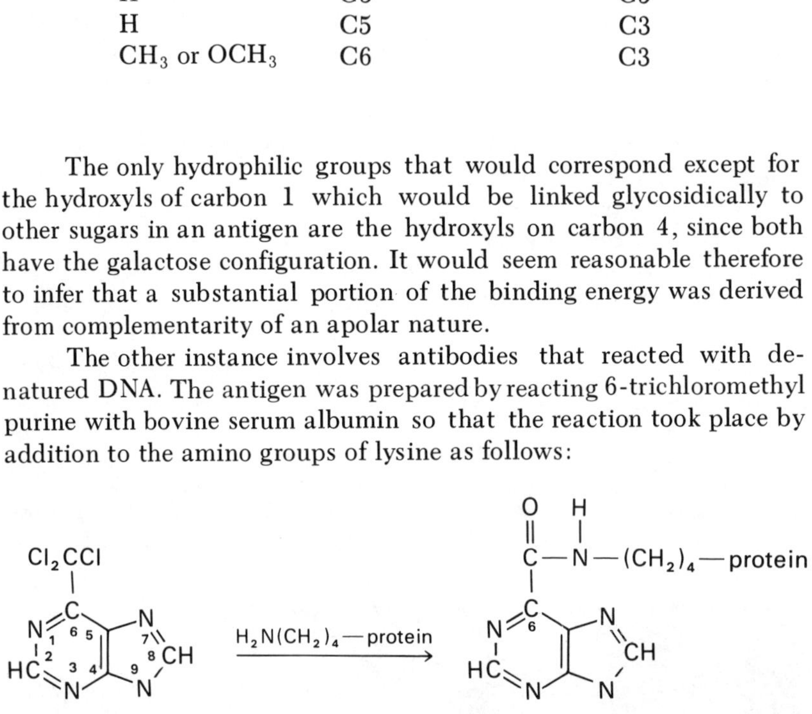

Cl_2CCl (at C6 of purine, positions 1–9) $\xrightarrow{H_2N(CH_2)_4\text{—protein}}$ purine-6-C(=O)—NH—$(CH_2)_4$—protein

It was puzzling that antibody to this antigen reacted with denatured DNA, since in DNA the purine was linked to deoxyribose at position 9 as in 2′-deoxyriboadenylic acid

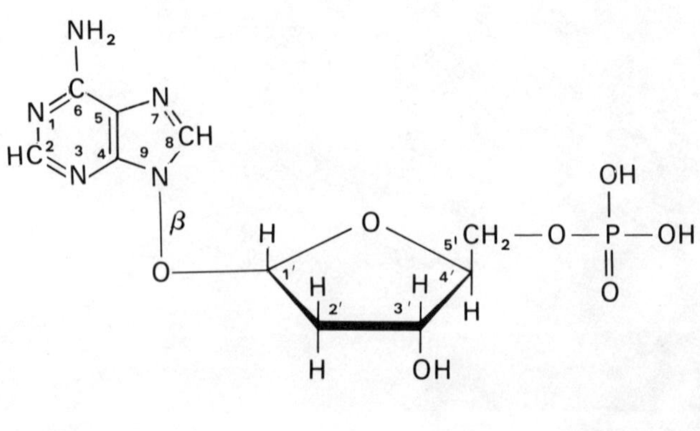

NH_2 (adenine, N9 β-linked to C1′ of 2′-deoxyribose; 3′-OH; 5′ CH_2—O—P(=O)(OH)—OH)

Molecular models, however, show that the N-C-N sequences 1-2-3 and 3-2-1 of the two compounds are identical and that there is a substantial similarity in profile of this portion of the molecule, which is again apolar or hydrophobic (Fig. 6.14).

The principles outlined in this chapter have proved applicable to the study of interactions between molecules other than antigen-antibody interactions. An example involving the plant seed hemagglutinins, lectins, with blood group specificity has already been given. Others include the reaction of the lectin, concanavalin A, with dextrans, mannans, and levans; virus-red cell interactions; and so forth. Findings from other areas will undoubtedly have considerable significance for immunochemical interpretations such as, for example, the demonstration by optical rotatory dispersion that the trinucleotide ApApCp can exist in a stacked and an unstacked form, the proportion of the latter increasing with temperature. Such observations suggest further ways by which antibodies of different specificities could be formed and how inhibition assays could be influenced.

Fig. 6.14 Molecular models of 2'-deoxyadenylic acid (left) and N-purin-6-oylglycine (right). (From Kabat, E. A., S. M. Beiser, and S. W. Tanenbaum. Cancer Research **26**: 459 [1966]; by permission of the copyright owner.)

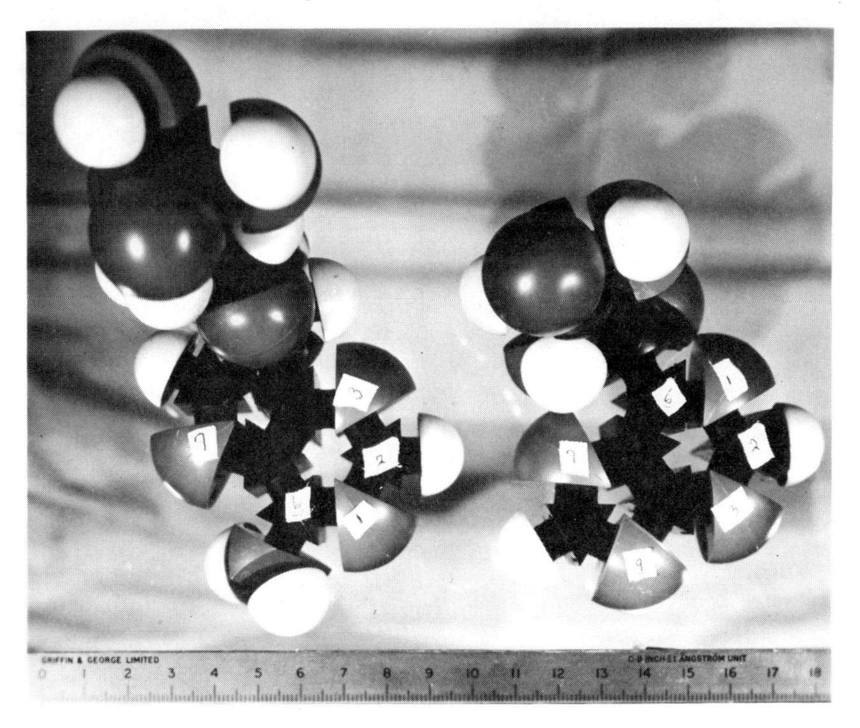

SUGGESTED READINGS

Kabat, E. A. Kabat and Mayer's Experimental immunochemistry. (2d ed.; 1961) Charles C. Thomas, Publisher, Springfield, Ill.; *Chapter 5 contains a fairly complete discussion of the homologous dextran-anti-dextran system and of cross reactions of dextran.*

Kabat, E. A. The nature of an antigenic determinant. Journal of Immunology **97**: 1 (1966); *a summary of the data on antigenic determinants and antibody combining site sizes. A good source of references to recent papers.*

Parker, C. W., S. M. Gott, and M. C. Johnson. The antibody response to a 2,4-dinitrophenylpeptide. Biochemistry **5**: 2314 (1966).

Gill, T. J., III, H. W. Kunz, E. Friedman, and P. Doty. Studies on synthetic polypeptide antigens. VIII. The inhibition of the antibody-synthetic polypeptide reaction by amino acids, dipeptides, amines, alcohols, and dicarboxylic acids. Journal of Biological Chemistry **238**: 108 (1963).

Lapresle, C. and T. Webb. Données actuelles sur les bases chimiques de la specificité des proteines. Bulletin de la Société de Chimie Biologique **46**: 1701 (1964).

Raynaud, M. *In* Mechanisms of hypersensitivity. Henry Ford Symposium. (1958) Little, Brown & Company, Boston.

Crumpton, M. J. and J. M. Wilkinson. The immunological activity of some of the chymotryptic peptides of sperm whale myoglobin. Biochemical Journal **94**: 545 (1965).

Young, J. D., E. Benjamini, M. Shimizu, and C. Y. Leung. Immunochemical studies on tobacco mosaic virus protein III. The degradation of an immunologically active tryptic peptide of tobacco mosaic virus protein and the reactivity of the degradation products with antibodies to the whole protein. Biochemistry **5**: 1481 (1966).

The last four references are recommended for additional insight into studies on antigenic determinants of proteins.

Kitagawa, M., Y. Yagi, and D. Pressman. The heterogeneity of combining sites of antibodies as determined by specific immunoadsorbents. II. Comparison of elution patterns obtained with anti *p*-azobenzoate antibodies by different kinds of immunoadsorbent and eluting hapten. Journal of Immunology **95**: 455 (1965); *heterogeneity of antibodies to* p-*azobenzoate.*

McCarty, M. The role of D-alanine in the serological specificity of group A streptococcal glycerol techoic acid. Proceedings of the National Academy of Sciences 52: 259 (1964); *the data on antibody to streptococcal techoic acids.*

Crumpton, M. J. Conformational changes in sperm whale metmyoglobin due to combination with antibodies to myoglobin. Biochemical Journal **100**: 227 (1966).

Breslow, E., S. Beychok, K. D. Hardman, and F. N. Gurd. Relative conformations of sperm whale metmyoglobin and apomyoglobin in solution. Journal of Biological Chemistry **240**: 304 (1965).

Springer, G. F. and P. Williamson. Immunochemical significance of L-and D-fucose derivatives. Biochemical Journal **85**: 282 (1962); *the basic data on methylated* D- *and* L-*fucoses showing blood group* H *specificity.*

Stewart, J. M., J. D. Young, E. Benjamini, M. Shimizu, and C. Y. Leung. Immunochemical studies on tobacco mosaic virus protein. IV. The automated solid-phase synthesis of a decapeptide of tobacco mosaic virus protein and its reaction with antibodies to the whole protein. Biochemistry **5**: 3396 (1966); *Synthesis of a decapeptide with tobacco mosaic virus protein specificity by the solid-phase procedure.*

Butler, V. P., Jr., S. M. Beiser, B. F. Erlanger, S. W. Tanenbaum, S. Cohen, and A. Bendich. Purine specific antibodies which react with deoxyribonucleic acid (DNA). Proceedings of the National Academy of Sciences **48**: 1597 (1962); *Data on antibodies to purine-6-oyl bovine serum albumin.*

Goldstein, I. J., C. E. Hollerman, and E. E. Smith. Protein-carbohydrate interaction II. Inhibition studies on the interaction of concanavalin A with polysaccharides. Biochemistry **4**: 876 (1965); *a nice study of a plant protein-polysaccharide interaction by immunochemical methods.*

Crumpton, M. J. The molecular basis of the serological specificity of proteins with special reference to sperm whale myoglobin. *In* Antibodies to biologically active molecules. (1966) Pergamon Press, Oxford, p. 61; *an up-to-date comprehensive review of antigenic determinants of proteins.*

Schlossman S., and H. Levine. Immunochemical studies on delayed and Arthus-type hypersensitivity reactions. I. The relationship between antigenic determinant size and antibody combining site size. Journal of Immunology **98**: 211 (1967); *the data on α-DNP polylysines as antigenic determinants and as antigens.*

7

The Antibody Combining Site for Elucidating Structures of Antigenic Determinants

In the previous chapter we have explored the size and shape of antibody combining sites, using the antigenic determinant as a molecular probe. The same concepts may be applied to obtain information about the structure of antigenic determinants on complex molecules. In this area almost all of the data have been obtained with polysaccharide determinants. A series of selected examples will be given to illustrate the principles involved.

There are two general approaches to the immunochemical elucidation of structure. The first examines either the cross reactions of naturally occurring polysaccharides of unknown structure with antisera to polysaccharides whose composition or structure is known, or the cross reactions of polysaccharides of known structure with antisera to polysaccharides of unknown structure. Cross reactions attributable to a sugar at the nonreducing ends of chains of branched polysaccharides tend to be stronger–that is, precipitate a larger fraction of the homologous antibody than do the cross reactions due to a sugar in the interior of a molecule, but the extent of cross reactivity will be greatly influenced by the degree of structural similarity between the cross-reacting and homologous antigenic determinants, such as the linkages and the number of sugars which are involved. While the occurrence of a cross reaction indicates structural similarity, there are many instances in which no cross reactions occur despite similarities in composition or even the presence of the same sugar at the nonreducing end of chains (see Chapter 6).

The second involves the comparison of oligosaccharides of known structure, preferably isolated from the antigen itself, for their capacity to inhibit precipitation or agglutination of the antigen-antibody system under study. These observations have proved especially rewarding when related to findings from bacterial genetics.

Of primary importance in such investigations is the assurance that the polysaccharide antigen under investigation and not some contaminant is actually reacting with the antibody in question and also that the antigen is not a mixture of substances only one of which is reacting with the antibody. These involve essentially establishing criteria of purity for the substance under investigation.

CRITERIA OF PURITY OF ANTIGENS

From the quantitative precipitin curves in Chapter 4 we are aware that in the region of antibody excess one does not find antigen in the supernatant; and studies with numerous antigens possessing some characteristic property such as color and enzymatic activity—some distinctive constituent like iodine, methylpentose, hexosamine, hydroxyproline, radioactivity, and so forth—have established that the antigen is actually in the precipitate formed with its specific antibody. Values may be somewhat low because of the solubility of specific precipitates and in cross reactions because all of the cross-reacting antigen often is not precipitated.

With unknown antigen-antibody systems, therefore, it is desirable to examine the system by gel diffusion (Chapter 3) to study the precipitin curve quantitatively to ascertain that it is a curve for a single antigen-antibody system, and not a mixture, and also to establish what proportion of the antigen is actually precipitated by the antibody.

For example, when it was discovered that the sera of patients with Lupus erythematosus reacted with DNA in precipitin and C′ fixation tests, it became very important to establish that it was the DNA, and not some contaminant, which was reacting. This was readily accomplished by analyzing the trichloroacetic acid extracts and the washed precipitates from various points on a quantitative precipitin curve spectrophotometrically at 2600 A. Results in Table 7.1 show

TABLE 7.1

Relation between the Composition of the Precipitate and the Amount of Added DNA

DNA Added (μg)	Protein in Precipitate (μg)	DNA found in Precipitate (μg)
0.25	7.0	0.25
0.5	13.5	0.50
1.5	29.0	1.62
3.0[a]	41.3	2.90
5.0[a]	41.3	4.02
10.0	16.0	4.25
20.0	12.5	1.62
50.0	7.5	1.50

From Deicher, H. R. G., H. R. Holman, and H. G. Kunkel. J. Exp. Med. **109**; 97 (1959).
[a] Equivalence zone.

clearly that in the antibody excess region all the DNA added is contained in the precipitate.

Another instance involved the question of whether the antibody formed in humans on injection of dextran was antibody to dextran itself or to some protein contaminant of the dextran. Using C^{14}-labeled dextran, prepared by growing the dextran-producing microorganisms on C^{14} sucrose, it could be demonstrated that a large proportion of the added C^{14} was contained in the antigen-antibody precipitate.

An unusual example of the use of immunochemical methodology to show that a polysaccharide was a mixture of two different substances was the case of teichoic acid of *Staphylococcus aureus*. This teichoic acid differs from that of the streptococcus (Chapter 6) in that it is a polymer of ribitol phosphate instead of glycerol phosphate

Fig. 7.1 Structure of the teichoic acid of S. aureus, strain Copenhagen. n = 10 to 14 (total units in the polymer, 12 to 16). (From Sanderson, A. R. J. L. Strominger, and S. G. Nathenson. J. Biol. Chem. **237**: 3603 [1962]; by permission of the copyright owner, the Amer. Soc. of Biological Chemists.)

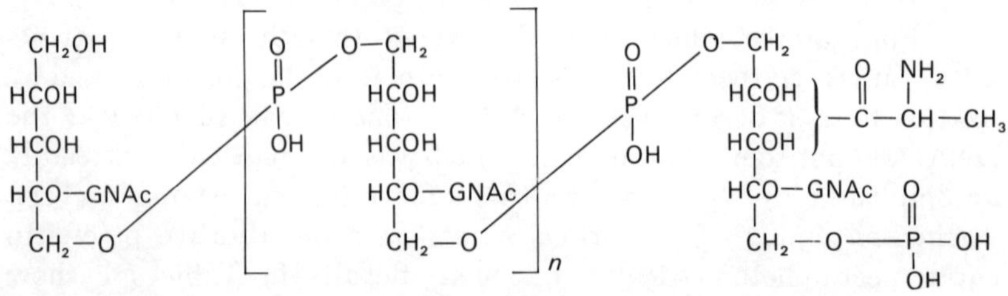

```
CH2OH
HCOH
HCOH
HCO—GNAc
CH2—O
[ O=P(OH)—O—CH2
  HCOH
  HCOH
  HCO—GNAc
  CH2—O ]n
O=P(OH)—O—CH2
HCOH }—C(=O)—CH(NH2)—CH3
HCOH }
HCO—GNAc
CH2—O—P(=O)(OH)—OH
```

and also has *N*-acetyl-D-glucosamine and alanine linked to the ribitol (Fig. 7.1). The teichoic acid used from the Copenhagen strain of *S. aureus* had been shown by action of α- and β-*N*-acetylglucosaminidases to contain 15 percent of the *N*-acetyl-D-glucosamine linked α to the ribitolphosphate backbone and 85 percent linked β; and it was thought to be a single polymer.

In studies on the antigenicity of this material in man, one subject gave an unusual type of quantitative precipitin curve (see Fig. 7.2) that appears to have two peaks. Analysis of specific precipitates formed at each peak of the curve showed that some hexosamine was present in the precipitates, which indicated that both antibodies were reacting with carbohydrate. Inhibition studies with *N*-acetyl-D-glucosamine and its methyl-α and methyl-β-D-glycosides showed the smaller peak to be specific for the β-glycoside and the larger peak to be specific for the α-glycoside, thus indicating that two polymers might be present. These were then recovered in highly purified form by forming specific precipitates corresponding to each peak of the curve and eluting the teichoic acid with trichloroacetic acid. The recovered teichoic acid from the small peak was all β-linked, while that from the larger was all α-linked; each gave a typical precipitin curve with the original antiserum (Fig. 7.3). By gel diffusion they could then be shown to cross completely and not fuse with each other (Fig. 7.4). The separated α- and β-teichoic acids behaved as expected with α-

Fig. 7.2 Precipitin curve of St. J_2 serum with teichoic acid Copenhagen. Key: ○ indicates before immunization; ● indicates after immunization. (Reprinted from Torii, M., E. A. Kabat, and A. E. Bezer. J. Exp. Med. **120**: 13 [1964]; by permission of The Rockefeller University Press.)

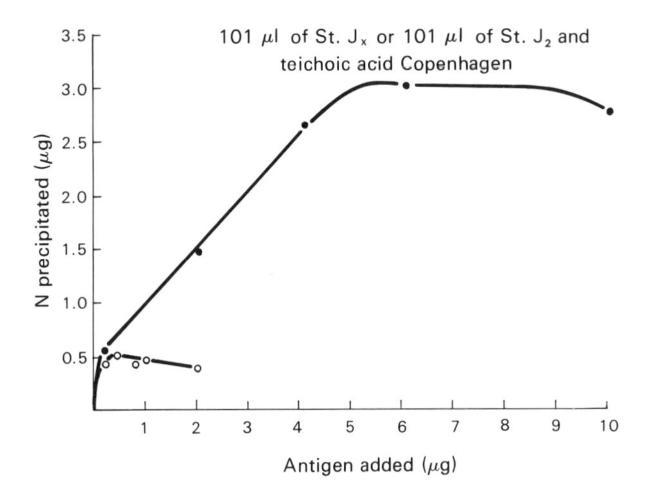

Fig. 7.3 Quantitative precipitin curves of St. J_2 with separated α- and β-teichoic acids. (Reprinted from Torii, M., E. A. Kabat, and A. E. Bezer. J. Exp. Med. **120**: 13 [1964]; by permission of The Rockefeller University Press.)

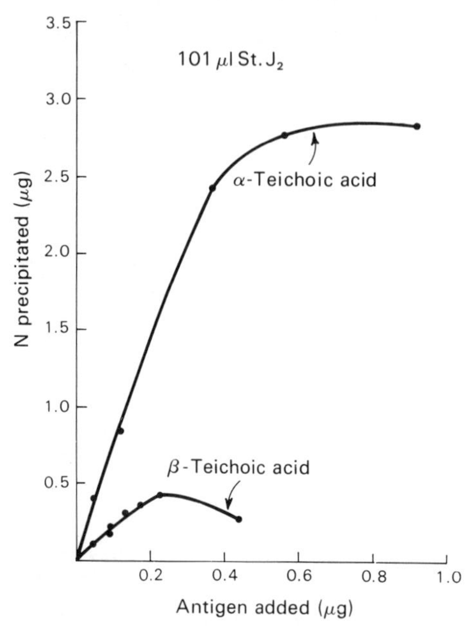

Fig. 7.4 Demonstration of two teichoic acids, one α- and one β- linked in a teichoic acid preparation by reaction with human antisera to teichoic acid. Antigens: α- = α-teichoic acid; β- = β-teichoic acid; N = teichoic acid from strain NYH-6, 0.8μg in A, 0.24μg in B; C_1, C_2 = teichoic acid Copenhagen strain 1.6 and 0.18μg respectively. Antisera: S = Subject St. J_2; I = Subject Is.; D = Subject Da. Note crossing of α and β lines in A and the two lines formed by N in A and B. (From Torii, M., E. A. Kabat, and A. E. Bezer. J. Exp. Med. **120**: 13 [1964]; by permission of The Rockefeller University Press.)

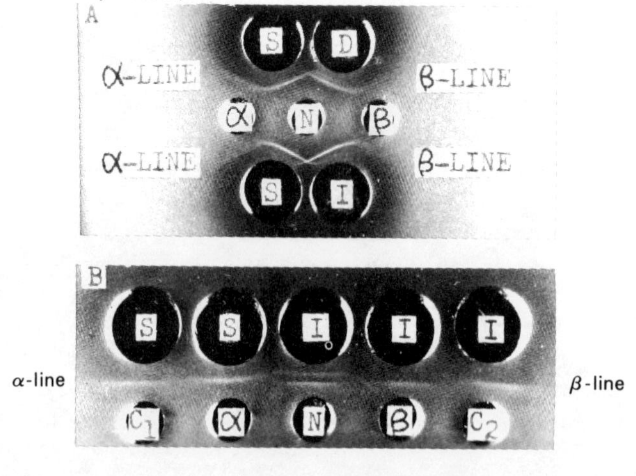

and β-*N*-acetylglucosaminidases. Teichoic acid from another strain was shown to contain close to equal proportions of the α- and β-polymers. It is of interest that the characteristic differences between β- and α-linked *N*-acetyl-D-glucosamine derivatives revealed by optical rotatory dispersion curves would permit the detection and quantitative analysis of mixtures of the two polymers, although a mixture of 85 percent β and 15 percent α might be close to the limit of detectability. It was also established that individual staphylococci are capable of synthesizing both polymers, although some strains apparently can synthesize one or the other.

IDENTIFICATION OF SUGARS IN POLYSACCHARIDE ANTIGENS BY CROSS-REACTIONS

Heidelberger has discovered an extraordinarily large number of cross reactions with the various type-specific antipneumococcal horse sera from which, knowing the composition of the sugars in the type-specific pneumococcal polysaccharides, he has been able to infer that certain sugars are constituents of the cross-reacting polysaccharides and to obtain important structural information relating composition and immunochemical specificity. The quantities of material required for probable identification are usually very small, and the information gained may greatly facilitate planning of chemical approaches to identification of constituents. Over 25 polysaccharides have been found which cross react with Type II antiserum. Cross reactions are best detected if carried out at 0°C.

Plant gums are among the polysaccharides that often cross react to varying extents with different antipneumococcal sera. For instance, early studies on ketha gum had reported it to contain arabinose, galactose, xylose, glucuronic acid, and an unidentified neutral sugar. The gum, however, cross reacted strongly with several Type I horse antipneumococcal sera, precipitating 20 to 45 percent of the type-specific antibody. Since the Type I capsular polysaccharide (S I) contains over 50 percent of D-galacturonic acid, it was anticipated that this sugar acid would be a constituent of the gum, and this was then readily demonstrated chemically. The component earlier identified as D-glucuronic acid was shown to be 4-*O*-methyl-D-glucuronic acid. This constituent was responsible for cross reactivity of this gum with Type II antipneumococcal serum, since S II contains D-glucuronic acid; in this instance the 4-*O*-methyl-group did not prevent cross reactivity, so that, an absolute identification cannot invariably be obtained. Inhibition of the ketha gum-anti-S I cross reaction was obtained with the sodium salts of D-galacturonic and D-glucuronic acids.

Another cross reaction between the group A specific carbohydrate of the hemolytic streptococcus that contains *N*-acetyl-D-glucosamine and L-rhamnose and Types II and VI antipneumococcal horse serum was attributed to the rhamnose moiety, since neither S II nor S VI contains *N*-acetyl-D-glucosamine. This inference became more probable when it was found that a variant carbohydrate that contained much less *N*-acetyl-D-glucosamine precipitated four times as much antibody from these antisera. Since the L-rhamnose in S II and S VI is linked (1 ⟶ 3), it was suggested that the streptococcal carbohydrates also contained (1 ⟶ 3)-linked rhamnose residues; and this was confirmed by methylation of the polysaccharide and hydrolysis and isolation of 2,4-di-*O*-methyl-L-rhamnose.

INHIBITION REACTIONS FOR ELUCIDATING STRUCTURES OF ANTIGENIC DETERMINANTS

This procedure, as already evident from data presented in Chapter 6, has great potentialities for aiding in the establishment of structure. Just as the terminal nonreducing end in the dextran-antidextran system, or the equivalent immunodominant group in linear polysaccharides contributed a very large proportion to the binding energy, so in an unknown antigen-antibody system, inhibition assays with the constituent monosaccharides often show that only one sugar gives appreciable inhibition, and this is assumed to be the immunodominant group. In the blood group A-anti-A reaction, of the four sugars present in the blood group A, B, H, and Le^a substances only *N*-acetyl-D-galactosamine was found to show significant inhibition; in the blood group B-anti-B reaction, D-galactose was the only sugar showing inhibition, while in the cross reaction of blood group H substance with eel anti-H, L-fucose was most active. Assays by inhibition of precipitation or by the inhibition of hemagglutination gave similar results. In the B-anti-B-system (Fig. 7.5) inhibition assays with methyl-α-D-galactoside and methyl-β-D-galactoside showed the former to be a better inhibitor, while the latter was a poorer inhibitor than D-galactose. Thus the galactose was considered to be linked to the next sugar by an α-linkage. This was confirmed when a disaccharide α-D-galactosyl-(1 ⟶ 3)-galactose was isolated from blood group B substance and shown to be a much better inhibitor than methyl-α-D-galactoside. Further increases in inhibiting power occur as trisaccharides of the proper structure are isolated, and in this manner the structure of the antigenic determinant is reconstructed.

Heterogeneity of antibody is of great importance in the selection of proper antisera. Thus with some antisera the concentration of mono-

Fig. 7.5 Inhibition by various sugars of precipitation of anti-B by blood group B substance. (Data from Kabat, E. A. and S. Leskowitz. J. Amer. Chem. Soc. **77**: 5159. Copyright 1955 by the Amer. Chem. Soc. By permission of the copyright owner.)

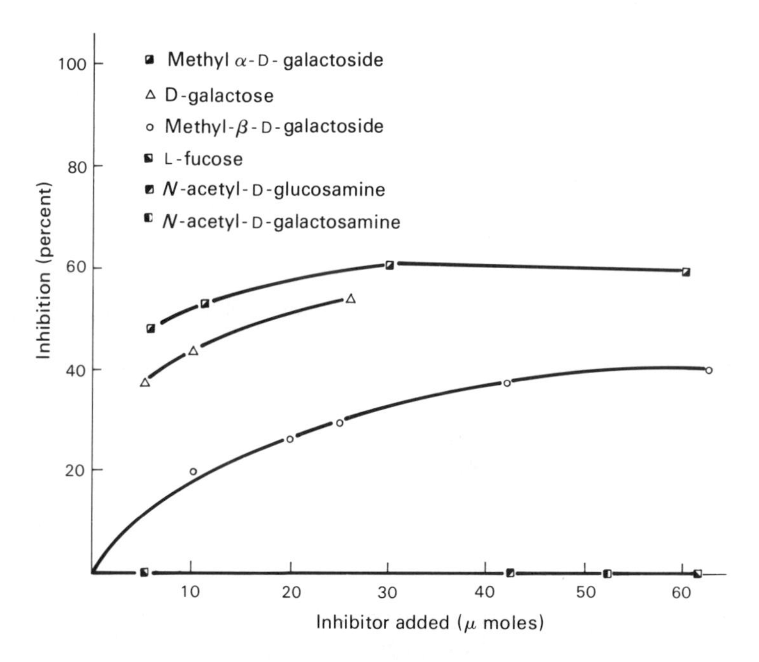

saccharides for inhibition of precipitation of the same quantities of antibody by a given amount of antigen may be much higher than those shown in Fig. 7.5. Such sera may be of limited utility in studying inhibition by monosaccharides and small oligosaccharides, but may be quite discriminating when larger oligosaccharides are being assayed (see Fig. 6.1).

Antigens of Salmonella

The most comprehensive series of coordinated chemical, genetic, and immunochemical studies have been carried out with the Salmonella and related enterobacteriaceae such as *E. coli*. In the almost forty years since serological classification was initiated by Kauffmann and White, over one thousand distinct species (serotypes) have been identified. The basis of the classification is the recognition of immunological differences among the flagellar (H) and somatic (O) antigens of the various species, and its original purpose was to facilitate diagnosis of salmonella infections. A detailed consideration of the entire scheme is not possible in this book, but some of the principles by which the structures of antigenic determinants responsible for the species differences among the O antigens of Salmonella are being worked out are especially illuminating.

By preparing antisera in rabbits to individual strains of Salmonella and testing them with a large number of strains, a classification based on differences in O antigens has established some forty serogroups. Strains within a group show cross reactions and are considered to possess very similar or identical antigenic determinants on their O antigens. Almost all strains have multiple antigenic determinants, one of which is designated as the characteristic group antigenic determinant. In Salmonella of group D, this is antigenic determinant 9, while in group B it is determinant 4. A species such as *Salmonella typhi* has determinants 9 and 12, while *Salmonella paratyphi* B possesses determinants 1, 4, 5, 12. The presence of such multiple determinants gives rise to a large variety of cross reactions, and it is often necessary to remove (absorb) antibodies to several determinants from an antiserum to render it specific for a given determinant. This is usually carried out by adding small portions of a heavy suspension of bacteria to the antiserum and centrifuging off the agglutinated organisms after each addition until all cross-reacting antibody has been removed and the antiserum has become specific for the antigenic determinant or factor desired. Thus the addition of a suspension of *Salmonella paratyphi A*, which contains antigenic determinants 1 ,2 and 12, to an antiserum to S. *typhi* containing anti-9 and anti-12 will remove the anti-12 and leave the antiserum specific for antigenic determinant 9; the antiserum will then be specific for group D.

The O antigen, which is a highly potent endotoxin, may be obtained as a high molecular weight lipopolysaccharide by extraction of the bacteria at 68°C with phenol-water (45 : 55). On cooling, two phases separate, the upper aqueous phase containing the lipopolysaccharide, nucleic acid, and any other polysaccharide materials. Further purification may involve dialysis, ethanol precipitation, and repeated ultracentrifugation at 100,000 g to sediment the lipopolysaccharide. From the lipopolysaccharide a non-toxic polysaccharide is prepared by mild hydrolysis in 0.1 N acetic acid at 100°C for 2 hr.; such polysaccharides have been used for the structural and immunochemical studies; the lipid is called lipid A.

Examination of the polysaccharides from a large number of Salmonella and *E. coli* strains for their sugar constituents showed them all to contain a basic core of five constituents: 2 keto-3-deoxyoctonate (KDO), heptose phosphate, and the three sugars, D-glucosamine, D-galactose, and D-glucose. In addition each strain might contain from one to three additional sugar constituents that are present as side chains on the basal core; any of nine different sugars may be used to form such side chains. These side chains attached in various ways to the main chain endow the polysaccharides with their characteristic O antigenic determinants. The classification of the polysaccharides on the basis of their constituent sugars into a series of chemotypes closely parallels the classification based on serological properties (serotype). In instances in which several serotypes fall into one chemotype, these are assumed to be caused by differences in linkage or sequence of the sugars.

A new family of sugars were first recognized among the Salmonella and *E. coli* strains. These are the 3,6-dideoxyhexoses, four of which have been identified:

tyvelose	3,6-dideoxy-D-mannose
abequose	3,6-dideoxy-D-galactose
colitose	3,6-dideoxy-L-galactose
paratose	3,6-dideoxy-D-glucose

A fifth member, ascarylose, 3,6-dideoxy-L-mannose has not been found in microorganisms, but was isolated from the parasitic worm Ascaris. When present, these dideoxyhexoses occur at the nonreducing ends of chains and constitute immunodominant groups of their respective antigenic determinants. Unfortunately they are readily split off by mild acid hydrolysis, so that oligosaccharides containing them have not yet been isolated. This disadvantage is in part compensated for by their resistance to oxidation with periodate, a property which permits the study of precipitin and inhibition reactions using periodate-oxidized polysaccharides in which other antigenic determinants have been largely destroyed and the system has been limited to the determinant in which the dideoxy sugar is involved. Models of these four dideoxyhexoses are shown in Fig. 7.6. The differences in contour which may be seen account for the differences in specificity of these four sugars as immunodominant groups.

Using α-and β-p-aminophenylglycosides of tyvelose, abequose, and colitose in inhibition assays, evidence was obtained (Table 7.2) that each of these sugars was linked α in determinants 9,4, and 35 respectively.

Certain antigenic determinants of Salmonella occur in a number of different groups, but in some instances may be associated with additional factors characteristic for another group. One such instance is antigenic determinant 1, which may occur by itself in group A but is always associated with factor 19 in group E4. Inhibition studies in the 1-anti-1 system and the 19-anti-19 system have shown these two specificities to be associated with portions of the same oligosaccharide sequence; this is clearly illustrated in Fig. 7.7. The 1-anti-1 system was studied with anti-E4 serum of specificity 1,3,19, using *Salmonella paratyphi B*, which contains determinants 1,4,12, as antigen. With the same antiserum the 19-anti-19 system was studied, using the

Fig. 7.6 Molecular models of four dideoxyhexoses. (From Kabat and Mayer's, Experimental immunochemistry. [2d ed.; 1961]. Charles C. Thomas, Publisher, Springfield, Ill.)

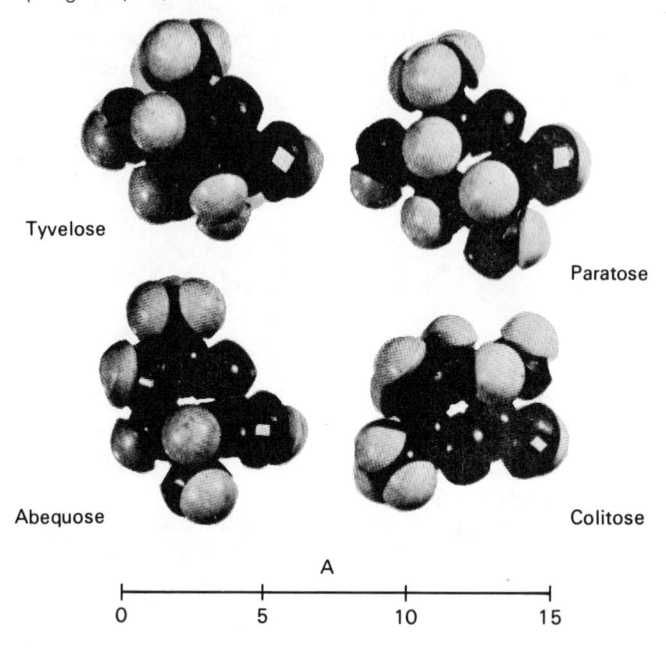

homologous E4 (1 ,3 ,19) antigen after removal of the anti-1 antibodies with *Salmonella paratyphi B* and of the anti-3 antibodies with an antigen from group E1 containing determinants 3 ,10. Five sugars were used for inhibition studies

glucose
methyl-α-D-glucoside
α-D-glucosyl-(1 $\longrightarrow$ 6)-D-galactose
α-D-glucosyl-(1 $\longrightarrow$ 6)-D-galactosyl-(1 $\longrightarrow$ 6)-D-mannose
α-D-glucosyl-(1 $\longrightarrow$ 6)-D-galactosyl-(1 $\longrightarrow$ 6)-D-mannosyl-L-rhamnose

The data in Fig. 7.7 show that the di-, tri-, and tetrasaccharides were all equally effective on a molar basis in the 1-anti-1 system, while in the 19-anti-19 system the tetrasaccharide was the best inhibitor with the smaller sugars being progressively less potent. Thus the specificity of factor 1 of group E4 is limited to the first two sugars, while the 19 determinant, which is specific for the E4 group, is at least as large as the tetrasaccharide. This is in good accord with the findings that two sugars in the same sequence are sufficient for cross reactivity to occur (see Chapter 6) and that the larger the size of the determinant, the greater is the degree of specificity.

TABLE 7.2

Inhibition of Precipitation by 3, 6-dideoxyhexoses and Their α- and β-glycosides

	Percent inhibition of precipitation with anti-								
	9 (*α-tyvelose*)			4 (*α-abequose*)			35 (*E. coli*) (*α-colitose*)		
Inhibitor	0.4 μmoles	2 μmoles	10 μmoles	0.4 μmoles	2 μmoles	10 μmoles	0.4 μmoles	2 μmoles	10 μmoles
α-glycoside	21	37	71	30	40	60	41	54	67
Sugar	10	22	45	—	18	27	5	18	31
β-glycoside	7	15	34	2	5	25	0	0	8

From O. Lüderitz, A. M. Staub, and O. Westphal. Bact. Rev. **30**; 192 (1966); by permission of the Amer. Soc. for Microbiology.

Fig. 7.7 Inhibition of 1 anti-1 and 19 anti-19 systems by oligosaccharides extracted from Salmonella E_4 (1, 3, 19) polysaccharide. (I) Anti-1 antibodies present in a rabbit anti-E_4 (1, 3 19) serum precipitated with Salmonella B (1, 4, 12) polysaccharide. (II) Anti-19 antibodies present in the same rabbit anti-E_4 (1, 3, 19) serum obtained by elimination of anti-1 by the system (I) and anti-3 by precipitation with an E_1 (3, 10) polysaccharide. Precipitation by the homologous E_4 (1, 3, 19) polysaccharide. Symbols: ●, glucose; X, methyl-α-D-glucoside; +, methyl-β-D-glucoside; ○, disaccharide, α-D-glucosyl-(1 → 6)-D-galactose; ▽, trisaccharide, α-D-glucosyl-(1 → 6)-D-galactosyl-(1 → 6)-D-mannose; △, tetrasaccharide α-D-glucosyl-(1 → 6)-D-galactosyl-(1 → 6)-D-mannosyl-L-rhamnose. (From Lüderitz, O., A. M. Staub, and O. Westphal. Bact. Rev. **30**: 192 [1966]; by permission of the Amer. Soc. for Microbiology.)

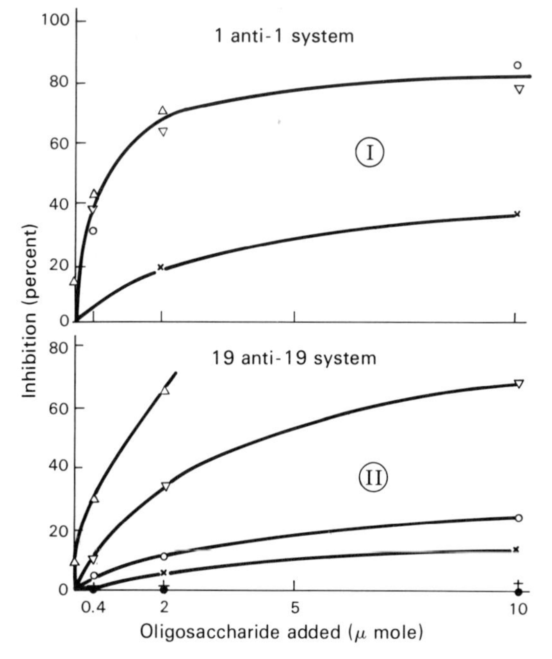

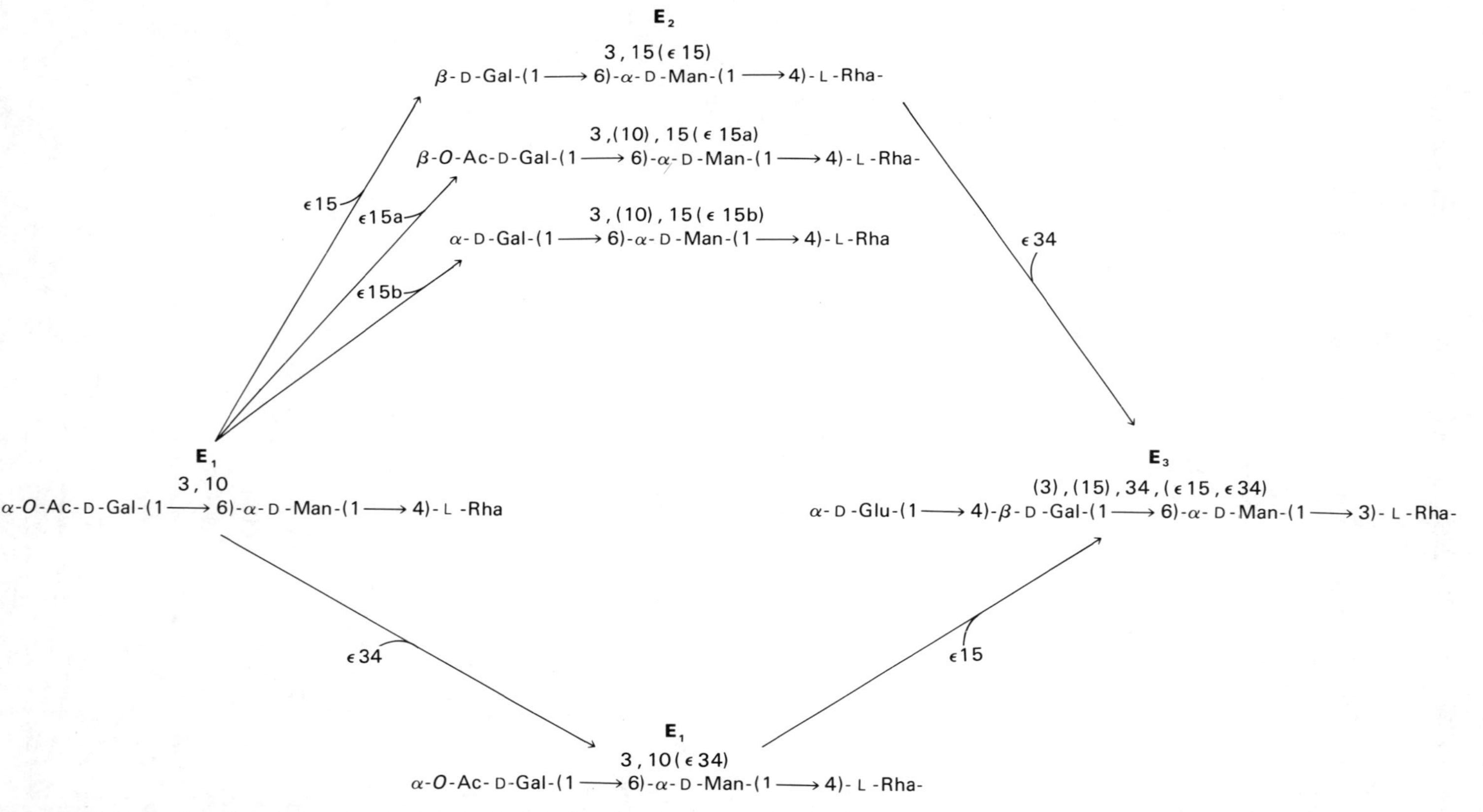

Fig. 7.8 Effect of lysogenic conversions on the antigenic determinants of Group E Salmonella (Data from Uchida, T. P. W. Robbins, and S. E. Luria. Biochemistry **2**: 663. Copyright 1963 by the Amer. Chem. Soc. Reproduced by permission of the copyright owner.)

Lysogenization of Salmonella by bacteriophages causes the appearance of new antigenic determinants and often produces weakened reactivity of other determinants that were initially present. Study of these lysogenic conversions has proved especially rewarding in delineating the kinds of genetic information transmitted by bacteriophages in determining biosynthesis of the different antigenic determinants. It is of special significance that the new factors appear 8 minutes after infection.

One extensively studied series of lysogenic conversions occurs in group E. Group E1, containing antigens 3 and 10, when lysogenized by phage ϵ15 is converted to group E2 and does not form antigen 10, but makes antigen 15 instead; antigen 3 is unaffected. E2 may be further lysogenized by a second phage ϵ34 to group E3 and makes antigen 34 in addition to antigens 3 and 15; the expression of the two latter antigens is weakened.

However, if lysogenization of E1 is first carried out with ϵ34 no change occurs and the strain remains E1, although lysogenized by ϵ34. If ϵ15 is now introduced, the change to E3 (3, 15, 34) occurs very rapidly. This is illustrated in Fig. 7.8.

A variety of oligosaccharides were isolated from the E1, E2, and E3 polysaccharides. Assays in the three systems by inhibition of C′ fixation are shown in Fig. 7.9, 7.10, and 7.11. The 3-anti-3 system is seen to involve α-D-mannosyl-(1 ⟶ 4)-L-rhamnose, since this disaccharide was maximally active whether it was isolated from a 3, 10 or a 3, 15 strain, and the substitution of an α- or a β-linked D-galactose on carbon 6 of the mannose did not significantly increase its inhibiting power (Fig. 7.9). In the 15-anti-15 reaction, the trisaccharide β-D-galactosyl-(1 ⟶ 6)-α-D-mannosyl-(1 ⟶ 4)-L-rhamnose was the best inhibitor followed by the disaccharide β-D-galactosyl-(1 ⟶ 6)-mannose, α-D-mannosyl-L-rhamnose, and the α-linked trisaccharide α-D-galactosyl-(1 ⟶ 6)-α-D-mannosyl-(1 ⟶ 4)-L-rhamnose. Thus, the 15 determinant evidently involves a β-galactosyl residue linked (1 ⟶ 6) to the mannose (Fig. 7.10). The 10-anti-10 system was found to involve an acetylated α-D-galactosyl-(1 ⟶ 6)-mannosyl-(1 ⟶ 4)-L-rhamnose determinant, and in the 34 system (Fig. 7.11) the trisaccharide α-D-glucosyl-(1 ⟶ 4)-β-D-galactosyl-(1 ⟶ 6)-D-mannose was the best inhibitor followed by the disaccharide α-D-glucosyl-(1 ⟶ 4)-D-galactose.

Accordingly, the lysogenic conversions in Fig. 7.8 show the changes in the structure of the antigenic determinants produced. Phage ϵ15 provides the information for repressing the synthesis of the enzyme producing α-*O*-acetyl-D-galactosyl as well as that for the synthesis of the enzyme adding β-D-galactosyl residues. The β-D-galactosyl linkage is the receptor necessary for ϵ34 information to be

Fig. 7.9 Inhibition of system 3 (lipopolysaccharide 3, 15 and anti-3, 10 serum) by oligosaccharides. The symbols used in this and the following two figures for oligosaccharides are as follows:
○, D-mannosyl-L-rhamnose of lipopolysaccharide (3, 10);
□, D-mannosyl-L-rhamnose of lipopolysaccharide (3, 15);
⊙, indicates α-1, 6-D-galactosyl-D-mannose of lipopolysaccharide (3, 10);
◬, indicates β-1, 6-D-galactosyl-D-mannose of lipopolysaccharide (3, 15);
⊡, indicates β-1, 6-D-galactosyl-D-mannose of lipopolysaccharide (3), (15), 34; x, α-1, 6-D-galactosyl 1, 4-D-mannosyl-L-rhamnose of lipopolysaccharide 3, 10; ●, β-1, 6-D-galactosyl-1, 4-D-mannosyl-L-rhamnose of lipopolysaccharide 3, 15; ▼, β-1, 6-D-galactosyl-1, 4-D-mannosyl-L-rhamnose of lipopolysaccharide (3), (15), 34; ◇, α-1, 4-D-glucosyl-D-galactose of lipopolysaccharide (3), (15), 34; ▽, α-1, 4-D-glucosyl-β-1, 6-D-galactosyl-D-mannose of lipopolysaccharide (3), (15), 34. (Reprinted from Uchida, T., P. W. Robbins, and S. E. Luria. Biochemistry **2**:663. Copyright 1963 by the Amer. Chem. Soc. Reprinted by permission of the copyright owner.)

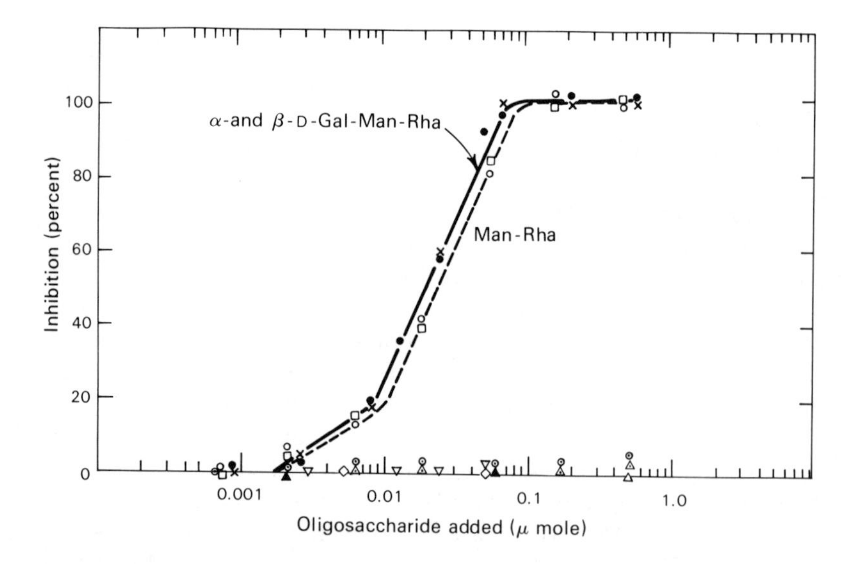

expressed by the addition of the α-glucosyl residue to carbon 6 of the β-D-galactose. Lysogenization of the 3,10 strain with ϵ34 does not manifest itself, since the receptor on antigen 10 is not suitable. When the 3,10 (ϵ34) strain is further lysogenized with ϵ15 the entire sequence of reactions can take place, and 3,15,34 is produced.

The action of ϵ15 was resolvable into two steps by the isolation of two mutant phages, ϵ15b and ϵ15a. Lysogeny by the former results in a determinant of the 3,10 structure but one lacking the *O*-acetyl group, while lysogeny by the latter results in conversion of the α-*O*-acetyl-D-galactose to a β-*O*-acetyl-D-galactose. In each case, galac-

Fig. 7.10 Inhibition of system 15 (lipopolysaccharide 3,15 and anti-15 serum) by oligosaccharides. Symbols explained in Fig. 7.9 (From Uchida, T., P. W. Robbins, and S. E. Luria. Biochemistry **2**: 663. Copyright 1963 by the Amer. Chem. Soc. Reproduced by permission of the copyright owner.)

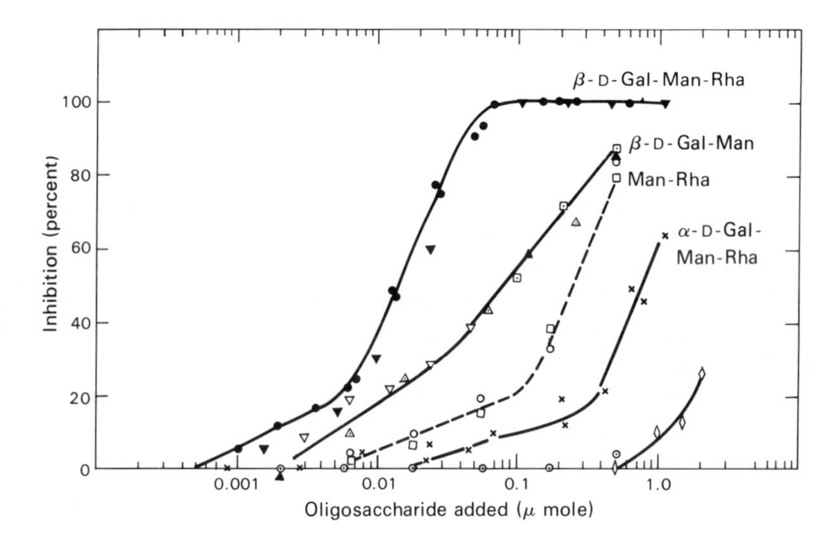

Fig. 7.11 Inhibition of system 34 (lipopolysaccharide (3), (15) 34 and anti-34 serum) by oligosaccharides. Symbols explained in Fig. 7.9. (From Uchida, T., P. W. Robbins, and S. E. Luria. Biochemistry **2**: 663. Copyright 1963 by the Amer. Chem. Soc. Reproduced by permission of the copyright owner.)

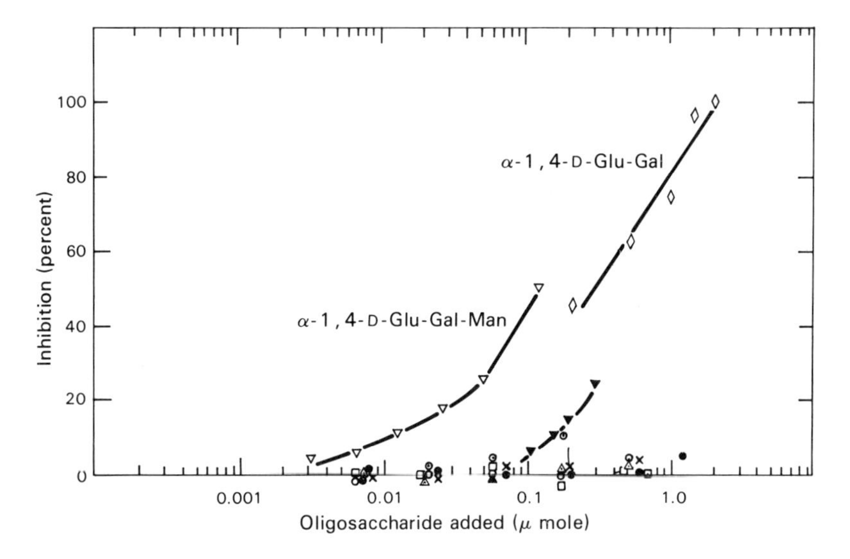

tose is linked to the mannosyl-rhamnose as in the other determinants. In both instances antigen-10 specificity is partially suppressed and antigen 15 specificity appears. ϵ 15a was selected out because it was resistant to a virulent ϵ34 phage and could thus be separated from the ϵ15-lysogenized organisms.

In the intact antigens, the chains of Gal-Man-Rha are linked by a (1 ⟶ 3)-linkage from the rhamnose to the galactose, as established by the isolation of 2, 4, 6 tri-*O*-methylgalactose after exhaustive methylation and hydrolysis of the E1, E2, and E3 polysaccharides. With this long sequence of repeating units, the inhibition data on the 3-anti-3 system furnished important evidence that antigenic determinants could occur in the middle of a linear polysaccharide and were not exclusively associated with the ends of chains.

The antigens of Salmonella thus far discussed have all been obtained from strains with colonies having a smooth appearance (S) on agar plates. Numerous other strains were known to have colonies on solid media with a rough (R) appearance. R mutants may be selected for by growing the S strains in type-specific anti-S serum. Studies of the lipopolysaccharides from R strains showed them to be higher in lipid content and to occur in lesser amounts in the microorganisms.

Fig. 7.12 Proposed scheme showing the structural relationships of the various rough and smooth forms of Salmonella. (From Lüderitz, O., A. M. Staub, and O. Westphal. Bact. Rev. **30**: 192 [1966]; by permission of the Amer. Soc. for Microbiology.)

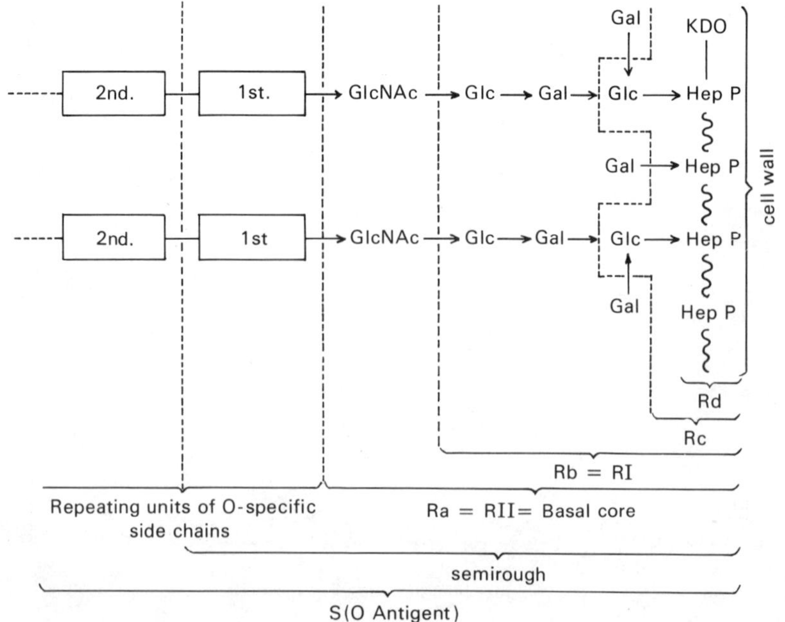

Lipopolysaccharides from most R strains contained only the basic core constituents (p. 120). Isolation of the polysaccharide portion of the R lipopolysaccharides by mild acetic acid hydrolysis permitted them to be subdivided into two groups. In one group the polysaccharide contained glucosamine, galactose, and glucose (Ra), while in the second group all the glucosamine was in lipid A and only galactose and glucose were in the polysaccharide (Rb). Additional rough mutants had polysaccharides lacking both glucosamine and galactose (Rc), a group containing only KDO and heptose phosphate (Rd) and one R strain containing only lipid A, KDO, and ethanolamine with no sugars (Re). There is thus a progressive sequence from Re to Ra, each step of which involves the addition of a sugar constituent (see Fig. 7.12).

Each of the steps in the sequence shown in Fig. 7.12 is under the control of a single gene, and individual mutants have each lost the ability to synthesize one of the enzymes in the biosynthetic pathway [Fig. 7.13(A)], thereby blocking not only the reaction it cata-

Fig. 7.13 Enzymatic synthesis of O-specific polysaccharides of Salmonella. (A) Enzymatic synthesis of the core polysaccharide; * indicates that the nonreducing galactose side chain attached to glucose is omitted. (From Osborn, M. J., S. M. Rosen, L. Rothfield, L. D. Zeleznick, and B. I. Horecker. Science **145**: 783. Copyright 1966 by the Amer. Ass. for the Advancement of Sci.) (B) Proposed scheme of the enzymatic synthesis of the O-specific chains of *S. typhimurium* (From Wiener, I. M., T. Higuchi, L. Rothfield, M. Saltmarsh-Andrew, M. J. Osborn, and B. L. Horecker. Proc. Nat. Acad. Sci., **54**: 228 [1965]; by permission.)

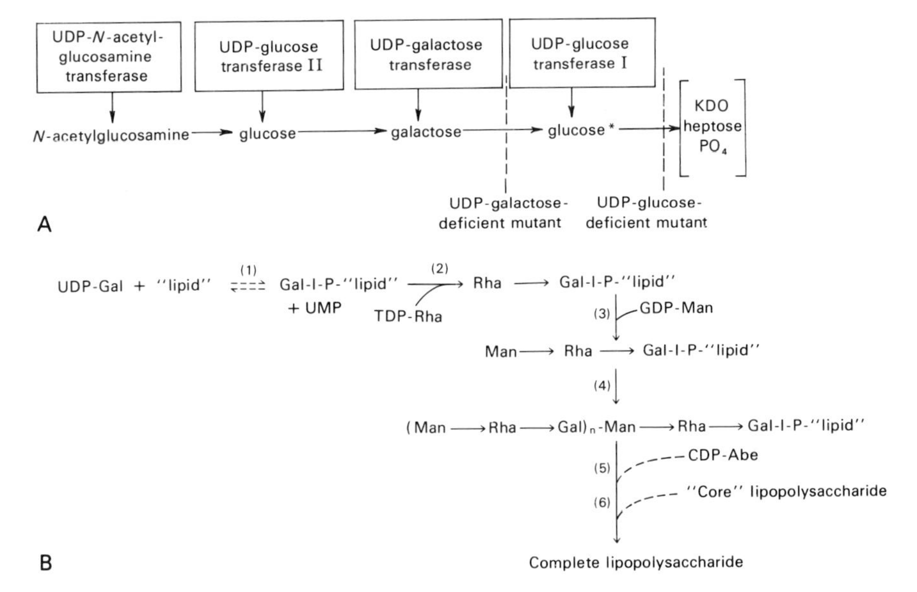

lyzes, but also the subsequent biosynthetic addition of the other sugars because an essential intermediate is lacking.

The relationship of the lipopolysaccharides formed by the various mutants to one another is established by isolating the oligosaccharides that represent their antigenic determinants and elucidating their structures. Thus the Rb and Ra mutants differ by a terminal α-*N*-acetyl-D-glucosamine residue since the tetrasaccharide

```
                α-D-galactosyl
                        |1
                        ↓6
α-D-glucosyl-galactosyl-glucose
```

was isolated from an Rb mutant of *Salmonella minnesota*, while from an Ra mutant the pentasaccharide

```
                                           α-D-galactosyl
                                                   |1
                                                   ↓6
α-N-acetyl-D-glucosaminyl-α-D-glucosyl-galactosyl-glucose
```

was obtained.

Ra and Rb mutants may be serologically distinguished, since erythrocytes coated with lipopolysaccharides of each are agglutinated only by homologous antiserum. Accordingly, each of these systems may be used in hemagglutination tests with lipopolysaccharides from various rough strains to classify them as Ra or Rb. Concentrations of from 1 to 8 μg per ml of an Ra lipopolysaccharide would inhibit hemagglutination of Ra lipopolysaccharide-coated erythrocytes by anti-Ra, while 250 μg per ml of an Rb polysaccharide would not. Similarly, 0.5 to 2.0 μg per ml of an Rb lipopolysaccharide would inhibit the Rb-anti-Rb reaction, while 250 μg per ml of an Ra lipopolysaccharide was inactive. Thus the *N*-acetyl-D-glucosamine constitutes an immunodominant group in the Ra antigens, while it at the same time prevents the expression of the Rb specificity.

Similarly, in a smooth lipopolysaccharide such as *S. adelaide*, which has antigen 35 specificity and contains colitose in addition to the basal Ra constituents, mild acid hydrolysis has been shown to release colitose with concomitant disappearance of type-specific O and the appearance of Ra specificity (Table 7.3). After 2.5 to 10 min of hydrolysis, less than 0.6 μg per ml of *S. adelaide* lipopolysaccharide gave inhibition of Ra hemagglutination of anti-Ra, while in the unhydrolyzed antigen no inhibition was obtained with 700 μg per ml.

TABLE 7.3
Release of Colitose and Appearance of Ra specificity on Mild Acid Hydrolysis of *S. adelaide* (35) Lipopolysaccharide

Time of Hydrolysis[a] *(min)*	*Colitose Bound (percent)*	*Minimum Quantity Giving Inhibition of Ra-Anti-Ra Hemagglutination*[b] *(μg/ml)*
0	100	>700
2.5	87	<0.6
5	81	<0.6
10	75	<0.6
20	66	1.1
40	49	5.5
30 (100°C)	0	>700

Data from O. Lüderitz, I. Beckmann and O. Westphal. Biochem. Z. **339**; 416 (1962).
[a] 0.25 *N* HCl at 65°C.
[b] Anti-Ra antiserum to *S. minnesota*, Ra lipopolysaccharide *S. djakarta*.

On further hydrolysis, as the Ra polysaccharide was itself being destroyed, larger quantities were required for inhibition.

Rb mutants derived from different species of Salmonella, although they may cross react, are not identical. In the preparation of the Rb lipopolysaccharide, the supernatant after high-speed centrifugation may contain a soluble polysaccharide composed of the sugars characteristic of the smooth antigen from which the Rb mutant was derived; and such mutants appear to be unable to attach the specific polysaccharide to the lipopolysaccharide core, perhaps because of the absence of the terminal *N*-acetyl-D-glucosamine.

Rc mutants grown in the absence of galactose form rough colonies on agar and produce a lipopolysaccharide containing only glucose and heptose in the carbohydrate portion; they are insensitive to bacteriophage; when grown in the presence of galactose they produce the complete O antigen, develop a smooth colonial form, and become sensitive to bacteriophage. These mutants lack the enzyme UDP-galactose-4-epimerase, which converts UDP-glucose into UDP-galactose, and thus are unable to form galactosyl residues to add to the lipopolysaccharides.

In addition to the Ra to Re mutants a group of semirough (SR) forms have been isolated with properties intermediate between the S and R forms (Fig. 7.12). They form a smooth colony on agar and were obtained as mutants or by recombination.

In Fig. 7.13(B), the proposed pathway for the attachment of the O antigenic side chains to the Ra core is given. Synthesis of the Man-

Rha-Gal side chains takes place via a lipid intermediate; the first Gal is joined to the lipid as Gal-1-P-lipid, with sequential addition of the others. Abequose is then added, and the O antigenic side chains are transferred to the completed core. Some studies on genetic mapping by study of recombinants among R mutants has also been carried out; two loci have been recognized in *S. typhimurium*. Rou A is involved in the synthesis of the basic core structure, and Rou B controls the synthesis of O specific side chains.

Many other determinants of the O antigens of Salmonella have been studied, and the general principles outlined above appear to have general applicability to the study of antigenic determinants. Of special interest is the finding in Salmonella of group U, which shows blood group B specificity of a sequence α-D-Gal-(1$\longrightarrow$3)-Gal which is identical with that of blood group B substance.

SUGGESTED READINGS

Kabat, E. A. Kabat and Mayer's Experimental immunochemistry. (2d ed.; 1961) Charles C. Thomas, Publisher, Springfield, Ill.; *Chapter 9 for studies on immunochemical criteria of the purity of proteins and polysaccharides.*

Heidelberger, M. Structure and immunological specificity of polysaccharides. *In* Progress in the Chemistry of Organic Natural Products, **18**: 503 (1960). (L. Zechmeister, ed.); *data on cross reactions with pneumococcal antisera.*

Torii, M., E. A. Kabat and A. E. Bezer. Separation of teichoic acid of *Staphylococcus aureus* into two immunologically distinct specific polysaccharides with α- and β-*N*-acetylglucosaminyl linkages respectively. Antigenicity of teichoic acid in man. Journal of Experimental Medicine **120**: 13 (1964).

Nathenson, S. G., N. Ishimoto, J. S. Anderson, and J. L. Strominger. Enzymatic synthesis and immunochemistry of α- and β-*N*-acetylglucosaminylribitol linkages in teichoic acids from several strains of *Staphylococcus aureus*. Journal of Biological Chemistry **241**: 651 (1966).

Lüderitz, O., A. M. Staub, and O. Westphal. Immunochemistry of O and R antigens of Salmonella and related enterobacteriaceae. Bacteriological Reviews **30**: 192 (1966); *a comprehensive review of the antigenic determinants of Salmonella and E. coli in more detail than could be presented.*

Uchida, T., P. W. Robbins, and S. E. Luria. Analyses of the serologic determinant groups of the Salmonella group E antigens. Biochemistry **2**: 663 (1963).

Molecular biology of Gram-negative bacterial lipopolysaccharides. Annals of the New York Academy of Sciences **133**: 277–786 (1966); *a symposium with numerous articles on the biosynthesis of lipopolysaccharides.*

8

Purification of Antibodies

Before one can study the structure of antibodies it is necessary to have suitable methods for obtaining them in highly purified form. For many biological and immunological purposes, actual purification is not so important as having the antibodies in higher concentration than they exist in serum. For such uses it is sufficient to prepare a concentrated γG immunoglobulin by chromatography on DEAE-cellulose, taking the major peak that is not held on the column on elution with 0.005 or 0.001 M phosphate buffer at pH 8.0, or by precipitation of the globulin at one-half saturation with $(NH_4)_2SO_4$ or Na_2SO_4 and so forth. For separation of γM and γG immunoglobulins, further fractionation of concentrated globulin solutions by zone electrophoresis, gel filtration on Sephadex or Biogel, density gradient ultracentrifugation in sucrose, or combinations of these methods may be used. These procedures do not generally separate the antibodies from the other immunoglobulins of the same class.

To obtain purified antibodies free of other immunoglobulins it is necessary to take advantage of their specificity and to remove them from solution through the use of antigen. This single step eliminates immunoglobulin molecules that have no complementarity for the antigen as well as other serum proteins, and these nonreactive components may be separated from the antigen-antibody aggregates by washing with 0.15 M sodium chloride solution (saline).

The next step involves separation of part, or preferably all, of the antibody from the antigen. The major problems are to avoid alteration of the antibody and to eliminate the antigen. This chapter will briefly indicate the principles of several methods, and detailed descriptions may be found in the Suggested Readings. Most are given in *Experimental Immunochemistry*, and *Methods in Medical Research* or in *Methods in Immunology and Immunochemistry* and the titles of the other references indicate the procedures given.

Specific methods fall into two general types: The first employs soluble antigen to precipitate the antibody and recovers the antibody from the washed antigen-antibody precipitate either by partial extraction and elimination of the antigen on the remaining antibody with which it is combined, or by complete solution of the antigen-antibody precipitate and removal of the antigen by some chemical method that separates it from the antibody. In special cases enzymes are used to digest the antigen, but leave the antibody intact.

The second type of method employs the antigen in an insoluble form, thereby permitting direct elution of the antibody without simultaneously causing the antigen to go into solution. This is especially advantageous because it may be carried out either batchwise or in chromatographic columns and also permits attempts to fractionate antibody by sequential elution with various reagents.

One of the earliest methods of the first type which is useful for obtaining ANTIBODIES TO POLYSACCHARIDES is the extraction of washed precipitates of pneumococcal specific polysaccharides and their antibodies with 15 percent NaCl, taking advantage of a shift in the equilibrium by which a given quantity of polysaccharide binds less antibody in high salt than in saline. The effect of the salt therefore shifts the equilibrium to the right.

$$\mathrm{S}_m\mathrm{Ab}_n \rightleftarrows \mathrm{S}_m\mathrm{Ab}_{n-x} + x\,\mathrm{Ab}$$

The residual specific precipitate is centrifuged off, and the antibody recovered from the supernatant. Such precipitates may be repeatedly used by removing the salt and absorbing an additional amount of antibody. Yields are generally poor with rabbit antibody, but reach up to 30 percent with horse antibody.

AZOPROTEIN ANTIBODIES are generally prepared by immunization with the haptenic group coupled to one protein and are precipitated with the same, or a closely related, haptenic group coupled to another protein. This procedure removes antibodies for which the haptenic group is immunodominant, but leaves in the supernatant antibodies to other determinants of the original antigen as well as those antibodies to the haptenic group in which the protein portion of the determinant contributes significantly to binding. Washed antigen-antibody precipitates may be dissolved in hapten and separated from the antigen chromatographically or by precipitation. Anti-lactosyl antibodies precipitated with lactosyl azofibrinogen, after washing, are dissolved in M /10 lactose, and the antigen is removed by precipitation in 0.6 M phosphate; with a hapten-azobovine serum albumin separation was accomplished by precipitation of the antigen at pH 4.7; with a hapten-azo egg albumin as the precipitating antigen, a DEAE-cellulose column on which the hapten-azo egg albumin was strongly bound separated it from the nonabsorbed antibody γG immunoglobulin. Hapten may then be removed by passage through a Sephadex or Biogel column, or by dialysis.

DINITROPHENYL ANTIBODIES are purified by precipitation with DNP-bovine-γG-globulin. The washed precipitate is extracted with dinitrophenol in the presence of streptomycin, which minimizes the solubility of the anionic DNP antigen. It is then passed through a Dowex-1 Cl^- column that retains any remaining antigen. The antibody is precipitated from the effluent with ammonium sulfate, and the precipitate dissolved and dialyzed. After extraction with dinitrophenol, additional antibody may be eluted from the residual specific precipitate with ε-DNP-lysine.

Hemocyanin conjugated with β-glucosyl-azo groups has been found to remove Type II ANTIPNEUMOCOCCAL ANTIBODY very effectively. The washed specific precipitate is dissolved in excess sodium glucuronate, and the hemocyanin removed by ultracentrifugation.

Washed precipitates have also been extracted in the cold at acid pH with partial recovery of antibody; pH 3.0 glycine-HCl has been used with rabbit antibodies. Human antibodies are more labile; and pH 3.6 acetate has been used, but yields are poor and changes in the antibody may occur. Solution in saturated aqueous carbonic acid (pH 5.0, 0.035 M) of egg albumin anti-egg albumin and hemoglobin anti-hemoglobin precipitates, and separation of the antibody by ultracentrifugation and by chromatography on carboxymethyl-cellulose (CM-cellulose) has also been used.

Another method that is applicable only in selected cases is digestion of the antigen with enzymes. DEXTRAN-ANTIDEXTRAN and DEXTRAN ANTIPNEUMOCOCCAL precipitates have been digested with the enzyme dextranase; as the antigen is destroyed the antibody goes into solution. It is very difficult to remove completely all bound oligosaccharide, since fragments of large sizes may remain. However, the enzymatically prepared antibody is very useful for physical and chemical—although perhaps not for binding—studies. Separation from split products is by dialysis. Amylase has been used to destroy glycogen in specific precipitates with cross-reacting Type II antipneumococcal antibody; lysozyme, for recovering antibody from precipitates of its substrate with anti-*M. lysodeikticus* serum; and collagenase, for digesting gelatin-antigelatin precipitates.

An ingenious method involves the introduction of SH groups into protein antigens using *N*-acetylhomocysteine thiolactone,

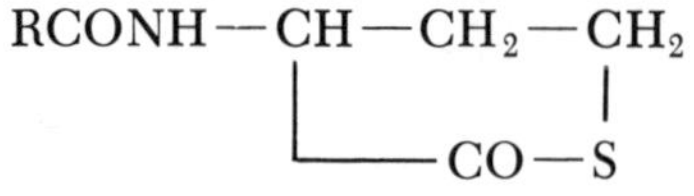

$$\mathrm{RCONH{-}\underset{\lfloor\_\_\_\_\_\_\_\_}{CH}{-}CH_2{-}\underset{CO-S}{CH_2}}$$

which reacts with the free amino groups of the antigen to form a CONH link and leaves an SH group free. This generally reduces to some extent the capacity of the antigen to precipitate antibody. The thiolated antigen is used to precipitate the antibody, the washed precipitate being dissolved in acid buffer pH 2.4 and the antigen rendered insoluble by cross linking the $-SH$ groups with an organic mercurial and separated from the antibody by centrifugation.

INSOLUBLE ANTIGENS AS ABSORBENTS

The earliest efforts to prepare insoluble antigens for absorbing antibody involved coupling of antigens to erythrocyte stromata. More recently, better-defined substances have been used, such as *p*-aminobenzyl-cellulose, polyaminopolystyrene, and a cellulose coupled to *m*-nitrobenzyloxymethylpyridinium chloride with subsequent reduction of the nitro to the amino groups. These compounds may be diazotized and coupled to protein antigens. The adsorptive capacity of the amino cellulose prepared with the pyridinium compound was greatly increased by solution in ammoniacal copper and precipitation as a very fine suspension. Ion exchange resins with the carboxyl or sulfonyl groups converted to acyl or sulfonyl chlorides have been coupled to antigens. The absorptive capacity of these materials is often limited, and although they have a tendency to absorb other proteins nonspecifically, they are nevertheless extremely useful.

Efforts to eliminate their undesirable features are being made. Whenever possible, insoluble adsorbents composed largely or exclusively of the antigen are highly desirable. For purifying antidextran antibodies, Sephadex (G-75) which is merely a cross-linked dextran has proved useful, and elution may be carried out with the isomaltose oligosaccharides. Polyleucyl blood group substances (already mentioned in Chapter 6) contain 50 percent by weight of antigen, and the attachment of the polyleucyl side chains to the ϵ-amino groups of lysine does not interfere with the antigenic determinants. Indeed, the hydrophobic leucyl side chains would tend to attract one another, leaving the carbohydrate determinants in an exposed position.

CROSS-LINKED PROTEIN ANTIGENS are also being developed. The mixed anhydride reaction using ethylchloroformate (see Chapter 2) has been used at acid pH to polymerize serum proteins or whole serum and to render them insoluble while not affecting their capacity to react with antibody. Another reagent used for cross linking is ethylene maleic anhydride, which reacts with amino groups and is used to cross link protein molecules to one another; the ethylene maleic anhydride in dioxane is added to the protein and flakes of the insoluble adsorbent settle out. *S*-acetylmercaptosuccinic anhydride and the previously mentioned *N*-acetylhomocysteine thiolactone may also be used to introduce -SH groups onto the amino groups of proteins, which may then be oxidized to produce insoluble polymers.

Human serum albumin could be coupled to polyaminopolystyrene and used to remove homologous rabbit antibodies. When these were eluted first with acetate buffer at pH 3 and then with 0.1 N HCl in 0.15 M NaCl, evidence of fractionation was obtained in that the latter eluate contained a higher proportion of antibody for the inhibitory fragments (see Chapter 6). The two fragments of molecular weight 11,000 and 6600 were then coupled to *p*-aminobenzyl-cellulose and columns of the conjugates were used to absorb rabbit anti-albumin. On elution with 0.5 M glycine-HCl, pH 1.0 antibodies specific for their determinants were recovered in good yield. The principle is clearly established that an insoluble absorbent consisting of a single antigenic determinant could be selectively used to remove part of the antibody from an antiserum and that these antibodies could be eluted and studied. Iodide salts have recently been shown to dissolve antigen-antibody precipitates completely and to elute antibody in high yield from insoluble adsorbents.

ISOLATION OF ANTIBODIES WITH DIFFERENT BINDING AFFINITY FOR ANTIGEN OR WITH DIFFERENT SIZE COMBINING SITES

Several procedures have been used. One involves sequential precipitation of portions of the antibody with antigen and elution of antibody from each precipitate with hapten. Antibodies with the highest binding affinity are precipitated by the smallest additions of antigen. This procedure was used to obtain rabbit anti-DNP antibodies of differing binding affinity as measured by fluorescence quenching (Chapter 5). Ten fractions (1 through 10) of antibody were obtained by successive small additions of DNP-bovine-γG-globulin, and each was purified as outlined above. Fluorescence quenching data on eight of the fractions are shown in Fig. 8.1. It is clear that there is a successive decrease in binding affinity, fraction 1 having the highest and fraction 10 the lowest.

Fig. 8.1 Fluorometric titrations of purified fractions isolated from the serum of a single rabbit by sequential precipitation with limiting amounts of DNP-B γG. Lowermost curve is fraction 1. Proceeding upward, the fractions are 3, 4, 5, 6, 7, 9, and 10. Fractions 2 and 8 are omitted to avoid overcrowding of data. (From Eisen, H. N. and G. W. Siskind. Biochemistry **3**: 996. Copyright 1964 by the Amer. Chem. Soc. Reproduced by permission of the copyright owner.)

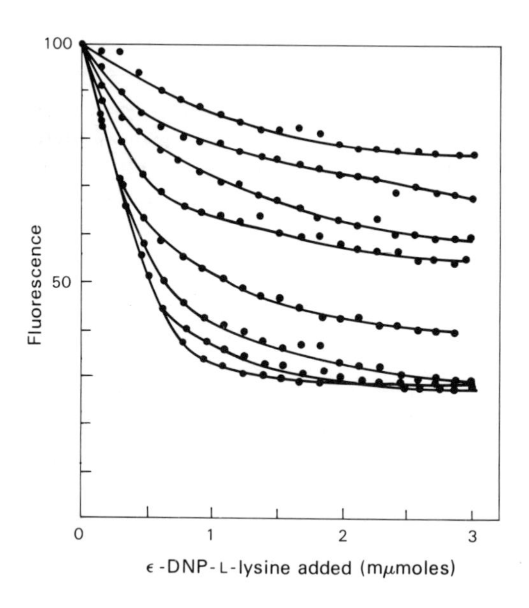

In the dextran-antidextran system, human antidextran from a single individual could be fractionated into subpopulations by sequential extraction with isomaltose oligosaccharides. Figures 8.2 and 8.3 show the results of absorbing human antidextran on G-75 Sephadex and eluting the washed Sephadex-antibody complex, first with IM3 and subsequently with IM6. The two fractions obtained were dialyzed to remove hapten and assayed for their capacity to fix C′ directly (Fig. 8.2). Larger amounts of the fraction eluted by IM3 were required for a given degree of C′ fixation than were needed of the IM6 antibody. In Fig. 8.3 the relative capacities of the isomaltose oligosaccharides to inhibit the fractions are shown as determined both by inhibition of the precipitin reaction and by inhibition of C′ fixation.

It is evident that the two methods give closely parallel results. The IM3 antibody is inhibited by both the di- and trisaccharides IM2 and IM3 (upper and lower left of the figure), but with the IM6 antibody these two oligosaccharides give no appreciable inhibition (upper and lower right). While with both fractions the tetrasaccharide IM4 and pentasaccharide IM5 are progressively better than IM3, with the

IM3 antibody fraction the penta-, hexa-, and heptasaccharides are of equal potency by inhibition of precipitation and the hexa- and hepta- are slightly better than the pentasaccharides by inhibition of C′ fixation. On the other hand with the IM6 antibody, inhibitng power continues to increase with chain length so that the heptasaccharide can be seen to be significantly better than the hexasaccharide, although in the original unfractionated antiserum (Fig. 6.2) they were of equal potency.

Fig. 8.2 Comparison by quantitative complement-fixation test of fractions of human antidextran. (Upper graph) Antibody extracted from washed Sephadex-antidextran precipitate by isomaltotriose. (Lower graph) Antibody subsequently eluted by isomaltohexaose. (From Gelzer, J. and E. A. Kabat. J. Exp. Med. **119**: 983 [1964]; by permission of The Rockefeller University Press.)

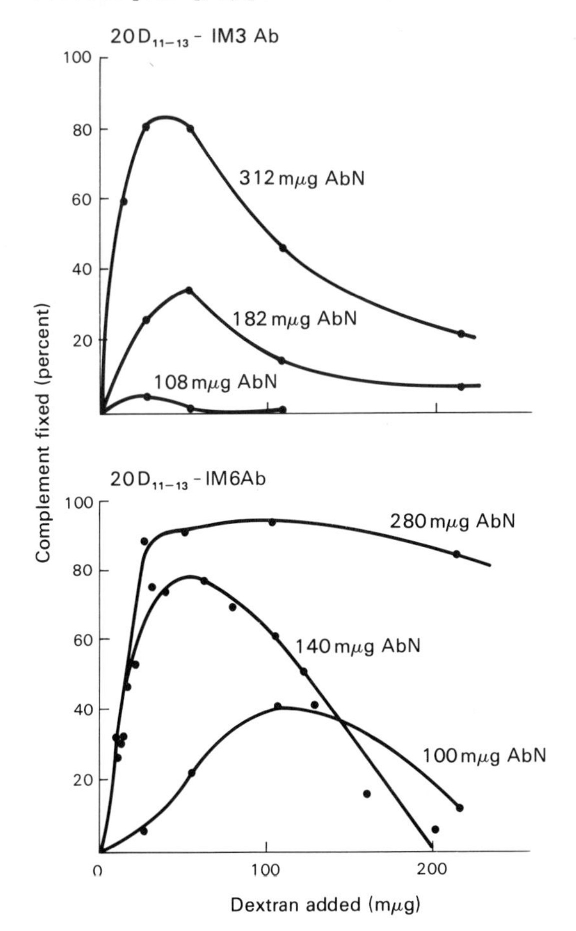

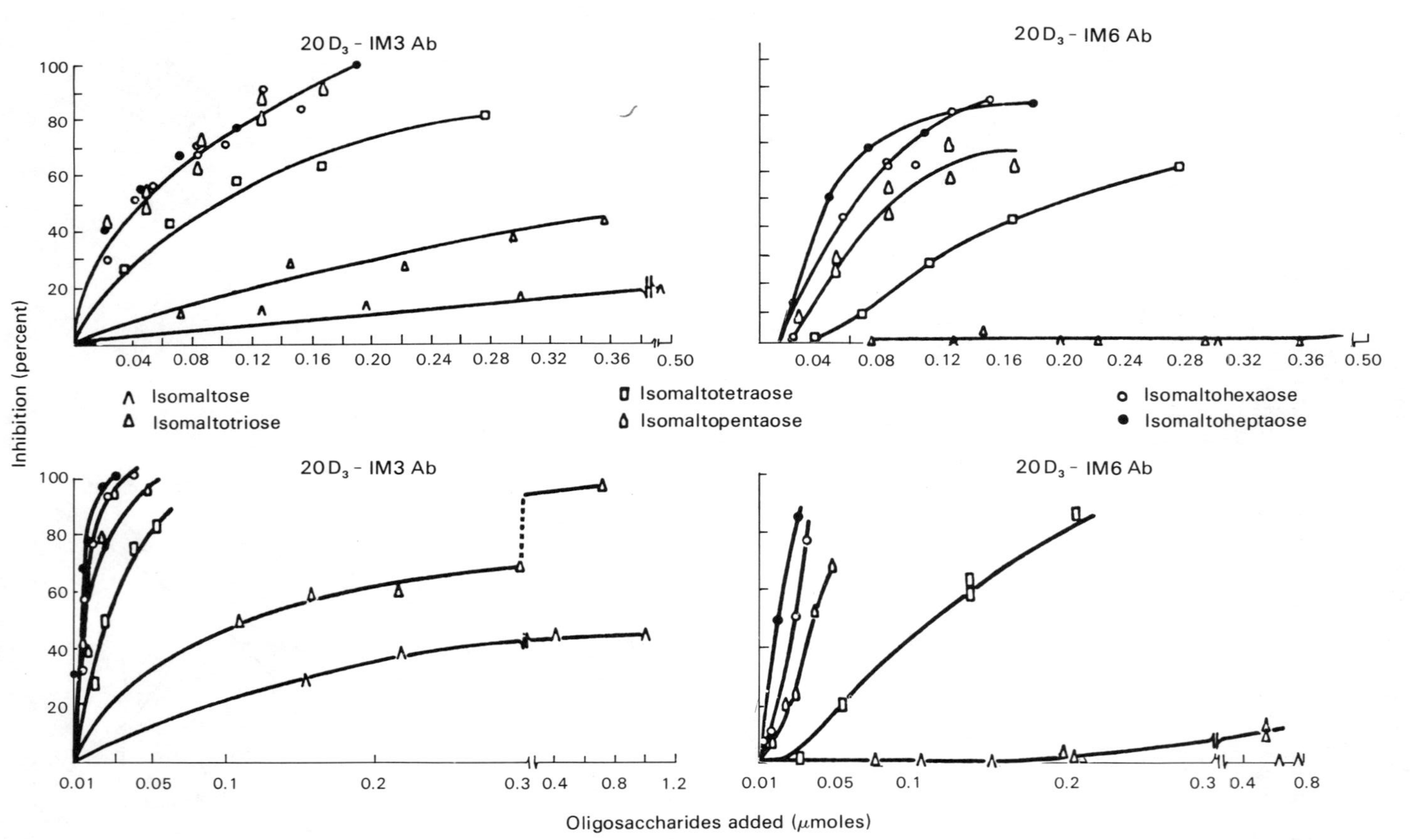

Fig. 8.3 Inhibition by isomaltose oligosaccharides of precipitation (upper graphs) and complement fixation (lower graphs) of human antidextran fractions by dextran. (Upper curves from Schlossman, S. F., and E. A. Kabat. J. Exp. Med. **116**: 535 [1962]; lower curves from Gelzer, J. and E. A. Kabat. J. Exp. Med. **119**: 983 [1964]; by permission of The Rockefeller University

PROPERTIES OF PURIFIED ANTIBODIES AND IMMUNOGLOBULINS

Many measurements of the molecular weight of purified antibodies and of the immunoglobulins have been made over the past 30 years and served to establish the macroglobulin and gamma globulin nature of these two classes. Recent interest in sequence of the immunoglobulin chains has led to additional measurements of molecular weight.

The most recent measurements for rabbit γG immunoglobulin gave values of about 140,000, and for horse γG immunoglobulin, values of 151,000. Early γM immunoglobulin values for purified horse, cow, and pig antibodies were about 900,000 to 1,000,000; for rabbit γM immunoglobulin a measurement of 850,000 to 900,000 was obtained. A detailed table of molecular weights and other properties of antibodies may be found in *Experimental Immunochemistry.* Precise molecular weights of γA immunoglobulins are not available, sedimentation constants from 7 to 15 S having been reported as compared with values of 7 S for γG and 19 S for γM. The γA immunoglobulins tend to form polymers that complicate the measurements.

γG immunoglobulin from rabbit, bovine, horse, and human sources has a carbohydrate content ranging from 2.4 to 2.9 percent, while human γM and γA immunoglobulins have 12.2 and 10.5 percent respectively. The carbohydrate is largely hexose and hexosamine with lesser amounts of fucose and sialic acid.

SUGGESTED READINGS

Kabat, E. A. Kabat and Mayer's Experimental immunochemistry. (2d ed.; 1961) Charles C. Thomas, Publisher, Springfield, Ill.; *Chapter 49 for concentration and purification of γG immunoglobulin; Chapter 51 for details of methods of purifying antibody; Chapter 7 for the physicochemical properties of antibody.*

Eisen, H. N., ed. Methods in Medical Research, Yearbook **10**: Sec. II, Chaps. 1-5 (1964). [Chicago].

Chase, M. W. and C. A. Williams, [eds.]. Methods in immunology and immunochemistry. Academic Press, New York. vol 1 (1967).

Sehon, A. H. Isolation and methods of characterizing antibodies. British Medical Bulletin **19**: 183 (1963).

Gurvich, A. E. The use of antigens on an insoluble support. *In* Immunological Methods (J. F. Ackroyd, ed.). Blackwell Scientific Publications, Oxford (1964).

Webb, T. and C. Lapresle. Study of adsorption on and desorption from polystyrene human serum albumin conjugates of anti-human albumin antibodies having different specificities. Journal of Experimental Medicine **114**: 43 (1961).

Lapresle, C. and T. Webb. Isolation and study of a fragment of human serum albumin containing one of the antigenic sites of the whole molecule. Biochemical Journal **95**: 245 (1965).

Avrameas, S. and Th. Ternynck. Biologically active water insoluble protein polymers. I. Their use for isolation of antigens and antibodies. Journal of Biological Chemistry **242**: 1651 (1967); *and* Use of iodide salts in the isolation of antibodies and the dissolution of specific immune precipitates. Biochemical Journal **102**: 37c (1967).

Cornell, I. and L. Wofsy. Specific purification of equine anti-SII antibodies by precipitation with a hemocyanin-glucuronide conjugate. Immunochemistry **4**: 183 (1967).

9

Heterogeneity and Structure of Immunoglobulins and Antibodies

The heterogeneity of antibody has been a recurrent theme throughout earlier chapters. We shall now consider the over-all structure of immunoglobulins with a view to understanding the basic patterns upon which these types of serum proteins are constructed. As yet, a specific localization of the antibody combining site to a given region of the various immunoglobulin molecules is not possible. We shall first look at the data on heterogeneity and then attempt to fit them into the chain structure of the immunoglobulins (p. 165) and relate them to what is known of sequence.

ANTIGENIC DIFFERENCES AMONG IMMUNOGLOBULINS

The three classes of immunoglobulin recognized by immunoelectrophoresis, γG, γM, and γA, in normal serum from many animal species have all been shown to be associated with antibody activity. However, there is as yet no evidence to indicate whether the immunoglobulins in normal serum are all antibodies formed to the many antigens with which one always comes into contact, or whether a population of non-antibody immunoglobulin molecules exists. The average levels and standard deviations (s.d.) in normal human serum of the three classes of immunoglobulin are:

		(s.d.)
γG	1240 mg per 100 ml	$\pm$ 270 mg per 100 ml
γM	120 mg per 100 ml	$\pm$ 35 mg per 100 ml
γA	280 mg per 100 ml	$\pm$ 70 mg per 100 ml

Each of these three classes differs from the other proteins of human serum in that they show a broad range of electrophoretic mobility and are not homogeneous (Fig. 3.10). Thus the γG globulin line in immunoelectrophoresis extends from the very slow γ region to the α_2 region. This heterogeneity—that individual γG molecules differ from one another in net charge is an intrinsic property of the immunoglobulin, since if various regions of the agar are cut out and subjected to a second immunoelectrophoresis, the faster-moving molecules again move at their original speed and the slower-migrating molecules continue to migrate slowly. A fourth class of immunoglobulin, termed γD, has recently been described and is present to the extent of < 0.3 to 30 mg per 100 ml.

Our understanding of the complexity of immunoglobulin heterogeneity has been greatly enhanced by studies on diseases that affect the synthesis of immunoglobulins. One of these, agammaglobulinemia, involves a defect in the ability to synthesize immunoglobulins with a corresponding failure to produce antibody on stimulation with various antigens and consequent high susceptibility to, and incidence of, bacterial infections. Its most severe form is congenital agammaglobulinemia due to a sex-linked recessive gene involving mostly males; its inheritance is very similar to that of color blindness in man. In one series of cases all 15 individuals were males, but in a second 9 of 50 were female. γG immunoglobulin levels may be as low as 5 to 100 mg per 100 ml. The disease is generally recognized very early in life, the age incidence ranging from birth to 14 years. Most cases of congenital agammaglobulinemia have very low levels of all three immunoglobulins, but cases are known in which only one or two classes may be affected. The observation that the three kinds of serum protein were involved provided the initial indication that all three immunoglobulins might be associated with the antibody forming mechanism. The second type of agammaglobulinemia, acquired agammaglobulinemia, affects males and females alike; and levels are not generally so low as those in the congenital type, the γG ranging from 100 to 300 mg per 100 ml.

The second group of diseases which have contributed to the clarification of immunoglobulin structure are the neoplastic diseases (cancers) involving synthesis of immunoglobulins. The diseases are called multiple myeloma and Waldenström macroglobulinemia and have been known for many years to be associated with excessive synthesis of serum immunoglobulins. The former disease involves excessive γG or γA immunoglobulin production, while the latter results in high γM levels. In both, the urine may frequently contain an unusual protein of low molecular weight—Bence Jones protein, known for over a century. This protein has been a great aid in diagnosis because of its unique behavior on heating in slightly acid solution, for example, precipitating at 56-64° and redissolving on boiling. Bence Jones protein will shortly be seen to be of great importance for immunoglobulin structure.

The unique character of the immunoglobulins in multiple myeloma and Waldenström macroglobulinemia is their relatively high degree of homogeneity as compared to the corresponding immunoglobulin in whole serum. In electrophoresis or immunoelectrophoresis they show a very narrow range of mobility. They thus are considered to be products of a highly selected population of cells rather than of the totality of cells synthesizing immunoglobulin. Indeed, the neoplastic cell producing each type of myeloma protein or macroglobulin may often be considered to be derived from a single clone. The extraordinary heterogeneity of the total serum immunoglobulin is further emphasized in that among the hundreds or perhaps even a thousand myeloma proteins that have been studied, no two have been found which are identical. Each may be readily classified as a γG or γA myeloma protein or as a macroglobulin; but within each class, they may differ in electrophoretic mobility, in immunological specificity, and in many other properties to be considered. They thus appear to be drawn at random from the total normal serum immunoglobulin pool that contains all the varieties, each being synthesized by a cell with slightly different synthetic capacity. Some evidence is accumulating of a hereditary predisposition to Waldenström macroglobulinemia, evidence of familial occurrence and of an increase in γM components, immunoglobulin levels, and antibodies to immunoglobulin in relatives having been found. Various workers are trying to find out whether myeloma proteins and Waldenström macroglobulins are at the same time antibody molecules. A knowledge of the complete amino acid sequence of a number of these proteins is being accumulated and will enormously contribute to our understanding of immunoglobulin and antibody heterogeneity and structure.

Recently a γA myeloma protein from a case with both myeloma and hyperlipidemia has been isolated which forms complexes with the serum α- and β-lipoproteins; and on ultracentrifugation in a medium of density 1.21, which causes the lipoproteins to float, the complexes moved upward with the lipoproteins and could be concentrated and purified. The myeloma protein was then separated from the lipoproteins by ultracentrifugation in acid-urea—in which the latter float and the former sediment—and by chromatography. It reacted with both

α- and β-lipoproteins in gel diffusion to give a single line that fused completely; it had a sedimentation constant between 7 and 19 S. The bulk, if not all, of the myeloma protein appears to have a unique autoantibody specificity for determinants present in both α- and β-human lipoprotein; rabbit antisera to human β-lipoprotein do not cross react with α-lipoprotein. Several other myeloma globulins with various antibody activities have also been isolated. γG myeloma globulins with antistreptolysin O and anti-α-staphylolysin have also been found as well as Waldenström macroglobulins with anti-γG globulin activity and anti-cholesterol activity. One γG myeloma globulin showed specific capacity to bind ϵ-DNP-lysine and appeared to be homogeneous with a K_0 of 10^4. Should the combining sites of these myeloma globulins with antibody activity prove to be homogeneous, the elucidation of the structure of the antibody combining sites will be greatly simplified.

Since these proteins are often present in very large amounts, the serum myeloma proteins and Waldenström macroglobulins and the urinary Bence Jones proteins have become available after purification in quantities sufficient for characterization and for the determination of amino acid sequence. In addition, it is possible to induce in mice, by injection of mineral oil, neoplasias that produce myeloma proteins and urinary Bence Jones proteins, and transplantable tumors may be obtained, thus insuring a supply of uniform material in genetically inbred lines. These mouse myeloma proteins also show the same narrow bands in electrophoresis and immunoelectrophoresis as do the human myeloma proteins, and each mouse protein differs from the others. Occasionally two proteins are formed in a single mouse and each may be established as a single line by tumor transplants.

Much additional insight into immunoglobulin heterogeneity and its structural basis has been obtained by efforts to sort myeloma globulins and Bence Jones proteins into various groups based on similarities of one kind or another. Similarities among antigenic determinants have proved especially useful. One basis for such a grouping was discovered by preparing antisera in rabbits to individual human Bence Jones proteins. Such antisera have established that almost all Bence Jones proteins fell into two groups termed K and L [earlier called I (B) and II (A)]. Not only could the Bence Jones proteins be so classified, but the myeloma globulins and the macroglobulins fell into the same two groups and normal immunoglobulin of all three classes could also be shown to consist of some molecules with K and some with L specificity. Fig. 9.1(A) shows that six type K Bence Jones proteins completely fused with one another in reacting with rabbit antiserum to whole γG immunoglobulin as did six type L Bence Jones proteins [Fig. 9.1 (B)]. The type K and type L proteins reacted with different antibodies [Fig. 9.1 (C)] as evidenced by the double spurs. In every case if the Bence Jones protein from a given individual was group K, his myeloma or macroglobulin protein was group K; similarly, if the Bence Jones protein was group L his myeloma protein or macroglobulin was group L. This at once established a structural relationship between the Bence Jones proteins, the myeloma and macroglobulins, and the normal serum immunoglobulins, since they possess similar antigenic determinants. It also raises important questions as to the interrelationships in the biosynthesis of immunoglobulin and Bence Jones protein. Individual molecules of immunoglobulin are generally only type K or only type L. In normal serum 60 percent of the molecules have been found to have type K determinants and 30 percent, type L, and this closely corresponds to the relative incidence of cases of multiple myeloma or Waldenström macroglobulinemia of these types. An analogous subdivision of mouse myeloma proteins has been made; guinea pig γG immunoglobulin has also been found to be of two antigenically distinct types, similarly termed K and L in the same proportions as human and mouse; but no such difference has been recognized among rabbit immunoglobulins. The K and L determinants are associated with one of the two types of polypeptide chain of which immunoglobulins are built (termed the light chains), of molecular weight about 25,000, and the Bence Jones protein represents an excess of light chains or light chain dimers that are excreted in the ur-

Fig. 9.1 Reactions in gel diffusion of type K and type L Bence Jones proteins with rabbit antiserum to human γG immunoglobulin. Central well: rabbit anti-human γG antiserum. Peripheral well: (A) Six type K Bence Jones proteins. (B) Six type L Bence Jones proteins. (C) Three type K (left two wells and bottom well) and three type L (right two wells and top well) Bence Jones proteins. (From Putnam, F. W., and C. W. Easley. J. Biol. Chem. **240**: 1626 [1965]; by permission of the copyright owner, the Amer. Soc. of Biological Chemists.)

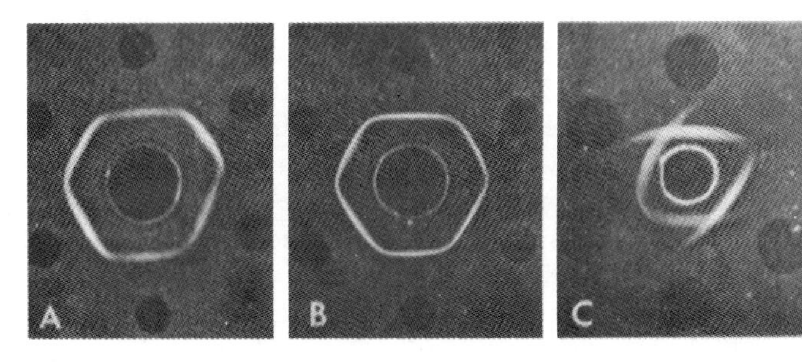

ine. Antisera to K and L determinants may also be prepared by immunization of rabbits with individual myeloma proteins, but they must be absorbed and rendered specific only for the K or L determinants.

Purified γG antibodies from humans immunized with dextran or with blood group A substance generally contained both K and L antigenic determinants, frequently in the proportions of 60 : 30 found for normal human γG molecules, but occasionally at a considerable divergence from this ratio. A sample of human antibody to levan contained only type K determinants, one sample of anti-A had 90 percent K and only 10 percent L determinants. Purified cold hemagglutinin, an unusual macroglobulin antibody that agglutinates erythrocytes at refrigerator temperatures but not at higher temperatures, from a great many cases that have been studied almost always had K determinants. Bone marrow cultures from patients producing cold hemagglutinins synthesized γM antibody containing exclusively K determinants. Guinea pig antibodies to various haptens also vary substantially in the proportion of molecules with K and with L determinants, some showing as little as 1 percent of L while others have a proponderance of L molecules. Thus the antigenic stimulus may effect some selection as to whether antibodies will have K or L determinants or both. In some instances this appears to be largely the result of chance, but with the human cold agglutinins and with some guinea pig antibodies, some unknown factor leading to their synthesis with only K determinants must be involved. Anti-thyroid antibodies from individual cases with thyroiditis have been found in each of the six immunoglobulin classes, γG K and L, γM K and L, and γA K and L. γG myeloma globulins have also been divided into subgroups by antisera to whole individual purified myeloma globulins. Such antisera have been produced in primates, monkeys and chimpanzees for example, and in rabbits. Before they can be used to subdivide individual myeloma globulins into classes, antibodies to the K and L determinants must be removed by absorption with Bence Jones proteins and the antibodies due to determinants occurring in all heavy chains must be absorbed through the use of myeloma globulin of another subgroup. When individual γG myeloma proteins are then studied they fall into four groups. In gel diffusion, members of a single group show no spurring. These four subgroups differ in antigenic determinants on their heavy chains, the other type chain of which immunoglobulin molecules are built. Individual γG immunoglobulin molecules are made up of only heavy chains of a single subgroup. Thus if the γG immunoglobulin of normal human serum is labeled with radioactive iodine, the proportion of molecules precipitated by antiserum specific for each of the subgroups can be measured and the percentage of each type of molecule in normal human serum can be calculated. The values found are as follows:

Subgroups	Older designations	Molecules in normal human serum γG immunoglobulin (percent)
γG1	γ_2b (We)	65
γG2	γ_2a (Ne)	23
γG3	γ_2c (Vi)	8
γG4	γ_2d (Ge)	4

The notations used for the subgroups of γG globulin are given. These subgroups of γG immunoglobulin differ in their susceptibility to digestion by papain, the γG1 antibody being readily split while the γG2 antibody is not split at all unless the disulfide bonds are thoroughly reduced.

Antibodies formed in humans to various antigens apparently represent selected populations of molecules. Human antidextrans from several individuals all formed predominantly—and some exclusively—γG2; since only 20 percent of the γG immunoglobulin in serum is of this subgroup, assuming equal numbers of cells involved in synthesis, this indicates a preferential response to dextran of cells making γG2 immunoglobulin. With other polysaccharide antigens, such as teichoic acid, γG2 was also predominant, but in some individuals considerable γG1 was present. In one person with anti-A, about equal amounts of γG2 and γG1 were formed; other antibodies might consist largely of one or the other subgroup. It is especially significant that many individuals whose antibodies were composed of a single heavy chain subgroup generally contained a mixture of K and L light chains in the usual proportions. The polypeptide chains on which the K and L determinants are found are often called κ and λ.

The human allotypes (see Chapter 2) of γG immunoglobulin, for example the Gm factors, have been shown to be associated with the different subgroups, each distinct genetic factor being associated with a particular heavy chain subgroup. The allotypic specificities are usually detected in whole serum or γG immunoglobulin by a hemagglutination inhibition test. The reagents are obtained, and the system set up in the following manner: Rh(D) positive human red cells are coated with a special kind of human antibody to the Rh(D) antigen. Any sample of anti-Rh(D) cannot be used, it must be a γG antibody that happens to contain γG anti-Rh(D) immunoglobulin possessing one of the Gm antigens. Such coated cells are agglutinated by antiserum from certain patients with rheumatoid arthritis, who tend to make autoantibodies to their γG immunoglobulin, or by the serum of a very small percentage of humans who, for unknown reasons, have such agglutinating antibodies or who have produced such specific isoantibodies as a consequence of multiple transfusions or injections of γG immunoglobulin. Having such a set of reagents, the capacity of individual human sera to inhibit hemagglutination of the Rh(D)-coated cells by the agglutinating antiserum is tested. Thus, if the anti-Rh(D) antibody coating the red cells contained the so-called Gm(a) antigen and the agglutinating rheumatoid or normal serum contained anti-Gm(a),the system would be inhibitable only by the γG immunoglobulin of individuals who were genetically Gm(a+) and not by those who were Gm (a−). Twenty-six such allotypic determinants have been described; those involving the heavy chain are the Gm factors, and those involving the light chain the Inv factors. The recognition of the individual genetic determinants is a difficult task, and only the exchange of reagents among various investigators avoids the utter chaos that could result if several investigators designated the same Gm factor by different symbols. The genetics of the Gm system became clear when these antigens were found to be associated with the heavy chain subgroups as follows:

	Gm factors present
γG1	a, y, f, z, x
γG2	n
γG3	b, b_3, b_4, s, t, c, g
γG4	none

No genetic factors have as yet been recognized in the γM and γA human immunoglobulins, but allotypic determinants in rabbit γM immunoglobulin have been found. More recently animal antisera have been obtained which may be used for identifying various Gm factors, and many Gm factors are present in primate γG immunoglobulins. With animal antisera, the Gm-containing immunoglobulin is coupled to erythrocytes with *bis*-diazobenzidine (Chapter 3), and the Gm factor in whole human sera is measured by a hemagglutination inhibition assay.

These associations between heavy chain subgroups and the Gm factors completely explain the findings that both γG myeloma globulins and antibodies could differ in their Gm groups from that of the total serum γG immunoglobulin of the same individual. Thus, if a myeloma globulin or an antibody is of the γG2 subgroup it will lack the Gm (a) or Gm (b) factors, even though these may be present in the individual's whole γG globulin. Thus an individual whose whole γG was genetically Gm (a+b+) produced the following antibodies

antidextran Gm (a− b−)
antilevan Gm (a− b−)
antiteichoic acid Gm (a− b−)
anti-A Gm (a+ b−)
antitetanus toxoid Gm (a+ b+)

In terms of the γG subgroups the molecules of antidextran and antilevan are found to be γG2, which lacks both these factors; the quantity of Gm (a) in the anti-A and antitetanus and of the Gm (b) in the antitetanus was much less than in normal serum, which indicates that the antibodies were produced by several kinds of cells making antibody belonging to different subgroups and that the proportion of γG1 in the anti-A and the γG1 and γG3 in the antitetanus toxoid was less than is usually found in normal γG immunoglobulin, probably because they were diluted with γG2 antibodies. Essentially the same situation obtains in rabbits; antibodies raised in rabbits of a particular allotype may lack certain allotypic determinants.

In addition to the antigenic determinants permitting classification into subgroups of the myeloma globulins and antibodies with respect to light and heavy chains, each individual myeloma globulin, Waldenström macroglobulin, and antibody has been shown to possess antigenic determinants that are uniquely specific for it and are absent in similar proteins derived from all other individuals. This is best illustrated in Table 9.1, in which antisera were prepared in rabbits with the use of purified anti-A antibodies from four different individuals.

TABLE 9.1

Reaction of Twenty-eight Isolated anti-A Antibodies with Rabbit Antisera to Four of the Isolated Antibodies

Isolated anti-A antibody	Antisera to Isolated anti-A Antibodies			
	Anti-Th[a]	*Anti-Ka*[a]	*Anti-Hb*[a]	*Anti-Wa*[a]
1.Th	5[b]	0	0	0
2.Wa	0	0	0	0
3.Ha	0	0	0	0
6.Ka	0	4	0	0
4, 5, 7, 8, 9, 10, 11	0	0	0	0
12.Hb	0	0	4	0
13 to 28	0	0	0	0

From Kunkel, H. G., J. Killander, and M. Mannik. Acta Med. Scand. Suppl. **445**: 63 (1966). By permission.
[a]Absorbed with normal serum of group AB + γG immunoglobulin Fr II.
[b]Precipitin reactions graded from negative 0 to 5 very strong.

Each antiserum was absorbed with normal human serum and with a purified pooled human γG immunoglobulin preparation (Cohn Fr II). The four antisera were then tested with the purified anti-A from 28 individuals as antigens—including anti-A from the four used to prepare the antisera. Reactions were obtained in three antisera only with the anti-A used to prepare the corresponding antiserum. Thus, each of these antisera recognized antigenic determinants present only in its homologous anti-A and absent in the anti-A of the 27 other individuals, the fourth antiserum had failed to produce individual specific antibody. Some determinants of individual specificity resided in the light chains, and others in the heavy. The same phenomenon has been shown to occur in rabbits.

CHAIN STRUCTURE OF γG IMMUNOGLOBULINS

The first definitive indication that γG immunoglobulin was built up of several chains was obtained by Edelman on reduction of the disulfide bonds with mercaptoethanol and alkylation in 8 M urea, by which two types of bands were observed on electrophoresis in starch gel 8 M urea-formate at pH 3. The faster-moving bands were the light chains, and the slower were the heavy chains. If normal γG immuno-

Fig. 9.2 Starch gel electrophoretic comparison of Bence Jones proteins before and after reduction and alkylation in 8M urea. (Left) Patient Haw. (Right) Patient S: (1) myeloma protein, (2) Bence Jones protein, (3) Bence Jones protein reduced and alkylated, (4) myeloma protein reduced and alkylated. L—light polypeptide chains; H—heavy polypeptide chains. (From Edelman, G. M. and J. A. Gally. J. Exp. Med. **116**: 207 [1962]; by permission of The Rockefeller University Press; the photograph here reproduced from printed halftone copy inevitably shows a loss of detail, and the quality of the results is not representative of the original.)

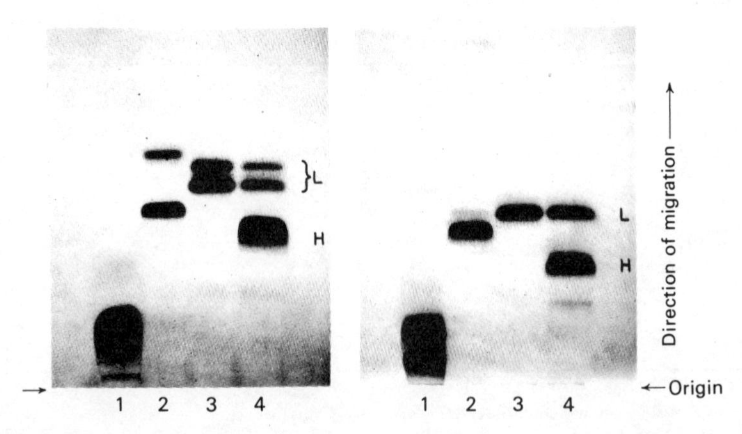

globulins were used both bands tended to be very diffuse; but with myeloma immunoglobulins the heavy chain remained diffuse, while the light chain bands were very sharp and tended to be few in number (Fig. 9.2) and corresponded closely to the bands obtained under similar conditions with the Bence Jones protein of the same individual. Purified antibodies from guinea pigs and humans also showed very sharp bands. When this technique was used at pH 7 increased resolution was obtained; normal human γG immunoglobulin was resolved into ten distinct light chain bands and normal rabbit γG immunoglobulin into 7 bands; γG immunoglobulins of other species also showed many bands (Fig. 9.3). The ten different light chain bands

Fig. 9.3 Electrophoresis in 8M urea glycine starch gel pH 7 of γG light chains of (1) guinea pig, (2) bovine, (3) horse, (4) baboon, and (5) human. (From Cohen, S., and R. R. Porter. Adv. in Immunol. **5**: 287 [1964]; by permission of the copyright owner, Academic Press, New York.)

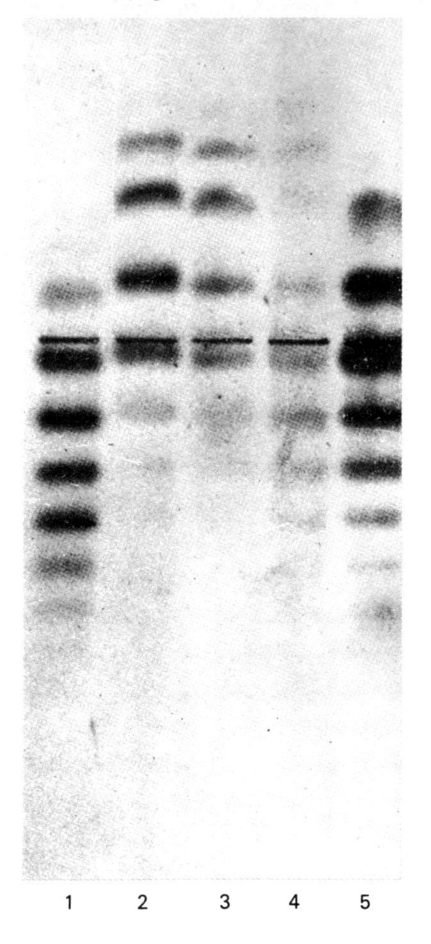

each appear to differ by a single charged group. This is illustrated in Fig. 9.4, in which the SH groups of myeloma light chains were blocked with neutral iodoacetamide or charged iodoacetic acid respectively. If two SH groups were blocked with iodoacetic acid the light chain occupied a position two bands faster than with iodoacetamide. Similarly, one SH group blocked with iodoacetamide gave a band displaced one position slower than with iodoacetic acid. Acrylamide gel electrophoresis also reveals many light chain bands and has also shown the heavy chains of rabbit immunoglobulin to be resolvable into several sharp bands. Rabbit antibodies gave all the seven light chain bands observed for whole rabbit γG immunoglobulin, and rabbit antibodies showed the same set of heavy chain bands in acrylamide gel. In the guinea pig, purified antibodies have shown some differences among themselves and from normal γG immunoglobulin in light chain bands at alkaline as well as at acid pH. Human anti-Rh antibodies from different individuals have been found to show four to

Fig. 9.4 Electrophoresis in 8M urea glycine starch gel pH7, of normal human light chain (1 and 4); a myeloma chain containing two sulphydryl groups blocked with (2) iodoacetic acid and (3) iodoacetamide; a myeloma light chain containing one sulphydryl group blocked with (5) iodoacetamide and (6) iodoacetic acid. (From Cohen, S. Roy Soc. [London], Proc. B. **166**: 114[1966]; by permission of the copyright owner.)

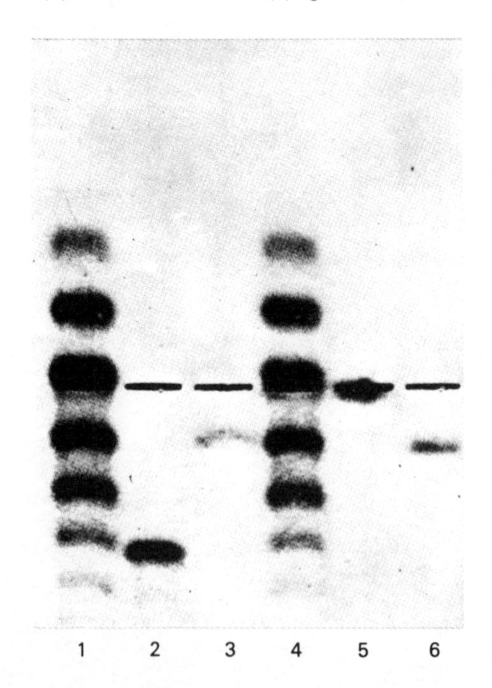

Fig. 9.5 Acrylamide gel electrophoresis of human γG myeloma polypeptide chains in Tris HCl at pH 9.4 in 8.5M urea. (Upper) Heavy chains of γG myeloma proteins of the four subgroups of human γG immunoglobulins. (Lower) Light chains from the same four myeloma proteins and from pooled normal human γG immunoglobulin. (From Terry, W. D., P. A. Small, Jr., and R. A. Reisfeld. Science **152**: 1628. Copyright 1966 by the Amer. Ass. for the Advancement of Science.)

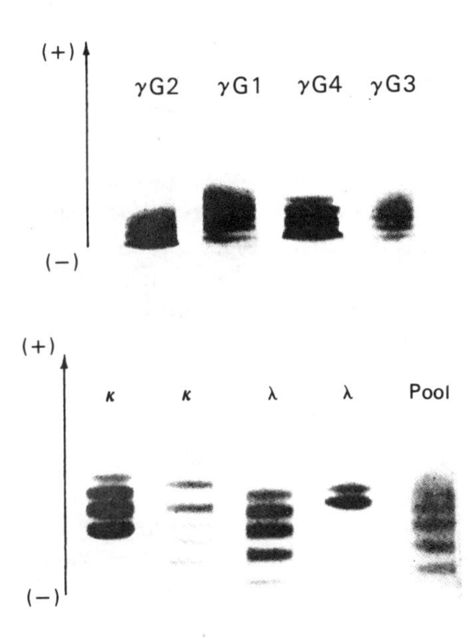

nine light chain bands on alkaline starch gel. The proportions of the bands varied from one individual to another.

Human myeloma globulins examined in acrylamide gel at alkaline pH after reduction and alkylation have been shown to be less homogeneous than was first believed. While as many as eight light chain and nine heavy chain bands were found for some myeloma proteins, others had fewer bands. This heterogeneity was present in K and L myeloma proteins as well as those of the four heavy chain subgroups (Fig. 9.5). The chemical basis of the heterogeneity is not known. In the mouse, however, newly synthesized myeloma protein has been found to be homogeneous, but in serum, changes occur with the appearance of five bands in starch gel; these changes have been produced by incubating newly synthesized myeloma globulin with sterile serum. How much such changes contribute to heterogeneity in other species is not clear. The charge differences could be the result of loss of labile groupings such as amide groups, sialic acid, and so forth and do not necessarily involve primary sequence differences.

The heavy and light chains obtained on reduction in 8 M urea were only soluble in this medium and this created serious obstacles to fractionation. However, reduction of the disulfide bonds in 0.75 M mercaptoethanol in Tris buffer at pH 8.2, followed by iodoacetamide or by sodium sulfite in the presence of Cu^{++} at pH 8.5 which converts the —S—S— linkage to $—S—SO_3^-$, and chromatography in cold N acetic acid or propionic acids on G-75 or G-100 Sephadex was found to give two peaks, the faster corresponding to the heavy chains and the slower to the light ones in the proportion of 70 to 75 percent by weight of the heavy and 25 to 30 percent of the light (Fig. 9.6). On examination in 8 M urea-formate starch gel electrophoresis, the first peak corresponded to the heavy chains and the second to the light chains. Molecular weights were about 50,300 and 19,400 for horse heavy and light chains, respectively. For rabbit heavy and light chains values range from 50,000 to 53,000 and from 22,000 to 25,000. Two heavy and two light chain molecules make up a molecule of molecular weight corresponding to γG globulin. The carbohydrate of γG immunoglobulin is associated almost exclusively with the heavy chains; traces, however, occur in the light chain peak.

Fig. 9.6 Separation of (A) heavy and (B) light chains of reduced rabbit γG immunoglobulin on Sephadex G-75 in 1 *N* acetic acid. (From Fleischman, J., R. H. Pain, and R. R. Porter. Arch. Biochem. and Biophys. suppl. 1: 174 [1962]; by permission of the copyright owner, Academic Press, New York.)

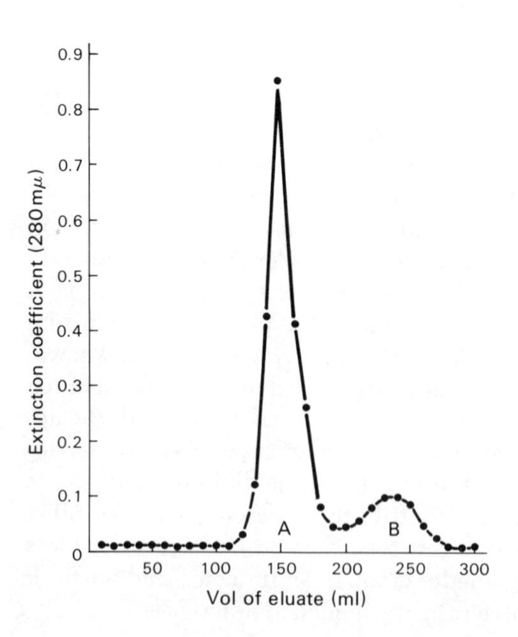

Studies on the light chain bands from normal human γG immunoglobulin showed that each of the ten bands was a mixture with both K and L determinants, while the bands seen in myeloma were either K or L. Thus, by these two criteria alone there are 20 varieties of light chains in human γG immunoglobulin.

Light chains as well as heavy chains tend to form dimers that dissociate in propionic acid, and most Bence Jones proteins occur as dimers having a molecular weight of about 45,000 (sed. constant 3.6 S), although monomers (1.8 S) and tetramers (5.5 S) have been found. The K light chain bands or Bence Jones proteins may be of three kinds based on their Inv determinants – Inv (a+ l+), Inv (l+), Inv (b+) or may have no Inv determinant. L chains also have no Inv determinants. Together with the ten bands in starch gel this would give 50 different light chains.

RECOMBINATION OF SEPARATED CHAINS TO FORM γG IMMUNOGLOBULIN

When the disulfide bonds are reduced as previously described the γG molecule does not fall apart into chains at neutral pH. Apparently it is still firmly held together by noncovalent forces – most likely hydrophobic bonds. These must be disrupted to obtain separation of chains. Disruption occurs in propionic or acetic acid solutions but even under these conditions complete separation of chains has proved difficult.

When the separated chains are mixed and brought to neutral pH they reassociate to form an intact γG molecule. If iodoacetamide has not been used or if the sulfite-Cu^{++} method has been used and mercaptoethanol is added, the —S—S— bonds may reform to produce a complete molecule, but association to give a molecule of sedimentation constant 7 S occurs even when the original disulfide linkages cannot reform.

Fig. 9.7 shows the results of such a recombination experiment. Separated heavy chains and light chains were labeled with I^{125} and I^{131}, respectively. On mixing and study by density gradient centrifugation it is evident that part of the radioactivity of the light chain becomes associated with the heavy chain. Comparison of (A) and (B) indicates the stoichiometric relationship between the amount of light chain combined with heavy chain and the ratio of heavy to light chain used.

Such recombination experiments have become especially useful for the demonstration of preferential specificity of light chains for their own heavy chains. Thus, recombination has been studied with heavy and light chains from myeloma globulins of various subgroups.

Fig. 9.7 Distribution of isotopic labels after gradient density centrifugation of $H_{I^{125}}L_{I^{131}}$ mixtures. Human H chain fractions labeled with I^{125}, L-chain fractions labeled with I^{131} and the products of their reconstituted mixture, $H_{I^{125}}L_{I^{131}}$, were each separately analyzed by density gradient centrifugation. (A) Mass ratio of H to L chains during reconstitution in 0.5 *N* propionic acid: 3.3/1. (B) Mass ratio of H to L chains during reconstitution: 6/1. △ – △, labeled L chain centrifuged alone; ○ – ○, labeled H chain fraction centrifuged alone; ▲ – ▲, L chain label in reconstituted mixture; ● – ●, labeled H chain fraction in mixture. Sedimentation proceeded from right to left. Percent total counts per minute in each fraction expressed as percent of total counts. This total accounts for soluble and insoluble material. ↓ indicates position of alkaline phosphatase marker. (From Olins, D. E., and G. M. Edelman. J. Exp. Med. **119**: 789 [1964]; by permission of The Rockefeller University Press.)

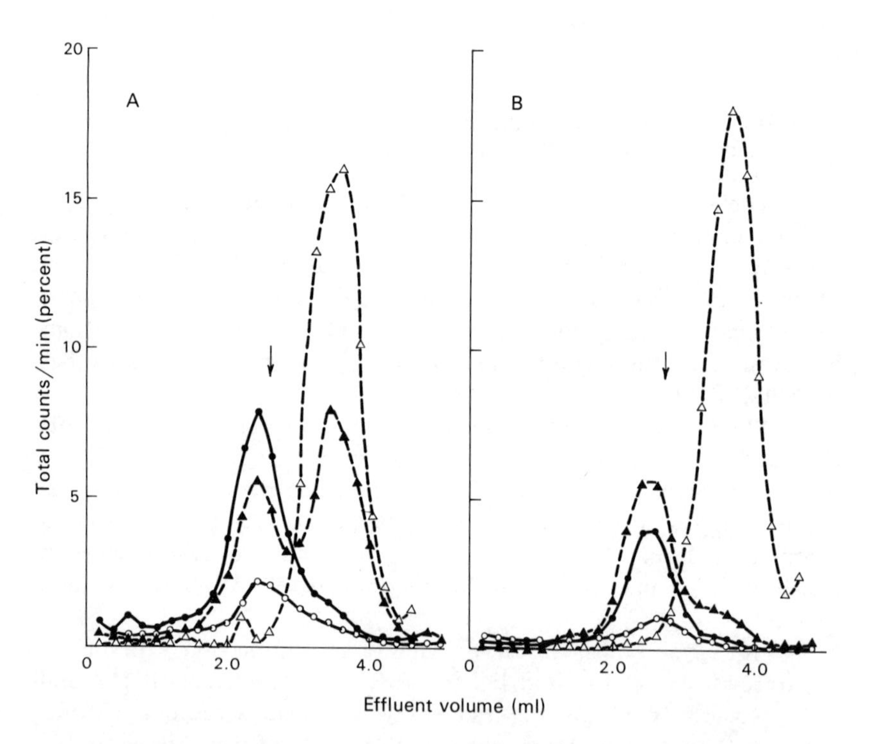

Figure 9.8 shows that light chains from a given myeloma protein will preferentially combine with their autologous heavy chains when both are present in a mixture. In Fig. 9.8 (A) it can be seen that the recombination of Ge* heavy chains with either Ge or Ne* light chains takes place to the same extent when only a single type of light chain is present. However, when a mixture of equal parts of Ge light chains

*In this experiment the chains were actually prepared from the myeloma proteins of individuals Ge and Ne.

Fig. 9.8 Sucrose density ultracentrifugation patterns illustrating the noncompetitive and competitive recombination of H and L chains. Gradient of 5 to 20 percent sucrose was utilized. (A) Patterns of two separate experiments are superimposed to show the degree of noncompetitive recombination of Ge H^2 chains with either Ge L or Ne L chains. (B) A competitive recombination experiment that illustrates the preferential recombination of Ge H^2 chains with Ge L chains. (C) A competitive recombination experiment that illustrates the preferential recombination of Ne H^1 chains with Ne L chains. (From Grey, H. M., and M. Mannik. J. Exp. Med **122**: 619 [1965]; by permission of The Rockefeller University Press.)

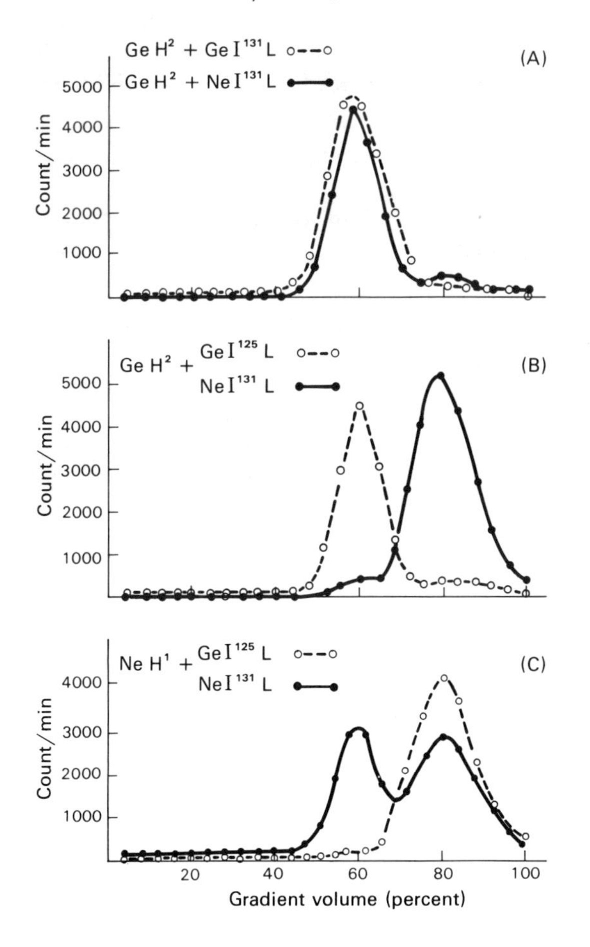

labeled with I^{125} and Ne light chains labeled with I^{131} were added to Ge heavy chains [Fig. 9.8 B] the peak of reformed γG globulin contained almost exclusively the Ge light chains. Similarly, the Ne heavy chains preferentially selected the Ne light chains from the mixture [Fig. 9.8 (C)]. Such recombination experiments can serve to establish specificity relationships among the various heavy and light chains. In a few instances light chains from unrelated myeloma proteins showed as high an affinity for an unrelated heavy chain as did its own light chain. Affinity of recombination was unrelated to whether the light chains were of the K or L antigenic type. The specificity of recombination must involve complementarity of regions of the heavy and light chains for one another and constitutes a recognition system that will probably become explainable in terms of primary structure of the chains.

Several investigators have shown that the recognition of heavy and light chains of antibodies for one another is substantial. Thus heavy and light chains, prepared from the γG immunoglobulin from whole rabbit antiserum to the *p*-azobenzoate hapten and recombined,

TABLE 9.2

Binding of C^{14}-2,4-dinitrophenol by Anti-DNP Antibodies of Different Combining Affinity from Rabbit HP and by Recombination of Light and Heavy Polypeptide Chains[a]

Sample	Concentration Hapten[b] Bound
	$10^6 \times$ moles/l
Fraction 1	13.4 (0.05)
Fr. 1, red, alk[c]	13.9 (0.69)
Fr. 1, red, alk, exposed to acid	6.86 (0.28)
$H_1 + L_1$	6.31 (0.29)
$H_1 + L_6$	3.44 (0.11)
$H_1 + L_N$[d]	2.28 (0.08)
Fraction 6	9.17 (0.04)
Fr. 6, red, alk	8.87 (0.34)
Fr. 6, red, alk, exposed to acid	3.29 (0.17)
$H_6 + L_6$	2.92 (0.07)
$H_6 + L_1$	2.54 (0.27)
$H_6 + L_N$	1.79 (0.38)
$H_N + L_1$	0.53 (0.10)
$H_N + L_6$	0.47 (0.06)
$H_N + L_N$	0.57 (0.22)

From Hong, R. and A. Nisonoff. J. Immunol. **96**: 622 (1966).

[a]Conditions of equilibrium dialysis. Protein concentrations, 0.8 mg per ml; free hapten concentration, 1.36×10^{-6} M. Standard deviations of the triplicate determinations are given in parentheses.

[b]C^{14}-2,4-dinitrophenol.

[c]Reduced and alkylated.

[d]normal

regained almost as much antibody activity as did the chains isolated and recombined from purified antibody. Light chains of a given antibody specificity prepared from one rabbit were not so efficient in recombining with heavy chains of the same antibody specificity from another rabbit as they were in recombining with their autologous heavy chains. Specificity of chain recognition has also been shown for fractions of antibody from a single rabbit, which varied in binding affinity for hapten. Six fractions of purified dinitrophenyl antibody from single rabbits were obtained by the sequential precipitation method (see Chapter 8). Chains were prepared from high-affinity fraction 1 and low-affinity fraction 6. Reconstitution of the heavy chains of fraction 1 with the light chains of fraction 1 gave antibody of higher binding affinity than when the low-affinity light chains of fraction 6 were used, and these were in turn better in reconstituting antibody activity than normal light chains. Similar specificity was noted, but was much less striking, when the low-affinity heavy chains were used (Table 9.2). It should be noted that exposure to N propionic acid causes substantial damage (50-65 percent loss of binding capacity) to the antibody even without separation of the chains, so that comparisons are made between the reduced and alkylated material exposed to acid and the recombined chains.

Although there is specificity of reformation of antibody and preferential recombination of antibody molecules with their own light chains in the absence of hapten, some data indicate that the presence of hapten further favors the recombination of antibody heavy with antibody light chains over normal light chains.

It is of interest that although molecules of γG globulin having one K chain and one L chain have never been found, it is possible to prepare such hybrid molecules by recombination experiments.

ANTIBODY ACTIVITY OF SEPARATED HEAVY AND LIGHT CHAINS

Antibody activity of separated heavy and light chains is a subject that has proved especially controversial, and it may eventually turn out that all investigators will have been right to some extent. For antibodies to several antigens, the isolated heavy chains have had considerable capacity to bind antigen. In one instance the heavy chains had 85 percent of the binding capacity of intact antibody. However, with antibodies to other antigens, heavy chains were found to be completely inactive, but some antibody activity was restored on interaction with light chains that by themselves were also inactive. Light chains derived from most antibodies studied were completely inactive, but phage neutralization by rabbit light chains has been reported provided antibody to rabbit light chains was added; and recently horse light chains from horse diphtherial antitoxin have been described which alone possess substantial antibody activity (5 to 10 percent of the original). Since recombination between heavy and light chains takes place so readily and since antibody activity can be measured only under conditions under which recombination would take place, the presence of even small contaminations of light chains in heavy chains would be expected to restore appreciable activity; and most doubts about the intrinsic antibody activity of the separated heavy chains were based upon this. The isolation of light chains free of heavy chains is not so subject to this criticism. In some ways the finding that either the heavy or the light chain may be of major importance in different antibodies may help in understanding the remarkable range of complementarity of antibody combining sites.

FRAGMENTS OF ANTIBODY AND NORMAL γG IMMUNOGLOBULIN OBTAINED BY ENZYMATIC DIGESTION

The study of fragments obtained by enzymatic digestion is an aspect of immunoglobulin structure which illustrates quite remarkably how difficult it sometimes is, and how long it may take, to appreciate the true significance of an observation made before there is a substantive theoretical basis for understanding its meaning. Over thirty years ago it was found that the digestion of horse antitoxins with pepsin at a pH close to 4 produced a molecule with intact antitoxic potency but with only two thirds the molecular weight of the native antitoxin, and shortly thereafter papain was shown to split horse antitoxin into "half and quarter molecules"; only one of the half-molecules flocculated with toxin. Pepsin-digested horse tetanus and diphtheria antitoxins came into widespread clinical use throughout the world, and probably thousands of liters have been used. Almost twenty years ago a fragment from rabbit anti-egg albumin was obtained by treatment with papain which inhibited precipitation of intact anti-egg albumin by egg albumin. Only in 1958 did the extraordinary significance of these observations for antibody structure become apparent when Porter placed a papain-digest of rabbit antibody on a carboxymethylcellulose column and obtained three peaks (Fig. 9.9). Peaks I and II were found to possess the antibody combining sites and are called the Fab fragments, while the third peak, which crystallized and showed no antibody activity, was called the Fc fragment. The two types of Fab fragments I and II have been shown not to occur on the same antibody molecule, but some antibody molecules have two molecules of fragment I combined with one Fc molecule,

Fig. 9.9 Chromatography of papain-digest of rabbit γG globulin on carboxymethylcellulose. Weight of digest 150 mg. Column 30 cm × 2.4 cm diam. Volume of mixing chamber 1200 ml. Gradient from 0.1 M sodium acetate, pH 5.5, to 0.9 M sodium acetate, pH 5.5, commencing at 200 ml eluate volume. (From Porter, R. R. Biochem. J. **73**: 119 [1959]; by permission of the copyright owner.)

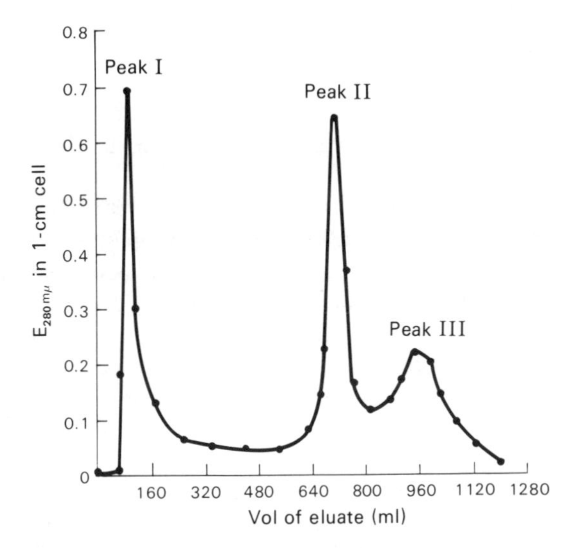

while others are built of two fragment II molecules and one Fc molecule. Recent studies have shown that these two types of rabbit γG immunoglobulin may be readily separated by chromatography on DEAE-Sephadex; various antibodies may be associated with one or another or both fractions. The charge on the antigen appears to have some determining influence on the fraction in which the antibodies appear. The separated Fab and Fc fragments have sedimentation constants of 3.5 S, as compared with 7 S for the original γG immunoglobulin.

When the action of pepsin on γG antibody immunoglobulin was reinvestigated, it was found that molecules of 5 S were formed and that a portion of the molecule was digested into small fragments. The 5 S material precipitated with antigen, but on treatment with cysteine or mercaptoethanol one disulfide link was broken to give two 3.5 S fragments that no longer precipitated with antigen but inhibited precipitation of intact antibody by antigen. The 3.5 S peptic fragments are designated Fab′ and the 5 S dimer as $F(ab')_2$; oxidation of Fab′ fragments in air gave dimers that again precipitated with antigen. The Fab′ fragments from antibody to two different antigens could be mixed and reoxidized to give bivalent 5 S hybrid antibodies. Papain

Fab fragments cannot be reoxidized, since the site of papain cleavage splits at a point at which the —S—S— bond linking the two Fab fragments to the Fc fragment is attached to the Fc fragment.

The 3.5 S Fab and Fab′ fragments obtained by papain and peptic digestion were found to have intact antibody combining sites by equilibrium dialysis; they showed the same heterogeneity distribution as did the intact γG antibody, and the binding curve extrapolated to a valence of one per Fab or Fab′ molecule.

A schematic view of the four-chain structure of γG immunoglobulin is given in Fig. 9.10; the relative sites of papain and pepsin action and the various fragments are shown. Treatment of the Fab or Fab′ fragments with mercaptoethanol and iodoacetamide splits them into a light chain and an Fd or Fd′ fragment. γG immunoglobulin could be reduced in 0.75 M mercaptoethanol and alkylated and then may be treated with papain and chromatographed on carboxymethylcellulose to give the same fractions seen in Fig. 9.9, since the chains are held by noncovalent bonds. These Fab fractions can then be separated into light chains and Fd fragments by chromatography on Sephadex in propionic acid. Most of the sequence and genetic data given in Fig. 9.10 are for human γG immunoglobulin, but the enzymatic splitting and the over-all scheme hold for other species as well. Rabbit allotypes A4, A5, and A6 controlled by the *b* locus have been associated mainly with the light chains while A1, A2, and A3 under the *a* locus are on the heavy chains. In any γG molecule the two light chains and the two heavy chains are identical in all respects as far as is known. The various structural features have only been indicated on a single chain in Fig. 9.10. The region around the inter-heavy chain disulfide bond which is susceptible to enzymatic attack is called the HINGE REGION.

With the light chains and Fd fragments from rabbit antibodies to *p*-azobenzoate, the same preferential specificity relationships for chain recombination as described for intact heavy and light chains have been found to hold. Fd fragment from the two Fab peaks (Fd^{I} and Fd^{II}) had less than 10 percent of the activity of the intact Fab fragments. When recombined with their own light chains or with light chains from the other Fab peak from the same rabbits, hapten binding activity was largely restored. However, light chains from another group of rabbits immunized with the same antigen or light chains from normal rabbit immunoglobulin gave no restoration of antibody activity. Recombination was shown to have taken place by immunoelectrophoresis and by disc electrophoresis in acrylamide gels. In mixtures containing Fd and light chains each derived from antibody and nonantibody γG immunoglobulin, antibody activity was largely restored on recombination.

Fig. 9.10 Schematic view of the four-chain structure of γG immunoglobulins.

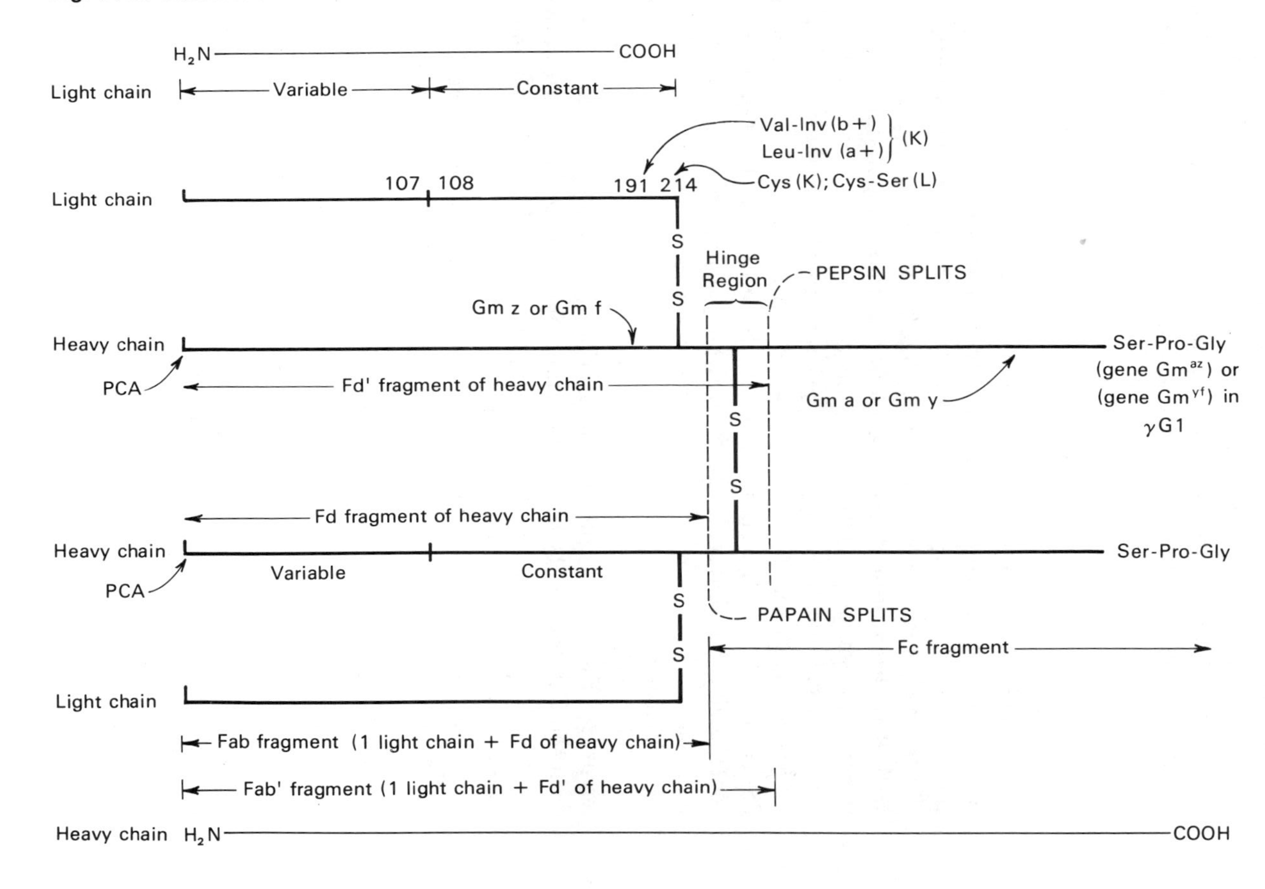

The Fab^{I} fragments from antibody to several antigens have also been subjected to extensive unfolding of the chains and opening of interchain disulfide bonds as well as to separation of the light chains from the Fd fragments using mercaptoethanol in guanidine hydrochloride; significant amounts of antibody activity have been recovered on removal of guanidine and slow reoxidation, but substantial amounts of insoluble material form. The optical rotatory dispersion curves of the original Fab^{I} fragments and of the reoxidized soluble materials were very similar.

The Fc fragment of papain digests of human γG immunoglobulin is not homogeneous, but shows several bands on immunoelectrophoresis and in starch gel. A faster moving band has been termed F′c fragment and is noted in papain digests of myeloma globulin as well; it is absent from digests of γA or γM immunoglobulins or from papain digests of γG unless cysteine is added (Fig. 9.11). F′c fragments of chimpanzee and human γG immunoglobulins cross react. They are smaller than Fc, having a sedimentation constant of about 2S. In addition to the splitting into Fab and Fc and F′c fragments, some dialyzable materials are formed on papain digestion. The F′c fragment is derived from the Fc region of the heavy chain and is also heterogeneous.

The antigenic determinants of the Fab and Fc fragments are different (see Fig. 9.11). Comparison of the determinants of the Fab′ with the Fab fragments from rabbit immunoglobulin showed them to be very similar as assayed with goat antisera to rabbit γG immunoglobulin and the Fab and Fc fragments.

The four-chain structure in Fig. 9.10 shows a single disulfide bond joining the two heavy chains together. There has been considerable controversy as to the exact number of —S—S— bridges between the two heavy chains. The site of papain action in Fig. 9.10 is based on the use of papain in the presence of cysteine. However, if papain

Fig. 9.11 Immunoelectrophoretic patterns showing G. Formation of Fab, Fc, and F'c fragments by digestion of human γG immunoglobulin in the presence of papain and cysteine and G' absence of F'c if papain is used without cysteine. (From Poulik, M. D. Nature **210**: 133 [1966]; by permission of the copyright owner, Macmillan [Journals] Ltd., London.)

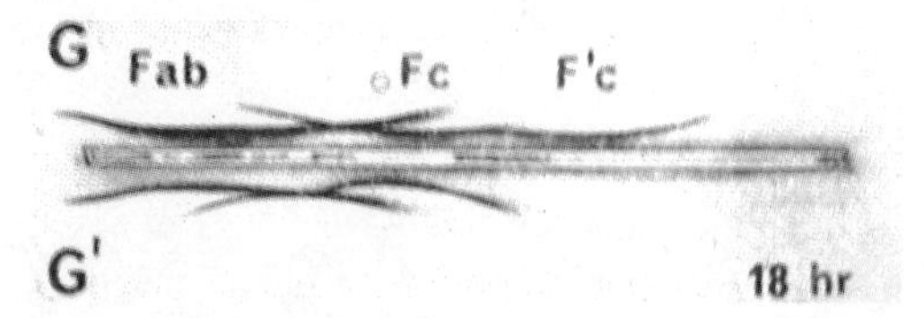

is used in the absence of cysteine, for example, as a water-insoluble polymer with long amino acid side chains, limited proteolysis occurs and after treatment with detergent a bivalent fragment $F(ab)_2$ resembling that produced by pepsin is obtained, which could be reduced by cysteine to monovalent Fab fragments as well as to an Fc fragment. This obviously would not fit with the scheme in Fig. 9.10, since the Fc portion of the heavy chains should be monomeric, there no longer being an —S—S— bond to link them together. Papain thus must be able to split on both sides of the disulfide bond. Other studies also showed that reduction of a single labile disulfide bond converted two thirds of the γG immunoglobulin molecules into half-molecules.

From a study of the fragments produced by peptic proteolysis of rabbit γG immunoglobulin and a comparison with the papain fragments, it has been inferred that the two heavy chains are connected by two crossed disulfide bridges

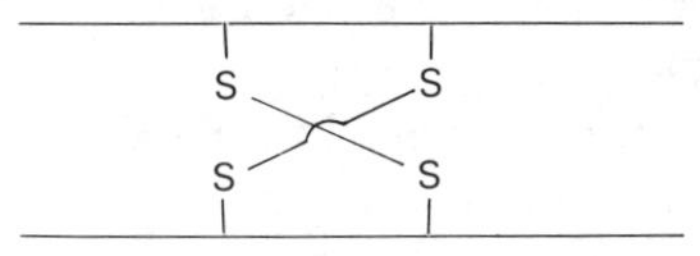

that may undergo disulfide interchange in the following ways:

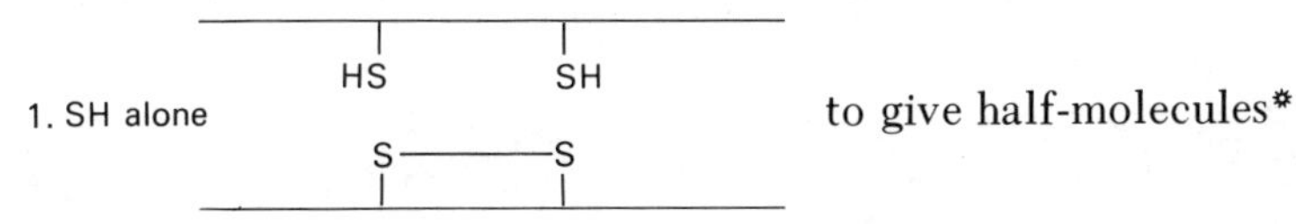

to give half-molecules*

(other interchanges in the equilibrium mixture would not yield half-molecules)

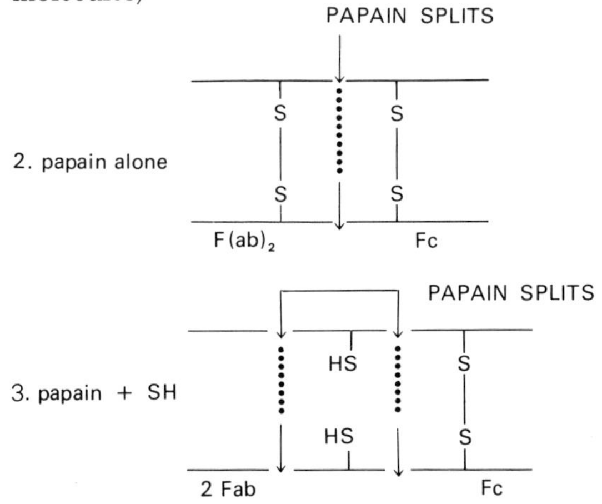

*Only the portion of the H chain involved is shown, but the entire molecule is being acted upon.

The crossed-disulfide scheme would appear to account satisfactorily for all of the data, but final proof will rest on the isolation of peptide with a crossed disulfide bridge.

RELATIONSHIP OF γG IMMUNOGLOBULIN IN MAN TO γM AND γA IMMUNOGLOBULINS

All three classes of immunoglobulin as well as the γD in man have been found to contain K and L light chains, thus giving a basis for their classification as immunoglobulins. More recent studies have shown that some antigenic determinants in the Fd or Fd′ fragment of the heavy chain are present in human γM as well as γG immunoglobulins. Rabbit antisera specific for the Fab′ fragment were prepared by injection of groups of rabbits with pepsin-digested γG myeloma globulins of type K or type L and with normal γG immunoglobulin. Antibody formed to the K and L determinants was removed by the addition of K or L chains, and the antisera were then specific for the Fd′ fragment. Certain of these antisera reacted with some purified γM preparations from cases of Waldenström macroglobulinemia. Thus some structural similarity exists between the Fd′ fragments in the γM and γG immunoglobulins. Since this portion of the heavy chain is associated with the region having antibody specificity, these findings provide another unifying feature of the immunoglobulins. Failure of many γM proteins to cross react may indicate subclasses among the Waldenström macroglobulins, just as there are heavy chain subgroups among γG myeloma globulins; evidence for subclasses of γA proteins is also being accumulated.

The Gm factors found in the Fc region of γG immunoglobulin are absent from a large number of γM and γA myeloma globulins as well as from normal γA and γM immunoglobulins. Thus these portions of the heavy chains of these three classes differ.

Papain digestion of human Waldenström γM immunoglobulins has also given fragments comparable to the Fab and Fc fragments, and pepsin digestion has given a fragment similar to Fab′ plus many small peptides.

Treatment of γM human antibodies when present in whole antiserum with mercaptoethanol causes loss of antibody activity as generally measured by hemagglutination tests. This has been related to the splitting of the γM antibody and γM immunoglobulin into monovalent subunits; on reoxidation random recombination of normal γM and antibody γM fragments occurs and antibody activity is not restored; with purified γM antibody, reoxidation of the subunits results in restoration of antibody activity. A Waldenström γM immunoglobulin of molecular weight 890,000 was split into five subunits, each of molecular weight about 185,000 on reduction of the disulfide bonds in aqueous solution using dithiothreitol at 0.001 M concentration. The valence of γM antibody appears to be 5. The structure of the γM subunit is not definitively clarified; structures of two light and two heavy chains and of three light and two heavy chains have been proposed.

ANTIBODIES IN OTHER SPECIES

The four-chain structure for γG immunoglobulin outlined for human and rabbit antibody and for the various classes of immunoglobulin has generally been found in all species that have been sufficiently studied. However, additional subclasses of antibodies have been found in other species.

Horse antibodies The horse has been found to form six distinct immunoglobulins possessing antibody activity to a lactosyl-azoprotein (Chapter 5). Three of these were γG immunoglobulins termed γGa, γGb, and γGc (Fig. 9.12); the others were γA, γM, and a protein with a sedimentation of 10 S and a mobility in the fast γ (γ_1) region. They could be separated chromatographically on DEAE-cellulose into γGab; γGc and γA fractions. The proportions of these antibodies changes with time and the binding affinity for hapten has been found to differ among the various antibodies. Thus the γA antibody isolated after six weeks and after six months of immunization gave Ko values $> 10^7$, while the γG a, b, c, showed a Ko of 10^5 at six weeks which increased to $> 10^7$ at six months. By equilibrium dialysis the γA antibody as well as the γG antibodies were found to have a valence of two. γA antibody did not precipitate with the lactosyl antigen, but was coprecipitated in an antigen-antibody precipitate of γGa, b; thus a bivalent antibody may not give precipitation with antigen, although it may have binding sites with very high affinity. Indeed, in suitable proportions it has been found competitively to inhibit precipitation with γG antibody.

Horse diphtheria antitoxic sera have also been found to exhibit complexity with respect to their immunoglobulin molecules. Two major types of diphtheria antitoxic globulin molecule have been recognized. One of these is the usual γG immunoglobulin of a slow γ_2 mobility, while the other, termed the T component, had a faster mobility occurring in the β_2 or γ_1 region and gave the flocculation rather than the precipitin type of curve (see Chapter 4). This T component was thought to be a γA immunoglobulin, but recent sequence studies (see

Fig. 9.12 The immunoelectrophoresis patterns of equine anti-Lac antibody prepared by the coprecipitation technique and fractions collected from diethylaminoethyl-cellulose chromatography developed against rabbit anti-whole horse sera. The top pattern shows the whole antibody preparation and shows at least four immunoglobulin components, $\gamma G_{a \text{ and } b}$ (the separation is not clear in this picture), γG_c, and γA seen as the major components. The second pattern is of FI and contains material from the ascending limb of the first peak. It shows only $\gamma G_{a,b}$, which runs from the γ_2 region into the β region. The third pattern is of FIII and shows the γG_c from the descending limb of the first peak; and fourth pattern shows the γA from the FIII, the material eluted after initiation of the NaCl gradient (From Klinman, N. R., J. H. Rockey, G. Frauenberger, and F. Karush. J. Immunol. **96**: 587 [1966]; by permission of the copyright owner, the Williams & Wilkins Company, Baltimore, Md.)

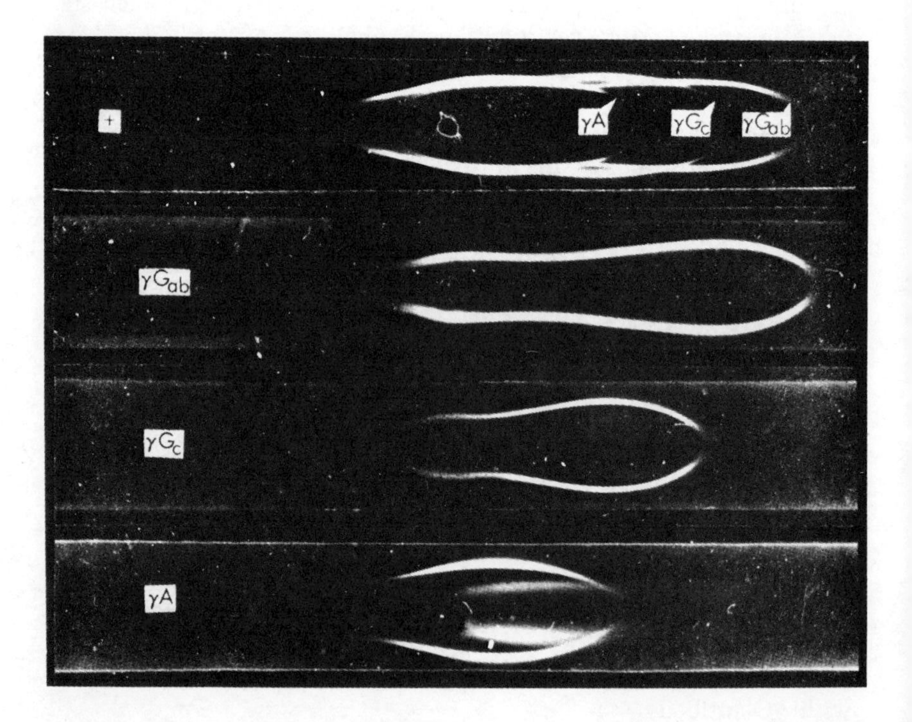

below) and assays for its carbohydrate content show it to be a γG type of immunoglobulin and it may be called $\gamma G(T)$. The proportions of these two antibodies change with continuous immunization, the $\gamma G(T)$ appearing early with a rise in the γG type later. The two antibodies may be separated by chromatography first on DEAE- and then on CM-cellulose. Other horse antitoxins correspond to the γGa, γGb, and γGc previously mentioned.

Horse antipneumococcal antibodies have long been known to occur predominantly in the γM fraction. On initial immunization the bulk of the antibody is of this type, but on continued immunization other lower molecular weight materials were present; and recently γG and another immunoglobulin class, either γA or γG(T), of antipneumococcal antibodies have been identified. Reduction of the γM antipneumococcal antibody did not inactivate the combining sites, and activity could be restored on reaggregation.

Guinea pig Purified guinea pig antibodies to DNP proteins and to insulin have been found to occur in two γG immunoglobulin fractions termed γ_1 and γ_2, the former migrating more rapidly in immunoelectrophoresis. These differ in biological properties; the γ_2 fixes C′ while the γ_1 antibody does not. For other biological properties, see Chapter 13. These two subclasses differ in their Fc fragments but when rabbit antisera to the Fab′ fragment of the γ_2 antibody were used, no antigenic differences in light chains or Fd′ fragments could be found.

Rat Rat antibodies have been studied to only a limited extent, but γA and γM immunoglobulins and two types of γG, each giving a long arc in immunoelectrophoresis and not equivalent to the γ_1 and γ_2 types in other species, have been recognized. A fifth type, detected only by its biological properties, is the anaphylactic type (see Chapter 13).

Mouse Mouse antibodies of the γM, γA, and γ_1 and γ_2 varieties of γG have been recognized. The γ_2 is further divided into γ_2a and γ_2b.

STRUCTURE AND SEQUENCE OF IMMUNOGLOBULINS

The ultimate understanding of the enormous heterogeneity of immunoglobulins and antibodies must rest on the determination of the sequences of the various chains and the formulation of detailed structures. To do this one must have reasonably homogeneous chains for study, and the best lead into the subject has been through the myeloma globulins and Bence Jones proteins. Two general tools have been used, one involving a study of the fingerprints or peptide patterns formed on tryptic digestion of the Bence Jones proteins, heavy and light chains, or Fc and Fd fragments of myeloma globulins; the other is the direct determination of the sequence of the various chains.

Fingerprinting

The protein is digested with trypsin which hydrolyzes the bond joining the carboxyls of lysine and arginine to the next amino acid to give a series of peptides. These are then placed on paper and subjected to chromatography in one direction and to high-voltage electrophoresis in the second dimension. The peptides are localized as distinct spots. These maps are characteristic and may be compared with one another if run under carefully standardized conditions.

Peptide maps of Bence Jones proteins of types K and L were found to have no tryptic peptides in common, indicating numerous

Fig. 9.13 Fingerprints of reduced and aminoethylated Bence Jones proteins (A) and BJ-subunit (B) separated from sample BJ-48. Tracing of the fingerprint of the Bence Jones protein (C) and of the BJ-subunit (D); peptides indicated as K1, K2, K3, K4, K5, K6, K7, K8, and K9 are the "common" tryptic peptides identified by comparison of the fingerprints of fourteen type K Bence Jones proteins. Peptide K8 overlaps a "distinctive" tryptic peptide; peptide K8 gives a positive reaction for tryptophan only, whereas the "distinctive" peptide gives a positive reaction for aminoethylcysteine only. (From Cioli. D., and C. Baglioni. J. Mol. Biol. **15**: 385 [1966]; by permission of the copyright owner, Academic Press, New York.)

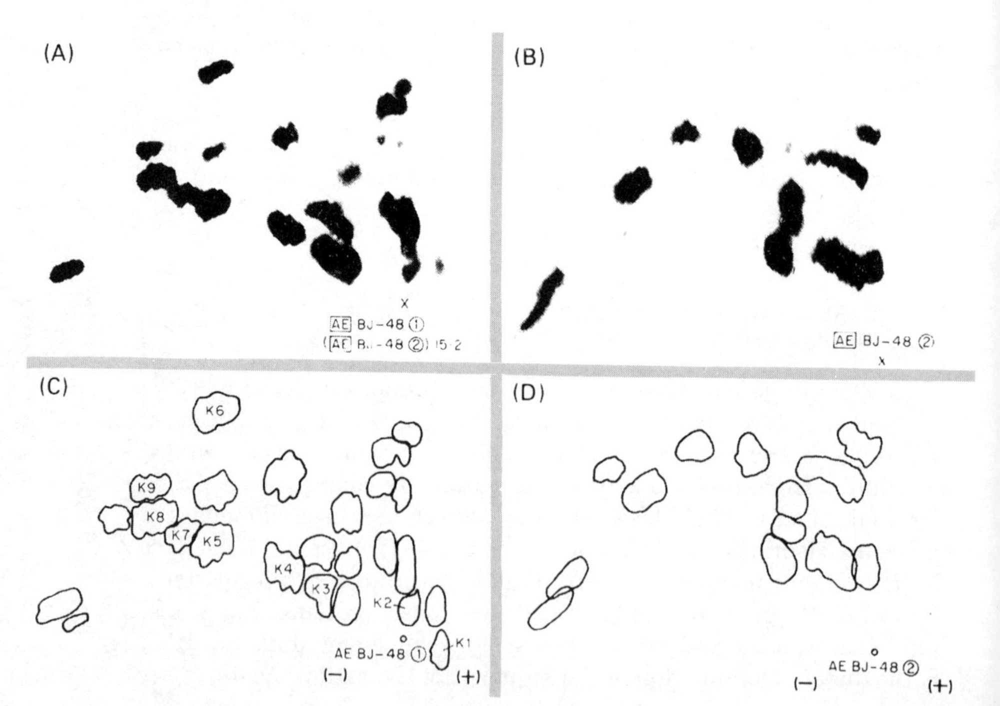

Fig. 9.14 Fingerprints of reduced and aminoethylated Bence Jones protein (A) and BJ-subunit (B) separated from sample BJ-38. Tracing of the fingerprint of the Bence Jones proteins (C) and of the BJ-subunit (D); peptides indicates as λ1, λ2, λ3, λ4, λ5, λ6, λ7, λ8, and λ9 are the "common" tryptic peptides identified by comparing the fingerprints of fifteen type L Bence Jones proteins. (From Cioli, D., and C. Baglioni. J. Mol. Biol. **15**: 385[1966]; by permission of the copyright owner, Academic Press, New York.)

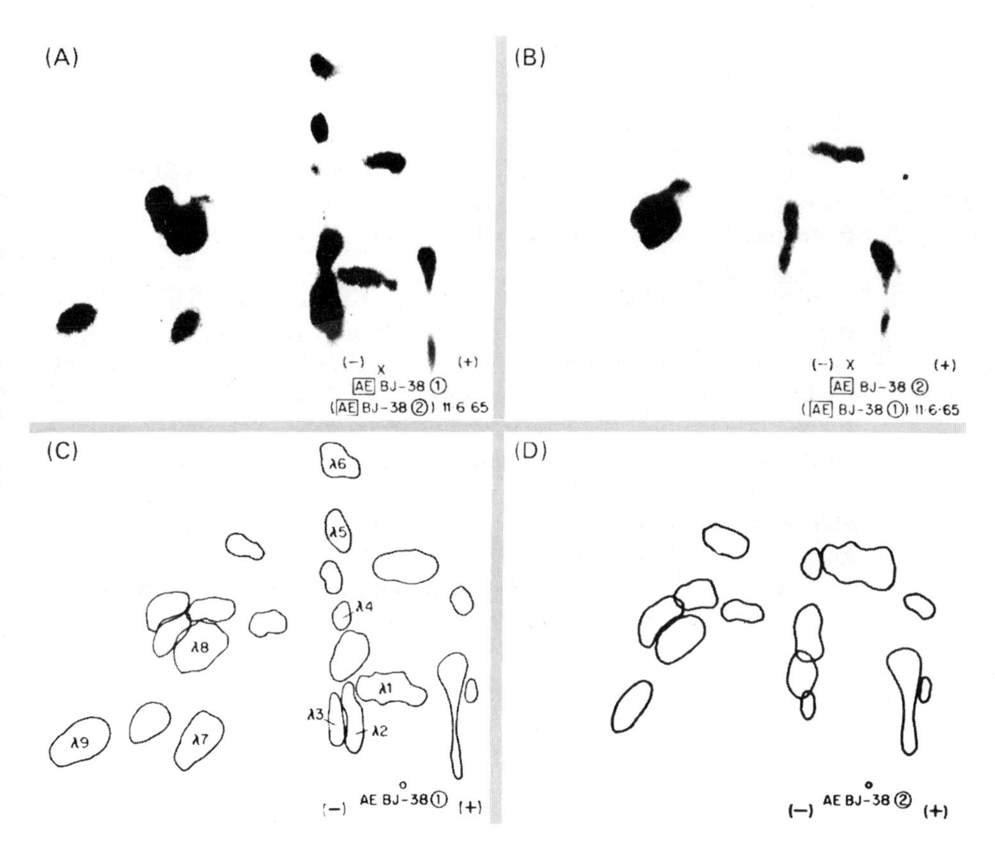

differences in the structures of the two chains (Figs. 9.13 and 9.14); they can, however, still have considerable similarity despite this. When a series of Bence Jones proteins of type K were examined they all showed a series of nine peptides in common, but the remaining peptides differed from protein to protein (Fig. 9.13); a series of type L Bence Jones proteins showed eight tryptic peptides in common (Fig. 9.14). These data led to the realization that the individual Bence Jones proteins and light chains were made up of a variable region and a constant one. This was reinforced by the finding that certain myeloma cases excreted in the urine not only intact Bence Jones proteins but a smaller fragment. This fragment in some instances corresponded only to the unique peptides of the intact Bence Jones protein, for example, the variable region as seen in Figs. 9.13 and 9.14, while in others it corresponded to the common peptides, for example, the constant region.

Similarly, fingerprinting has been carried out on the Fc fragments of the heavy chains of myeloma globulins. Within a given heavy-chain subgroup the Fc fragments were quite similar. With the γG1 subgroup, variation in the Fc fragment appeared primarily related to the Gm groups.

Comparing peptide maps of the entire heavy chain with the corresponding Fc fragment from each myeloma globulin showed the presence of from 6 to 13 additional peptides. These were ascribed to the Fd fragment, for example, (heavy chain minus Fc = Fd). Some of these were also present in the Fd fragment from normal human γG immunoglobulin and may indicate a region of structural similarity in the Fd fragment. There were, however, from two to seven spots that were unique to the individual myeloma Fd fragment from γG1 heavy chains and one to three spots unique to γG3 heavy chains. Study of the peptide maps of the Fab fragments from most of the myeloma proteins also permitted identification of spots due to the Fd portion of the molecule. These studies suggest that the Fd fragment has a variable and a constant region, but the relative extent of each is not known.

The variable regions of the light and heavy chains would appear to possess structural requirements for imparting the wide range of antibody specificities.

The tryptic peptide map of normal γG immunoglobulin was found to contain spots identical with those in both K and L Bence Jones proteins, providing additional strong evidence that Bence Jones proteins are structural subunits of γG immunoglobulin. A major uncertainty in our knowledge is the relationship of the multiple bands in starch gel electrophoresis of Bence Jones and myeloma proteins to the other parameters, including sequence, in which they appear to be homogeneous.

Sequences of Chains from γG Immunoglobulins

The standard techniques of sequence determination developed so successfully by Sanger in working out the detailed structure of insulin, and which have been so successfully applied to elucidating the complete sequences of ribonuclease, myoglobin, cytochrome C, hemoglobin, and other proteins, have been applied to the chains of myeloma globulins, purified antibodies, Bence Jones proteins, and the invariant portions of the heavy chains of whole γG immunoglobulins. This area of study is being pursued very actively, and large areas of sequence have already been worked out. In considering the known sequences we shall proceed first to consider the constant regions of γG immunoglobulin molecules (for details of the procedure see Chapter 1, Suggested Readings, Loewy-Siekevitz).

Carboxyterminal Regions of the Heavy Chains

By treating the heavy chains of γG immunoglobulins and antibodies with cyanogen bromide, the peptide bond between the COOH of methionine and the amino group of the next amino acid is split and the carboxyterminal methionine is converted to homoserine. In the case of a γG heavy chain this liberates an octadecapeptide whose sequence has been established in five instances (Table 9.3). The extent of the similarity of the five proteins from three animal species is extraordinary, 12 of the 19 amino acids (including the methionine) being in exactly the same position. Two additional amino acids, the Leu and the His at positions 4 and 5 of the octadecapeptide, were identical in all γG globulins except the horse γG(T). At two other positions, 7 and 8, four proteins were identical and only the human γG3 was different. At position 13 the amino acid was different for each species, while at position 15 the human samples were the same but all three others had a different amino acid.

SEQUENCE OF THE CONSTANT REGION OF TYPE K BENCE JONES PROTEINS

Eight type K Bence Jones proteins have been studied. While the sequence for only a few of these has been completely determined, the partial sequences for the others lend support to the inference that all type K Bence Jones proteins have the same sequence for the carboxyterminal half of the chain from residues 108 to 212,* with the exception of residue 191 which is leucine for Inv(a+) chains and valine for Inv(b+) chains in all eight specimens; twenty-seven type K Bence Jones proteins studied by fingerprinting showed the same leucine-va-

*The numbering of the residues has been made sequential by changing residues 70a, 70b, and 70c to 70, 71, and 72. Data in the literature are based on the specimen Roy, but studies on protein Ag established two additional residues between 70 and 71 of Roy.

TABLE 9.3

Sequences of Carboxyterminal Octadecapeptides from Heavy Chains of Several γG Immunoglobulins

	COOH terminal 18
Human γG myeloma γG1	(Met)-His-Glu-Ala-Leu-His-Asn-His-Tyr-Thr-Gln-Lys-Ser-Leu-Ser-Leu-Ser-Pro-Gly
Human γG myeloma γG3	(Met)-His-Glu-Ala-Leu-His-Asn-Arg-Phe-Thr-Gln-Lys-Ser-Leu-Ser-Leu-Ser-Pro-Gly
Horse γG(T)	(Met)-His-Glu-Ala-Val-Glu-Asn-His-Tyr-Thr-Gln-Lys-Asn-Val-Ser-His-Ser-Pro-Gly
Horse γG	(Met)-His-Glu-Ala-Leu-His-Asn-His-Tyr-Thr-Gln-Lys-Ser-Val-Ser-Lys-Ser-Pro-Gly
Rabbit γG	(Met)-His-Glu-Ala-Leu-His-Asn-His-Tyr-Thr-Gln-Lys-Ser-Ile-Ser-Arg-Ser-Pro-Gly

From Weir, R. C., R. R. Porter, and D. Givol. Nature **212**: 205 (1966). By permission.

line substitution to correlate with Inv(a) and (b) respectively. The sequence is given in Table 9.4. For comparison, the COOH-terminal half of the chains of human type L and mouse K Bence Jones proteins are also given. The human type L has a COOH terminal serine attached to the cysteine which links to the heavy chain, while in the type K the cysteine itself is the COOH terminus. A most significant implication of these data is that the constant regions of the K and L light chains are not identical and hence that in the biosynthesis of the complete chain the variable regions of the K chains associate only with K constant regions and L variable regions associate only with L constant regions. The sequences have been aligned to give maximum correspondence, and deletions are assumed to have occurred at positions 169, 201, and 202 in the human L chain. Some portions of the human K and L chains are identical, and a tryptic peptide has been identified in a type L Bence Jones protein in which nine of the first eleven amino acids are identical with those of residues 111 to 121 of the type K protein (Table 9.4).

In eight of these nine amino acids the sequence for mouse K at positions 111 to 121 also appears to be identical, although the final sequence has not been established. In comparing the three classes of proteins, 35 positions are identical for all three (in some the position of an amide has not been established); an additional 10 are the same for the human K and L proteins; human K and mouse K, and human L and mouse K are the same at an additional 29 and 7 positions, respectively. This leaves 31 positions at which all three proteins have a different amino acid. The mouse K protein differs from both human proteins at 36 positions, and these differences may be considered to be species specific. Such sequence differences among species are generally considered to be the result of mutations during evolution from a common ancestor. It is of interest that position 191 associated with the Inv factor in human K is serine in both human L, which lacks the the Inv determinants, and in the mouse K protein. A structural and allotypic difference among various human L Bence Jones proteins has also been found; at position 190 one group (Oz+) have lysine, and the other Oz−) have arginine.

The constant region of all Bence Jones proteins has 35 invariant residues. These include 3 residues each of alanine, valine, and leucine and 2 of histidine. It is of special interest that none of these amino acids are invariant in the variable portion. The constant region contains no invariant glycine, while the variable region has five such glycines. The hydrophobic invariant alanines, leucines, and valines, and the invariant histidines are perhaps of importance for the tertiary

TABLE 9.4

Sequence of the Constant Region of Type K Human and Mouse Bence Jones Proteins and of a Human Type L Bence Jones Protein

Residue Number	
108 110 115 120 125 130 135 140	
Arg-Thr-Val-Ala-Ala-Pro-Ser-Val-Phe-Ile- Phe-Pro-Pro-Ser-Asn-Glu-Gln-Leu-Lys-Ser-Gly-Thr-Ala-Ser-Val-Val-Cys-Leu-Leu-Asn-Asn-Phe-Tyr-	Human K
Gln-Pro-Lys-Ala-Ala-Pro-Ser-Val-Thr-Leu-Phe-Pro-Pro-Ser-Ser-Glu-Glu-Leu-Gln-Ala-Asn-Lys-Ala-Thr-Leu-Val-Cys-Leu-Ile- Ser-Asp-Phe-Tyr-	Human L
Arg-Ala-Asx-Ala-Ala-Pro-Thr-Val-Ser (Ile Phe Pro Pro Ser Ser) Glu-Gln-Leu-Thr-Gly (Gly Ser Ala Ser) Val-Val-Cys-Phe-Leu-Asn-Asn-Phe-Tyr-	Mouse K
141 145 150 155 160 165 170	
-Pro-Arg-Glu-Ala-Lys-Val-Gln-Trp-Lys-Val-Asp-Asn-Ala-Leu-Gln-Ser-Gly-Asn-Ser-Gln-Glu-Ser-Val-Thr- Glu-Gln-Asp-Ser- Lys-Asp-	Human K
-Pro-Gly-Ala-Val-Thr- Val-Ala-Trp-Lys-Ala-Asp-Ser-Ser-Pro-Val-Lys-Ala-Gly-Val- Glu-Thr-Thr-Thr-Pro- Ser-Lys-Gln- Ser-[ ]-Asn-	Human L
-Pro-Lys-Asp-Ile-Asn-Val-Lys-Trp -Lys-Ile-Asp-Gly-Ser-Glu-Arg-Gln-Asx-Gly-Val- Leu(Glx Ser Asx Thr Asx Trp) Asp-Ser- Lys-Asp-	Mouse K
171 175 180 185 190 Inv 195 200	
-Ser-Thr-Tyr-Ser-Leu-Ser-Ser-Thr-Leu-Thr-Leu-Ser-Lys-Ala-Asp-Tyr-Glu-Lys-His-Lys ↓ -Val-Tyr-Ala-Cys-Glu Val- Thr- His- Gln-Gly-	Human K
-Asn-Lys-Tyr-Ala-Ala-Ser-Ser-Tyr-Leu-Ser-Leu-Thr-Pro-Glu-Gln-Trp-Lys-Ser-His-↓Arg[a]-Ser-Tyr-Ser-Cys-Gln-Val-Thr- His- Glu-Gly-	Human L
-Ser-Thr-Tyr-Ser-Met-Ser-Ser-Thr-Leu-Thr-Leu-Thr-Lys-Asx-Glx-Tyr-Glx-Arg-His- Asx-Ser-Tyr-Thr-Cys-Glx-Ala-Thr- His- Lys-Thr-	Mouse K
201 205 210 214 COOH terminal	
-Leu-Ser-Ser-Pro-Val-Thr-Lys-Ser-Phe-Asn-Arg-Gly-Glu-Cys	Human K
[ ] -Ser-Thr-Val-Glu-Lys-Thr-Val-Ala -Pro-Thr -Glu-Cys-Ser (COOH Terminal)	Human L
-Ser-Thr- Ser-Pro -Ile-Val-Lys-Ser-Phe-Asn-Arg-Asn-Glu-Cys	Mouse K

Data from K. Titani, E. Whitely Jr., L. Avogardo, and F. W. Putnam. Science **149**: 1090 (1965); C. Milstein. Nature **205**: 1171 (1965); Roy Soc. (London), Proc., B. **166**: 138 (1966); W. R. Gray Roy Soc. (London), Proc., B. **166**: 146 (1966) C. Milstein, J. Mol. Biol. **21**: 203 (1966); W. Gray, W. Dreyer, and L. Hood. Science **155**: 465 (1967); K. Titani, M. Wikler and F. W. Putnam. Science **155**: 828 (1967); M. Wikler, K. Titani, T. Shinoda, and F. W. Putnam. J. Biol. Chem. **242**: 1668 (1967); C. Milstein, J. B. Clegg, and J. M. Jarvis. Nature: **214**: 270 (1967); E. Appella and D. Ein, Proc. Nat. Acad. Sci. **57**: 1449 (1967).

[a]Human L chains of type Oz + have lysine, those of Oz − have arginine at position 190.

structure of the constant region and perhaps contribute to the complementarity involved in its noncovalent binding to heavy chains. There are also four prolines, five serines, and three tyrosines in the constant region which are invariant. Also, the sequence of residues 113-124 in human K and L and in mouse K Bence Jones proteins (Table 9.4) has five of the invariant residues including three of the prolines, one glutamic acid, and one valine and a similar sequence in which these same invariant residues occur has been found in the constant region of rabbit and human heavy chains. As more sequences are established, relationships between the two chains should help clarify their origins and functions. Fig. 9.15 shows the sequence of the Bence Jones proteins with the invariant residues inserted.

Sequences of Amino Terminal Regions of Light Chains

Table 9.5 summarizes the sequences thus far established for the amino terminal regions of human K and L and mouse K Bence Jones proteins and also gives data on normal rabbit γG immunoglobulin and rabbit anti-DNP antibody. A deletion has been assumed to occur at position 9 or 10 of the human L protein. Variable positions for human K and L and mouse K proteins are in boldface type. Position 6 is the same for all human and mouse proteins and for the major portion of the rabbit normal and anti-DNP γG immunoglobulin. If the dele-

Fig. 9.15 Light chain of human K and L and mouse K Bence Jones proteins to give maximum homology and showing the nature and distribution of the invariant residues. The arrow indicates the transition from the variable (left) to the constant region.

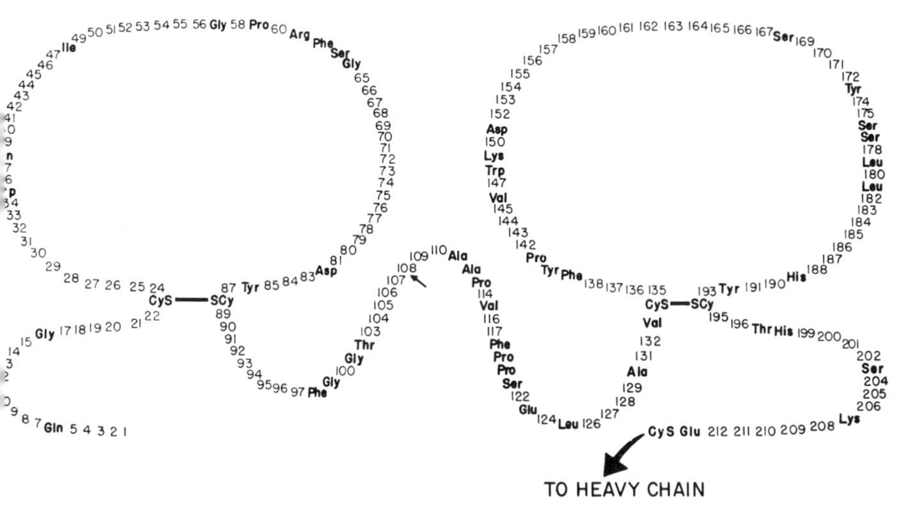

TABLE 9.5

Comparison of Amino Terminal Sequences of Type K and L Human Bence Jones Proteins, Type K Mouse Bence Jones Protein and Rabbit γG Immunoglobulin, and anti-DNP Antibody

Protein	Type of Chain	Residue (Variable Positions of Human K and L and Mouse K Proteins are in Boldface Type) **1** **2** **3** **4** 5 6 **7** 8 **9** 10 11 12 13 14 15 16 **17** 18 **19** 20 **21** **22** 23
Human		
Ag	K	Asp-Ile-Gln-Met-Thr-Gln-Ser-Pro-Ser-Ser-Leu-Ser-Ala-Ser-Val-Gly-Asp-Arg-Val-Thr-Ile-Thr-Cys
Roy	K	Asx-Ile-Glx-Met-Thr-Gln-Ser-Pro-Ser-Ser-Leu-Ser-Ala-Ser-Val-Gly-Asp-Arg-Val-Thr-Ile-Thr-Cys
Cum	K	Glu-Asp-Ile-Val-Met-Thr-Gln-Thr-Pro-Leu-Ser-Leu-Ser(Ala Pro Val Gly Glx Pro Pro Thr Ile Ser Cys)
BJ	K	Asx-(ValGlx)Met-Thr-Gln(Ser Pro Ser Ser Leu Ser Ala Ser Val Gly Asp)Arg-Val-Thr-Ile-Thr-Cys
Ker	K	Asx (ValGlx)Met-Thr-Gln (Ser Pro Ser Ser Leu) Ser-Ala-Ser-Val-Gly-Asp-Arg- Ile -Thr-Ile-Thr-Cys
Day	K	Val
Rad	K	Ala-Thr-Leu-Ser-Cys
HBJ 3	K	Asp-Ile-Val-Leu-Thr-Gln
HBJ 12	K	Glu-Ile-Val-Val-Thr-Gln
HBJ 10	K	Asp-Ile-Gln-Met-Thr-Gln
HBJ 6	K	Asp-Ile-Gln-Met-Thr-Gln
HBJ 1	K	Asp-Ile -Met-Thr-Gln
HBJ 5	K	Glu-Ile-Val -Thr-Gln
HBJ 4	K	Asp-Ile-Val -Thr-Gln
HS 4	K	Glu-Ile-Val-Leu-Thr-Gln
HS 6	K	Glu-Ile-Val-Leu-Thr-Gln

		3 5 7 8 9 11 13 14 15 18 19 20
HBJ 11	L	PCA*-Ser-Val-Leu
HBJ 2	L	PCA-Ser-Ala-Leu-Thr-Gln-Pro-Pro-Ser-[ ]-Ala-Ser-Gly-Ser-Pro-Gly-Gln-Ser-Val-Thr
HBJ 7	L	PCA-Ser-Val-Leu-Thr-Gln-Pro-Pro-Ser-[ ]-Ala-Ser-Gly-Thr-Pro-Gly-Gln-Gly-Val-Thr
HBJ 8	L	PCA-Ser-Ala-Leu-Ala-Gln-Pro-Ala-Ser-[ ]-Val-Ser-Gly-Ser-Pro-Gly-Gln-Ser-Ile-Thr
Sh	L	Ser-Glu-Leu-Thr-Gln-Asp-Pro-Ala-[ ]-Val-Ser-Val-Ala-Leu-Gly-Gln-Thr-Val-Arg-Ile-Thr-Cys

Mouse		3 4 9 12 13 19 20 21 22
MBJ 41	K	Asp-Ile-Gln-Met-Thr-Gln-Ser-Pro-Ser-Ser-Leu-Ser-Ala-Ser-Leu-Gly-Glu-Arg-Val-Ser-Leu-Thr-Cys
MBJ 70	K	Asp-Ile-Val-Leu-Thr-Gln-Ser-Pro-Ala-Ser-Leu-Ala-Val-Ser-Leu-Gly-Glu-Arg-Ala-Thr-Ile-Ser-Lys

Rabbit

γG Immunoglobulin	*Main*	Ala-	Val-	Val-	Val-	Gln-	Gln
	other small components	Ile	Leu	Leu	Gln		Thr
		Asp		Gln	Glu		Ala
		Glu		Glu			
Anti-DNP	*Main*	Ala-	Val-	Val-	Val-	Gln-	Gln
	other small components	Ile		Leu		Ala	Ala
		Asp		Gln	Gln		Thr
		Glu		Glu	Glu		

From N. Hilschman and L. C. Craig. Proc. Nat. Acad. Sci. **53**: 1403 (1965): F. W. Putnam, K. Titani, and E. Whitely, Jr. Roy Soc. (London), Proc., B. **166**: 124 (1966) and earlier papers. C. Milstein. Roy Soc. (London), Proc., B. **166**: 138 (1966); Biochem. J. **101**: 352 (1966) and earlier papers; L. Hood, W. Gray, and W. Dreyer. J. Mol. Biol. **22**: 179 (1966); W. R. Gray. Roy. Soc. (London), Proc., B. **166**: 146 (1966); R. F. Doolittle. Proc. Nat. Acad. Sci. **55**: 1195 (1966); W. Gray, W. Dreyer, and L. Hood. Science **165**: 465 (1967) K., Titani, M. Wikler, and F. W. Putnam. Science **155**: 828 (1967); M. Wikler, K. Titani, T. Shinoda, and F. W. Putnam, J. Biol. Chem. **242**: 1668 (1967) N. Hilschmann, Nobel Symposium on Gamma Globulins. Almqvist and Wiksell, Uppsala, 1967; F. W. Putnam, T. Shinoda, K. Titani, and M. Wikler, Science **157**: 1050 (1967).

*Pyrollidone carboxylic acid

tion is assumed to occur at position 9 and the serine corresponds to position 10, then all human K and L proteins and mouse K proteins have serine at this position and they all have glycine and cysteine at residues 16 and 23. Despite the relatively few proteins of each type analyzed, 19 of the first 23 positions have been found to be variable in one or another of the three proteins—that is, within each class, human K or human L or mouse K, individual proteins may have a different amino acid. For example, at residue 3 all three proteins have been shown to vary from one sample to another. Human K and mouse K proteins may have Gln and Val, human L contain Ala or Val or Glx;* all three classes also are variable at positions 9 and 19. In addition human K and mouse K both vary at residues 4, 7, 21, and 22; human L and mouse K at residues 12, 13, and 20, Sh. Thus far, residues 1 and 2 are variable only in human K; residues 5, 8, 11, 14, 15, and 18 only in human L; and residue 17 only in mouse K. Protein Cum has an additional residue at the N terminus.

SEQUENCE OF THE VARIABLE PORTION OF THE TYPE K AND L BENCE JONES PROTEINS

Table 9.6 gives the most complete sequences thus far established for the first 107 residues of type K human Bence Jones protein Ag, human type L Bence Jones protein Sh, and for two mouse type K proteins. Almost complete sequences are also available on two other human K and two human L proteins. Additional partial sequence data are available for six human type K proteins and for residues 1 to 6 for nine other type K proteins, and for residues 1-20 for three other human type L proteins (Table 9-5); amino acid substitutions that have clearly been established to occur at various positions are also tabulated. Fifty-seven positions in human K Bence Jones proteins in which a different amino acid may be substituted — that is, the variable positions—have thus far been encountered, at which 135 different interchanges have occurred. Bence Jones protein Cum has six additional residues between 27 and 28. Of the two mouse K Bence Jones proteins studied thus far, one has 4 amino acids more than the other between residues 27 and 28; these are numbered 27a, 27b, 27c and 27d (see footnote to Table 9.6). Excluding these four there are 40 variable positions (80 interchanges). For the human type L Bence Jones proteins, there are 55 variable positions (135 interchanges). For all three types of protein there are 86 variable positions; 18 of these are variable in all three, 10 more are variable in both human K and mouse K, 14 in

*Glx indicates that there is uncertainty as to whether the residue is glutamine or glutamic acid.

human K and in human L, and 6 in mouse K and in human L. With the data thus far available 15 variable positions are unique to human K, 17 to human L, and 6 to mouse K proteins. In all proteins the cysteines at positions 23 and 88 are joined as a disulfide bond to form a loop. If antibody specificity and the complementarity of the antibody combining site is determined by sequence differences in the variable regions of the light and heavy chains, the data on Bence Jones proteins thus far permit an enormous degree of variation.

Of those residues that as yet are nonvariable, 19 – including the two cysteines at residues 23 and 88 and residue 38 for which in some samples the presence or absence of an amide has not been established have the same amino acid in all specimens of each of the three kinds of Bence Jones protein. At 5 of the 19 invariant positions (16, 57, 64, 99, 101) the amino acid is glycine and glycine also occurs at position 68 in all proteins analyzed with the exception of one human L sample; the small side chains of glycine may be of importance for tertiary structure and may be necessary to give the variable portion of the molecule the flexibility it needs to permit the substitutions that occur at the variable positions. Of the 2 remaining residues to make up the 107 in the variable region, in one the same amino acid is present in human K and in mouse K and in the other the same amino acid occurs in human L and mouse K. At none of the 107 positions is there any evidence of species specificity.

There is thus a remarkable degree of similarity among the variable regions of the different proteins as compared with substantial species specificity for the constant region (Table 9.4). This appears even more evident when one considers the substitutions that are seen thus far at the variable positions. In 46 of the 86 variable positions with 319 interchanges for human K, human L, and mouse K, one of the possible amino acid substitutions is the same in all three types of protein. At 34 variable positions, the same amino acid occurs as one of the possibilities in human K and mouse K and at 6 positions in human L and mouse K. Thus in a total of 86 of the 319 interchanges, at the variable positions an identical amino acid occurs in the mouse and in one or both of the human Bence Jones proteins. At only 8 of the 86 positions that are variable (33, 43, 50, 55, 60, 80, 92 and 96) are the substitutions in the mouse different from those in the human Bence Jones proteins. Inasmuch as the relatively small number of individual human K, human L, and mouse K proteins studied were randomly drawn each from perhaps one thousand different kinds of light chains of each type, the similarity in variable positions is extraordinary. An understanding of the significance of the variable region, of its origins, and of the genetic control of its biosynthesis is crucial to resolution of the problem of antibody formation.

TABLE 9.6

Sequence and Other Substituents Found at Variable Positions of Human K and Mouse K Bence Jones Proteins. Sequence of a Human L Bence Jones Protein (Variable positions for Human and Mouse are in Boldface Type)

NH_2 Terminal	**1**	**2**	**3**	**4**	5	6	**7**	8	**9**	10	11	12	13	**14**	15	16	**17**	**18**	**19**	20	**21**	**22**	23	**24**	**25**	26	27[b]	**28**	**29**	**30**	
	Asp-	Ile-	Gln-	Met-	Thr-	Gln-	Ser-	Pro-	Ser-	Ser-	Leu-	Ser-	Ala-	Ser-	Val-	Gly-	Asp-	Arg-	Val-	Thr-	Ile-	Thr-	Cys-	Gln-	Ala-	Ser-	Gln	(Asx	Ile	Asx	Ag(K)
	Glu	Val	Val	Val			Thr		Leu					Pro(?)			Glx	Pro	Ala		Leu	Ser		Arg	Ser			Asp	Asp	Asn	
Glu				Leu															Ile									Gly(?)	Ser	Lys	
																												Ser(?)		Ser	
																														Gly	

1	2	**3**	**4**	5	6	7	8	**9**	10	11	**12**	**13**	14	15	16	**17**	18	**19**	**20**	**21**	**22**	23	24	25	26	**27**	28	**29**	**30**	
Asp-	Ile-	Gln-	Met-	Thr-	Gln-	Ser-	Pro-	Ser-	Ser-	Leu-	Ser-	Ala-	Ser-	Leu-	Gly-	Glu-	Arg-	Val-	Ser-	Leu-	Thr-	Cys-	Arg-	Ala-	Ser-	Gln-	Asx-	Ile-	Gly	Mouse 41(K)
		Val	Leu					Ala			Ala	Val				Gln		Ala	Thr	Ile	Ser					Glu[a]		Gly	Ile	Mouse 70(K)

1	2	**3**	4	**5**	6	**7**	**8**	**9**	10	**11**	12	**13**	**14**	**15**	16	17	**18**	**19**	**20**	21	**22**	23	**24**	25	**26**	27	**28**	**29**	**30**	
	Ser-	Glu-	Leu-	Thr-	Gln-	Asp-	Pro-	Ala-[	]-	Val-	Ser-	Val-	Ala-	Leu-	Gly-	Gln-	Thr-	Val-	Arg-	Ile-	Thr-	Cys-	Gln-	Gly-	Asp-	Ser-	Leu-	Arg-	Gly	Sh(L)
PCA		Ala		Ala		Pro	Ala	Ser		Ala		Gly	Thr	Pro			Ser	Ile	Thr		Ser		Thr		Thr		Ser	Asp	Asx	
		Val											Ser				Gly						Ser		Gly			Asn	Asn	
																	Arg													

31	**32**	33	34	35	36	**37**	38	**39**	**40**	**41**	**42**	**43**	44	**45**	**46**	47	48	49	**50**	**51**	52	**53**	**54**	**55**	**56**	57	58	59	**60**	
Ser-	Phe)	Leu-	Asn-	Trp-	Tyr-	Gln-	Gln-	Gly-	Pro-	Lys-	Lys-	Ala-	Pro-	Lys-	Ile-	Leu-	Ile-	Tyr-	Asp-	Ala-	Ser-	Asn-	Leu-	Glu-	Thr-	Gly-	Val-	Pro-	Ser	Ag
Lys	Tyr					Leu		Lys	Ala	Gly	Gln	Ser(?)		Glx(?)	Leu				Thr	Leu		Lys	Arg	Ala	Ala				Asp	
Asn	Phe																					Tyr			Ser					
Ile																														
Thr																														
Ser																														

31	**32**	**33**	34	35	**36(?)**	37	38	39	40	41	42	43	**44**	45	**46**	47	48	49	50	**51**	52	**53**	**54**	**55**	56	57	58	59	**60**	
-Ser-	Leu-	Ser-	Asx-	Trp-	Leu-	Glx-	Glx	(Gly	Pro	Asx	Glx	Thr)	Ile-	Lys-	Arg-	Leu-	Ile-	Tyr-	Ala-	Thr-	Ser-	Ser-	Leu-	Asx-	Ser-	Gly-	Val-	Pro-	Lys	Mouse 41(K)
	Phe	Met	Asn		(Phe	Glx)		-Lys-	Pro-	Gly-	Glx-	Pro-	Pro		Leu					Ala		Asn	Gln	Gly					Ala	Mouse 70(K)

31	**32**	**33**	**34**	35	36	37	38	**39**	40	41	**42**	43	44	**45**	46	**47**	48	**49**	**50**	**51**	**52**	**53**	54	55	56	57	**58**	59	60	
-Tyr-	Asp-	Ala-	Ala-	Trp-	Tyr-	Gln-	Gln-	Lys-	Pro-	Gly-	Gln-	Ala-	Pro-	Leu-	Leu-	Val-	Ile-	Tyr-	Gly-	Arg-	Asn-	Asn-	Arg-	Pro-	Ser-	Gly-	Ile-	Pro-	Asp-	Sh(L)
Lys	Tyr	Val	Ser					His			Arg			Lys		Leu		Phe	Glu	Val	Ser	Glx					Val			

61	62	63	64	**65**	66	**67**	68	69	70	71	72	**73**	**74**	75	76	**77**	**78**	**79**	**80**	81	82	**83**	**84**	**85**	86	87	88	89	**90**	
-Arg-	Phe-	Ser-	Gly-	Ser-	Gly-	Phe-	Gly-	Thr-	Asp-	Phe-	Thr-	Phe-	Thr-	Ile-	Ser-	Gly-	Leu-	Gln-	Pro-	Glu-	Asp-	Ile-	Ala-	Thr-	Tyr-	Tyr-	Cys-	Gln-	Gln	Ag(K)
				Thr		Ser						Leu	Lys			Arg Ser	Val	Glu	Ala			Phe Val	Gly	Val					Met	

61	62	63	64	65	**66**	67	68	**69**	70	**71**	72	73	**74**	75	**76**	**77**	**78**	79	**80**	**81**	82	**83**	**84**	**85**	86	87	88	**89**	90	
-Arg-	Phe-	Ser-	Gly-	Ser-	Arg-	Ser-	Gly-	Ser-	Asp/	Tyr-	Ser-	Leu-	Thr/	Ile-	Ser-	Ser-	Leu/	Glu-	Ser-	Glu-	Asp-	Phe-	Val-	Asp-	Tyr/	(?)/	Cys-	Leu-	Gln	Mouse 41(K)
					Gly			Thr		Phe			Asn		His	Pro	Met		Glx	Asx		Thr	Ala	Met		Phe		Glx		Mouse 70(K)

61	62	63	64	65	**66**	67	**68**	**69**	**70**	71	72	73	**74**	**75**	**76**	77	**78**	**79**	**80**	81	82	83	84	**85**	86	**87**	88	**89**	**90**	
-Arg-	Phe-	Ser-	Gly-	Ser-	Ser-	Ser-	Gly-	His-	Thr-	Ala-	Ser-	Leu-	Thr-	Ile-	Thr-	Gly-	Ala-	Gln-	Ala-	Glu-	Asp-	Glu-	Ala-	Asp-	Tyr-	Tyr-	Cys-	Asn-	Ser	Sh(L)
					Lys		Asn	Asp Thr	Ser				Ala	Val	Ser		Leu	Arg	Ser					His		His		Ser Ala	Ala	

91	**92**	**93**	**94**	95	**96**	97	98	99	**100**	101	102	103	**104**	**105**	**106**	**107**	
-Tyr-	Asp-	Thr-	Leu-	Pro-	Arg-	Thr-	Phe-	Gly-	Gln-	Gly-	Thr-	Lys-	Leu-	Glu-	Ile-	Lys-	Ag
Arg Phe	Leu Glu	Asn Asp Glu	Ser Ile		Pro Thr Tyr Leu				Pro Gly				Val- Leu-	Asp- Glx-	Phe- Ile-	Lys- Arg-	

91	**92**	**93**	**94**	95	96	97	98	99	100	101	102	103	104	105	106	107	
-Tyr-	Ala-	Ser-	Ser-	Pro-	Trp-	Thr-	Phe-	Gly-	Gly-	Gly-	Thr-	Lys-	Leu-	Glu-	Ile-	Lys-	Mouse 41(K)
Ser	Lys	Glu	Val														Mouse 70(K)

91	**92**	**93**	**94**	**95**	**96**	**97**	98	99	100	101	102	**103**	104	105	106	**107**	
Arg-	Asp-	Ser-	Ser-	Gly-	Lys-	His[c]	Phe-	Gly-	Gly-	Gly-	Thr-	Lys-	Leu-	Thr-	Val[c]	Gly-	Sh(L)
Tyr Trp	Val	Asx Tyr	Asx Arg	Asx Leu	Asx Ser	Phe Ala						Gln				Arg	

The sequence of residues 39-43 is tabulated for Mouse 70 as well, since it is not definitely established for Mouse 41.

[a]Mouse K Bence Jones Protein 70 has four additional residues between 27 and 28 in the following sequence: 27 27a, 27b, 27c, 27d, and 28. Glu-Ser-Val-Asx (Ser Asx).

[b]Human Bence Jones Protein Cum has six additional residues between 27 and 28 in the following sequence: 27, 27a, 27b, 27c, 27d, 27e, 27f, 28 Glx-Ser-Leu-Leu-Asp-Asp (Ser Gly).

[c]Two additional residues, Val and Leu, occur between positions 97 and 98, and an additional Leu is found between residues 106 and 107.

Data from K. Titani, E. Whitely Jr., and F. W. Putnam, Science **152**: 1513 (1966); F. W. Putnam, K. Titani, and E. Whitely, Jr. Roy. Soc. (London), Proc. B. **166**: 124 (1966); C. Milstein. Nature **209**: 370 (1966); Roy. Soc. (London), Proc., B, **166**: 138 (1966); Biochem. J. **101**: 338, 352 (1966); L. Hood, W. Gray, and W. Dreyer, Proc. Nat. Acad. Sci., 55,826 (1966) J. Mol. Biol. **22**: 179 (1966); W. R. Gray, Roy. Soc. (London), Proc., B. **166**: 146 (1966); W. Gray, W. Dreyer and L. Hood, Science **165**: 465 (1967); N. Hilschman and L. C. Craig, Proc. Nat. Acad. Sci. **53**: 1403 (1965); K. Titani, M. Wikler and F. W. Putnam, Science, 155, 828 (1967); M. Wikler, K. Titani, T. Shinoda and F. W. Putnam, J. Biol. Chem., **242**: 1668 (1967); N. Hilschmann, Nobel Symposium on Gamma globulins. Almqvist and Wiksell, Uppsala, 1967; F. W. Putnam, T. Shinoda, K. Titani, and M. Wikler, Science **157**: 1050 (1967).

Implications of Sequence Studies

In addition to the data presented, about one half of the sequence of the Fc fragment of rabbit γG immunoglobulin has been worked out, since this portion of the heavy chain appears to be the same in the bulk of rabbit γG immunoglobulin. The Fd fragment, however, is also heterogeneous and this portion of the molecule has the greatest significance for antibody structure, since it is associated with the combining site.

The sequence of the hinge region of the heavy chain of rabbit γG immunoglobulin which is present in the peptic F(ab′)$_2$ fragment but absent in the papain Fab fragment has been shown to be:

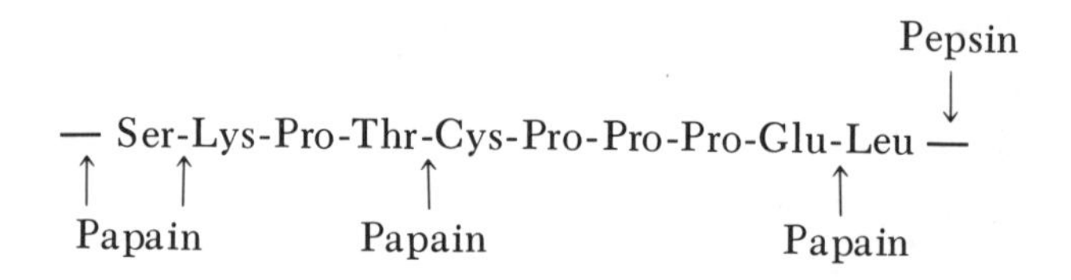

The bonds split by pepsin and papain are shown by arrows. Thirty five percent of the heavy chains contain carbohydrate on the threonine adjacent to the cysteine which makes the threonine-cysteine peptide linkage resistant to papain.

It is generally agreed that the number of sequence differences between a given protein in two species (for example, species specific residues) is a function of random mutations arising during evolution from a common ancestor. On this assumption, the finding that there are no species specific residues in the variable portion of human and mouse Bence Jones proteins as compared with 36 in the constant half of the same chain suggests that the mechanism responsible for the variable region may have developed at an early stage in vertebrate evolution and was of sufficient survival value, perhaps because of its importance for antibody combining sites, to have been maintained largely unchanged despite the divergent evolutionary pathways leading to mouse and to man. This would tend to favor a hypothesis of a single gene controlling during embryogenesis the development of the entire range of variability of the light chains, rather than 1000 genes (one for each variable region). Sequence studies have led to the concept that the heavy chain developed from the light chain by gene duplication. The smooth dogfish *Mustelus canis* which forms γM antibody had a 7 S immunoglobulin with heavy chains corresponding in molecular weight to those of γM immunoglobulin, which suggests that the γM heavy chain was the first heavy chain to evolve. These findings also tend to favor an early evolution of the antibody forming mechanism.

It will be of substantial importance to resolve the problem of the heterogeneity of the chains of myeloma proteins in starch and acrylamide gel electrophoresis in relation to structure and sequence. One wonders whether some lines of myeloma cells may not have a more restricted capacity to synthesize immunoglobulin than do normal cells.

The sequence studies should provide information on the other allotypic determinants and on the nature of the residues responsible for their specificity. Peptides from the Fc fragment with Gm (a+) specificity have been found to have the sequence Asp-Glu-Leu-Thr-Lys while Gm (a−) proteins had Met-Glu-Glu-Thr-Lys. It should also be possible to establish the structural basis of heavy chain subgroups and the location of antigenic determinants on heavy and light chains.

Structural studies on heavy and light chains of antibodies would be greatly facilitated by the preparation of homogeneous populations of antibody molecules. These should not only be homogeneous with respect to antigenic and physicochemical parameters, such as having a single heavy and light chain, but must also represent antibody to a single antigenic determinant and in addition the antibody must be fractionated so that the combining sites are of the same size. To accomplish this by fractionation of the heterogeneous antibody populations in whole serum and obtain suitable quantities for sequence studies may prove very difficult and one would like to have methods for producing less heterogeneous populations of antibody molecules (see Chapter 15). Naturally the sequence studies have great significance in regard to the biosynthesis of antibody (see Chapter 10).

AFFINITY LABELING OF THE ANTIBODY COMBINING SITE

An important approach to identifying amino acid sequences at the antibody combining sites involves the use of a hapten possessing a reactive grouping. The hapten is preferentially bound and positions itself in the antibody combining site in such a manner that the reactive group is free to form a covalent bond with some neighboring amino acid residue in the site. This procedure has been extensively used with enzymes to identify amino acids at active sites. As applied to antibodies, haptens containing a diazonium group have been used (see Chapter 2) which can couple to tyrosine, histidine, lysine, and other residues. Table 9.7 shows three types of antibody and the diazonium reagents used for labeling. The labeling has been shown to involve the active site since (1) with specific antibody the rate of azo-bond formation is much greater than with non-antibody immunoglobulin; (2) the prior addition in suitable concentration of the specific hapten lacking the reactive grouping to fill up the sites prevents the reagent from labeling the site; (3) the reagent labels only antibodies specific for its haptenic portion and not antibodies of another specificity; (4)

TABLE 9.7
Affinity-Labeling Systems[a]

Antibody Directed to		Labeling Reagent	Mole ratio of Label (Heavy; Light Chain)
$AsO_3H^- - C_6H_4 - N{=}N -$ {Tyr, His, Lys}	(R)	$AsO_3H^- - C_6H_4 - N_2^+$	2.1
$NO_2 - C_6H_3(NO_2) - NH(CH_2)_4 - CH<$	(DNP)	$NO_2 - C_6H_4 - N_2^+$	1.3
		$C_6H_4(NO_2) - N_2^+$	1.8
$(CH_3)_3\overset{+}{N} - C_6H_4 - N{=}N -$ {Tyr, His, Lys}	(TMA)	$(CH_3)_3\overset{+}{N} - C_6H_4 - N_2^+$	1.5

[a]From Singer, S. J. and R. F. Doolittle. *Science* **153**: 13(1966).

with the reagents in Table 9.7 only tyrosine residues of specific antibodies have been labeled, while with normal γG immunoglobulin the reagent has labeled histidine and other linkages in addition to tyrosine; (5) the reaction of the antibody with the labeling reagent inactivates the antibody combining site irreversibly.

The heavy and light chains are then obtained from the affinity-labeled antibody, and the amount of label on each is assayed. With all three antibodies (Table 9.7) both chains were labeled and there was generally more label in the heavy chain than in the light chain, with the ratios ranging from about 1.3 to 2.1. In Table 9.7, two types of haptens were used with anti-DNP antibody, one with *p*-nitrophenyl and the other with the *m*-nitrophenyl diazonium reagents. The ratio of label in the heavy and light chains was 1.3 and 1.8 respectively, which indicated heterogeneity in the antibody populations. Study of the light chains of the labeled antibody by acrylamide gel electrophoresis showed the label to be distributed relatively uniformly among all of the five to seven light chain bands present. Tryptic digestion of performic acid-oxidized heavy and light chains of labeled antibody showed the labeled peptides to be very heterogeneous. The average size of the labeled peptides, from the heavy as well as the light chains, was about 25 amino acids. On the light chains the label was found by Singer to be on the invariant tyrosine at position 86 in anti-DNP antibodies.

The affinity-labeling studies thus fit very nicely with the sequence analyses on immunoglobulins and with the other evidence for the heterogeneity of antibody combining sites. The application of this technique to relatively homogeneous fractions of purified antibody, if such can be obtained, or the ability to separate the various labeled peptides and the determination of the sequences involved should yield important information about the structure of the site. The length of 25 amino acids for the labeled peptides encompasses the variable regions that exist around cysteine 88 of the Bence Jones proteins studied; the performic oxidation would have oxidized the disulfide bond, and digestion would give at least two peptides.

AMINO ACID COMPOSITION OF PURIFIED ANTIBODIES

The heterogeneity shown by almost all purified antibodies when studied by the various procedures previously outlined would necessarily be expected to be revealed in gross differences in amino acid composition. In studies of purified human γG antibodies to four different antigens of relatively simple structure—for example, antidextran, antilevan, antiteichoic acid of *Staphylococcus aureus* and anti-blood group A substance—produced in a single individual, substantial differences in amino acid composition occurred. Maximum differences per molecule from one antibody preparation to another of 32 valines, 20 glycines, 7 leucines, 11 tyrosines, 12 arginines, and 14 lysines were found. In further studies on antidextran produced in several individuals, differences of the same order were seen. Individuals immunized with a dextran containing two kinds of linkages α-$(1 \longrightarrow 6)$ and α-$(1 \longrightarrow 2)$ formed two distinct antibody populations, α-$(1 \longrightarrow 6)$ specific and α-$(1 \longrightarrow 2)$ specific, and these two antibody populations also showed substantial differences in amino acid composition; these were often in opposite directions. Thus the α-$(1 \longrightarrow 6)$ and α-$(1 \longrightarrow 2)$ antidextrans of one individual have 131 and 123 valines, while with another the values were 122 and 129, respectively. The differences are generally of the same order as those between an individual K and an L Bence Jones protein calculated to a molecular weight of 160,000 to make them comparable to that of the antibody γG immunoglobulin. The differences among the various antibodies probably indicate some selection during the antibody response which produced deviations from the average of the various heterogeneous antibody populations. The variation in composition of the purified antibodies could be accounted for on the basis of selection from the variable regions of Bence Jones proteins but could not be ascribed to differences in the constant region resulting from differences in the proportion of K and L chains.

On the other hand antibodies formed in individual allotypically homozygous rabbits to two different haptenic groups showed relatively small variations in amino acid composition, differences of from three to six residues per molecule of 160,000 molecular weight in aspartic acid, serine, alanine, valine, and tyrosine having been found. These differences were associated with both the heavy and light chains. The relationship of these findings to the antibody combining site is not clear. Antibodies to these haptenic groups have been found to show numerous light chain bands in starch or acrylamide gel electrophoresis and to consist of populations of molecules with antibody combining sites of different affinity.

ANTIBODY-HAPTEN COMPLEXES IN THE ELECTRON MICROSCOPE

Examination of aggregates of a bivalent hapten and specific antibody in the electron microscope by Valentine and Green has yielded unique insight into the structure of the γG antibody molecule. The hapten used, bis-N-DNP-octamethylene-diamine

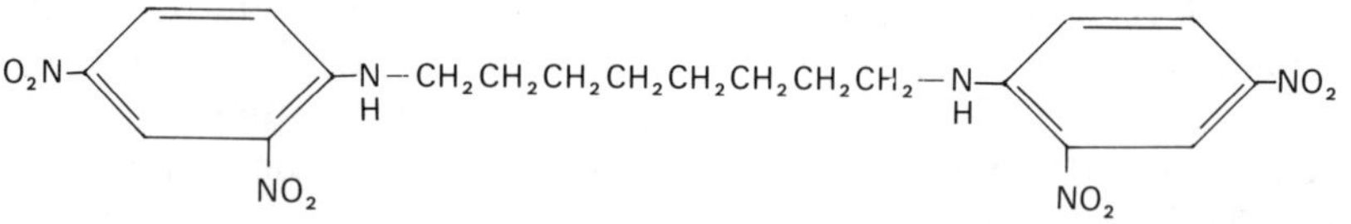

$$O_2N-C_6H_3(NO_2)-NH-CH_2CH_2CH_2CH_2CH_2CH_2CH_2CH_2-NH-C_6H_3(NO_2)-NO_2$$

has its two DNP groups sufficiently apart so that each haptenic group does not interfere with the binding of the other to antibody. When rabbit γG anti-DNP is bound to the hapten and examined in the electron microscope a set of discrete geometric patterns is seen which represents the different possibilities for combination of a bivalent antibody having two relatively flexible sites for binding with hapten. There are flat dimers, trianglular-shaped trimers, square-shaped tetramers, and pentamers. The triangular trimer is diagramatically illustrated in Figure 9.16. The Fc fragment is connected to the two Fab fragments by a flexible (hinge) region that permits the angle between the two Fab regions of each molecule to vary substantially. Fig. 9.17 shows the aggregates in the electron microscope; the unique geometric triangular, square, and pentagonal shapes and the flat dimers are clearly seen. At each corner of the triangle, square, and pentagon, the Fc portion appears as a small knoblike structure. This was proved to be the Fc portion by digesting the aggregates with pepsin; in Fig. 9.18 the knoblike Fc portions have disappeared without affecting the unique geometrical shapes of the aggregates. On reduction of the disulfide bonds of the complexes in Fig. 9.18 with dithiothreitol, the aggregates fell apart. The flexibility of the Fab relative to the Fc fragments had

Fig. 9.16 Diagram illustrating schematic arrangement of triangular-shaped aggregate of three anti-DNP molecules connected by three bivalent hapten molecules. (From Valentine, R. C., and N. M. Green, J. Mol. Biol. **27**: 615 [1967]; by permission of the copyright owner, Academic Press, New York.)

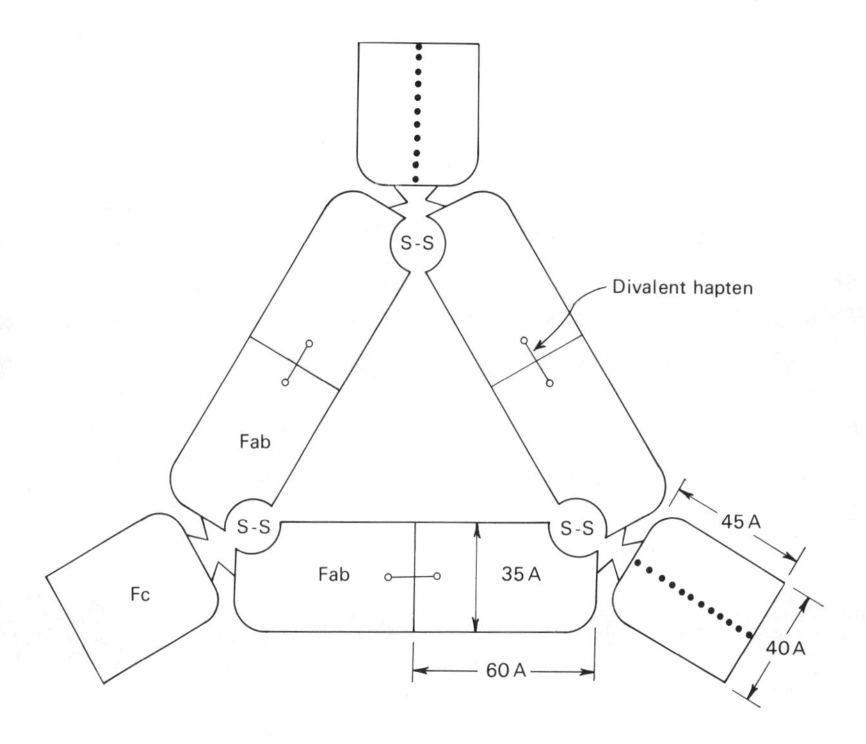

been put forward earlier from physicochemical considerations, and some electron microscopic evidence had also been obtained (see the Suggested Readings). A more highly magnified view of selected dimers, trimers, tetramers, and pentamers is seen in Fig. 9.19; the Fc portions are clearly visible. These aggregates show more structure for the antibody than do those in Chapter 1.

IMMUNOGLOBULINS OF SECRETIONS

Although in serum the γA immunoglobulin is generally found in much lower concentration than the γG immunoglobulin, in certain secretions—notably in parotid saliva, colostrum, tears, and nasal and bronchial fluids—γA immunoglobulin is present in the largest amount. Studies of the γA immunoglobulin in human parotid saliva and colo-

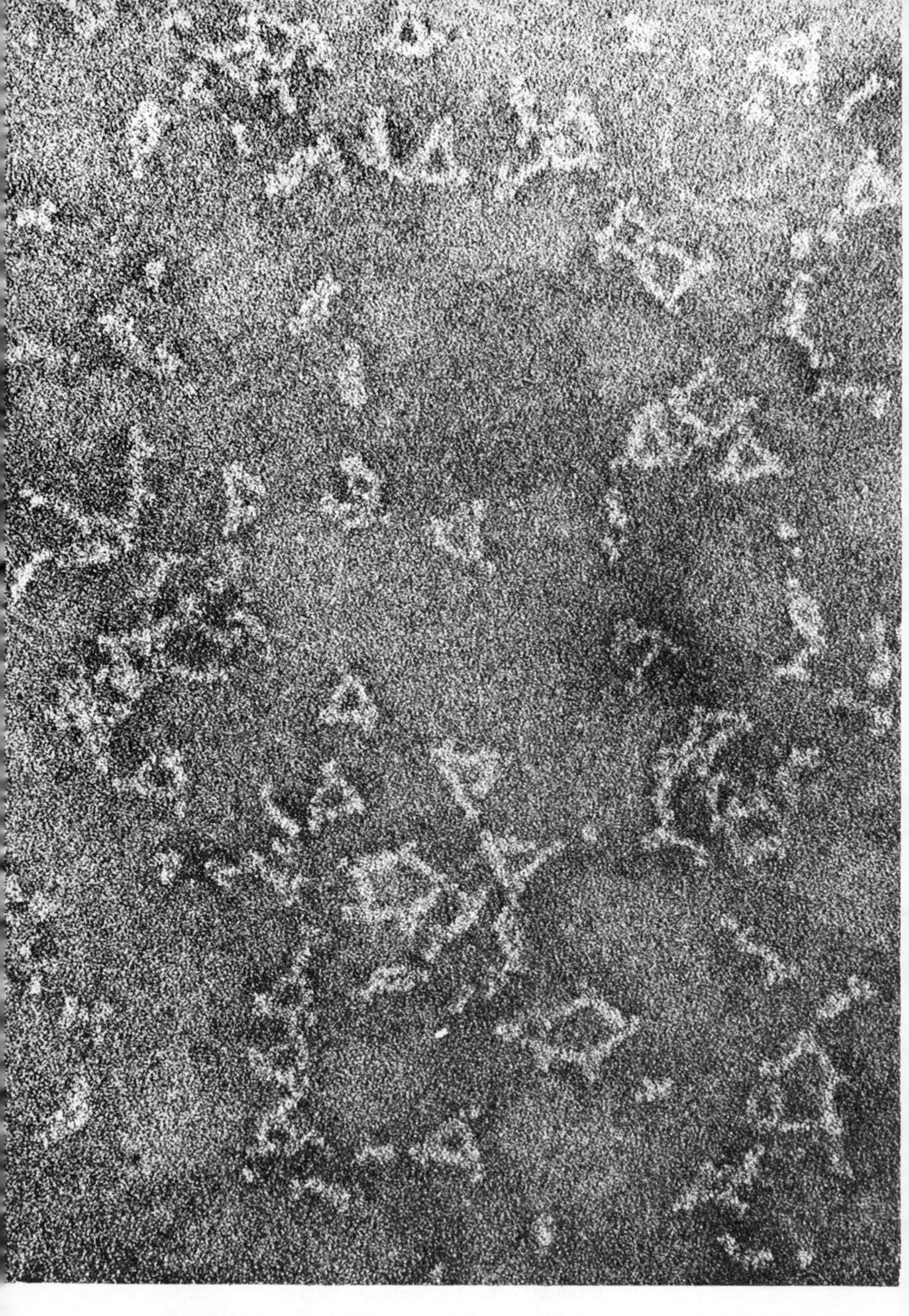

Fig. 9.17 Electron micrograph of various polymers formed on mixing rabbit anti-DNP γG with bivalent DNP-hapten magnification $\times$ 500,000. (After Valentine, R. C., and N. M. Green. J. Mol. Biol. **27**: 615 [1967]; courtesy of Dr. R. C. Valentine and with the permission of Academic Press, New York.)

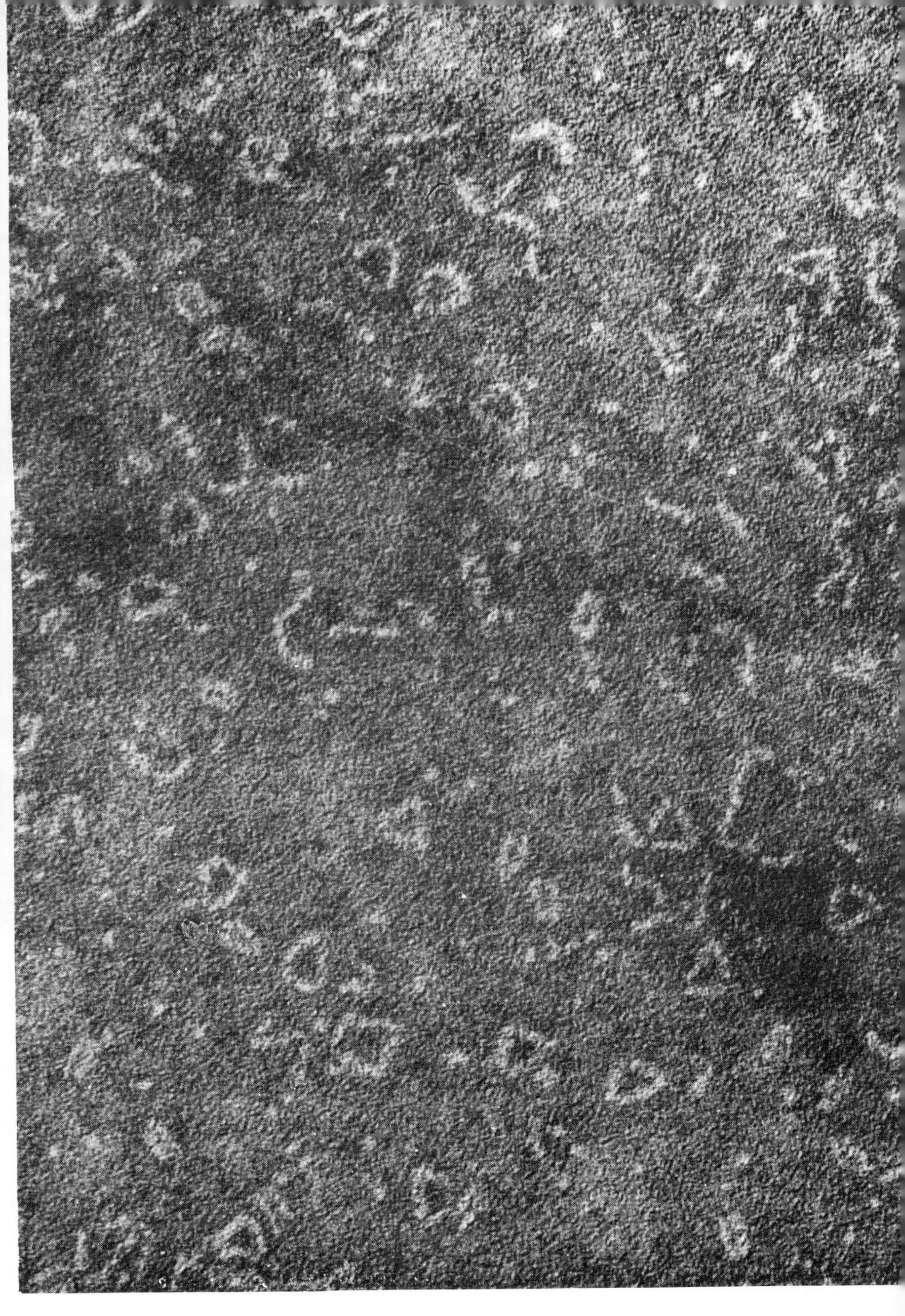

Fig. 9.18 Polymers after digestion of Fc fragments with pepsin × 500,000. (After Valentine. R. C., and N. M. Green. J. Mol. Biol. **27**: 615 [1967]; courtesy of Dr. R. C. Valentine and with the permission of Academic Press.)

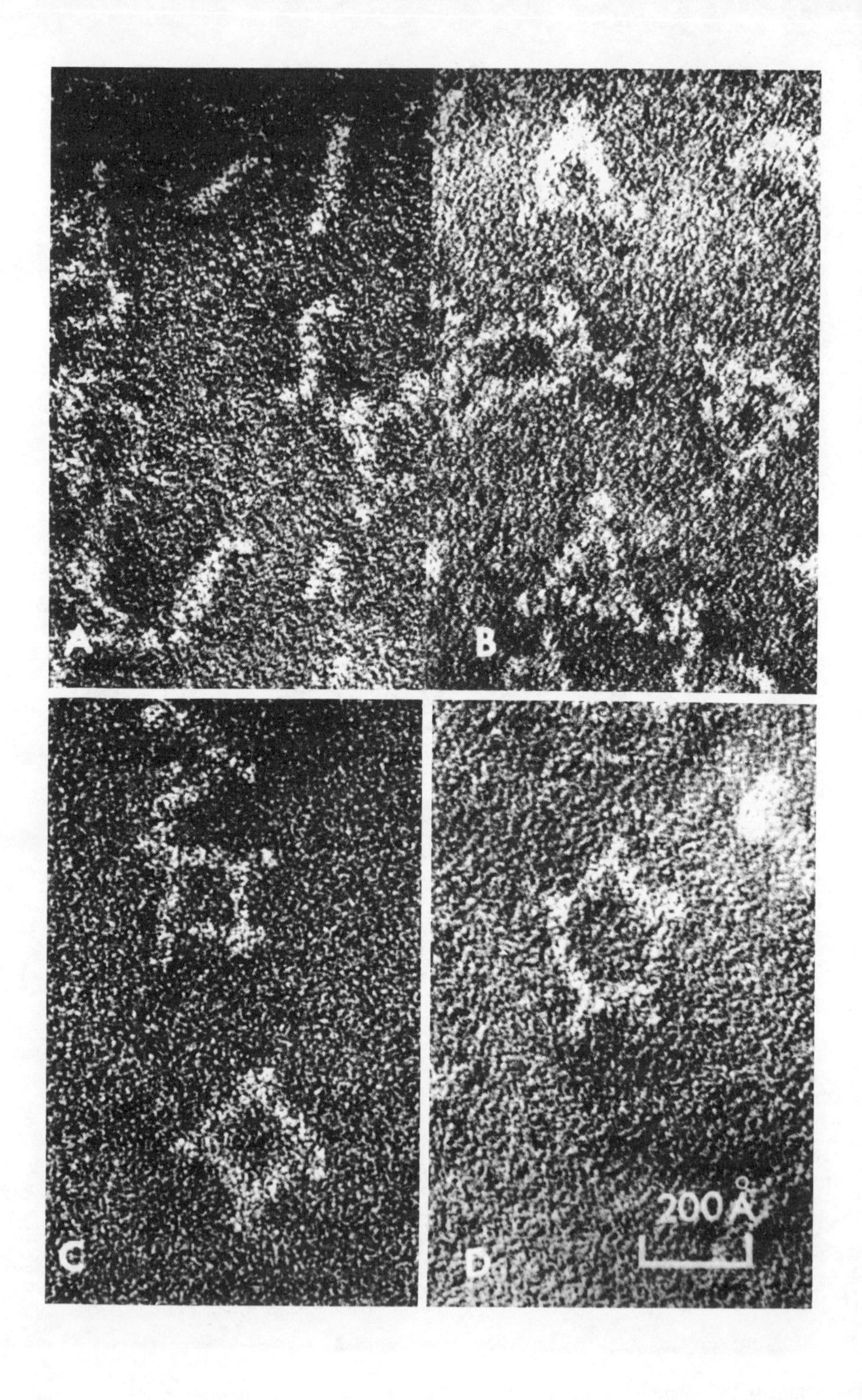
A
B
C
D
200 Å

Fig. 9.19 [Facing page] (A) Dimer, (B) Trimer, (C) Tetramer, and (D) Pentamer forms of antibody-hapten complexes in Fig. 9.16 × 800,000. (After Valentine, R. C, and N. M. Green. (From R. C. Valentine. Electron microscopy of γG immunoglobulins in Nobel Symposium III. Gamma Globulins. [1967] J. Killander [Ed.] Almqvist and Wiksell, Stockholm Courtesy of Dr. R. C. Valentine.)

strum have shown it to have a higher sedimentation constant (11S) and to be combined with an additional antigenic constituent with a specificity not present in the serum γA immunoglobulin. Fluorescent antibody localizations with antisera to serum γA and to salivary γA, as well as with antisera rendered specific for the additional component, have shown the specific component to be localized in a different region of the parotid gland than the γA immunoglobulin, the latter being in plasma cells while the former was in acinar cells adjacent to the collecting ducts. Salivas of agammaglobulinemics and of a healthy adult lacking γA in serum or saliva have been shown to contain this additional component in unbound form. The extra component may be dissociated from the salivary γA immunoglobulin by mercaptoethanol. Infusion of normal serum into agammaglobulinemics resulted in the appearance of γA immunoglobulin but not of γM or γG in the saliva. Rabbit and human colostrum γA immunoglobulin have the same sedimentation constants. γA immunoglobulin in secretions may be of importance in protecting mucous membranes against infections.

BIOLOGICAL ACTIVITIES OF ANTIBODIES

The heterogeneous populations of antibody molecules with specificities even to single antigens is accompanied by a host of different biological properties that can be exhibited by some antibodies and not by others. Many of these properties were discovered by chance in biological investigations; only a few of them have been accounted for in terms of immunoglobulin structure, and some may turn out to be different ways of measuring the same antibody. Most of these properties will be considered in subsequent chapters.

Placental passage The property of passing through the placental barrier from mother to fetus is possessed only by γG and not by γA or γM immunoglobulins. Digestion with pepsin destroys this property, while the Fc fragment from papain digestion traverses the placenta readily, although some Fab fragment may also pass. It is generally thought that the Fc fragment contains a specific site determining placental passage by some active process.

SUGGESTED READINGS

Cohen, S. and R. R. Porter. Structure and biological activity of immunoglobulins. Advances in Immunology **4**: 287 (1964). [Academic Press, New York].

Kabat, E. A. Structure and heterogeneity of antibodies. Acta hematologica **36**: 198 (1966).

The above two general reviews give numerous specific references.

Holborow, E. S. [Scientific ed.] Antibodies. British Medical Bulletin **19**: 169 (1963); *a series of articles on antibodies and their properties.*

Schultze, H. E. and J. F. Heremans. Molecular biology of human proteins with special reference to plasma proteins. (1966) Elsevier Publishing Company. Amsterdam, vol. **1**.; *a comprehensive reference on serum proteins.*

Rohult, O., G. Radzimski, and D. Pressman. Specificity in the combination of Fd fragments with L chains to form hapten-binding sites. Journal of Experimental Medicine **123**; 921 (1966).

Singer, S. J. and R. F. Doolittle. Antibody active sites and immunoglobulin molecules. Science **153**; 13 (1966); *a comprehensive review of efforts to establish structure at the combining sites of antibody molecules.*

Bernier, G. M. and F. W. Putnam. Myeloma proteins and macroglobulins: Hallmarks of disease and models of antibodies. Progress in Hematology **4**: 160 (1964).

Mangalo, R., S. Iscaki, and M. Raynaud. Presence d'activité anticorps dans des préparations de chaines légéres. Comptes Rendus de L'Académie des Sciences **263**: 204 (1966). Paris. *the highest antibody activity reported thus far for light chains.*

Seligmann, M. A genetic predisposition to Waldenström' macroglobulinemia. Acta Medica Scandinavica Suppl. 445: 140 (1966). [Stockholm].

Beaumont, J. L. Une spécificité commune aux α- et β-lipoproteínes du sérum révélée par un autoanticorps de myélome-L'antigène Pg. Compte Rend. Acad. Sciences **264**: 185 (1967) [Paris] and earlier papers; *an unusual case in which a* γA *myeloma protein has the properties of an autoantibody to* α*-and* β*-human lipoproteins.*

Symposium on differentiation and growth of hemoglobin and immunoglobulin synthesizing cells. Journal Cellular Physiology **67** (Suppl 1): 1-224 (1966).

Grabar, P. and P. Miescher [ed.]. Immunopathology IV International Symposium (1965); B. Schwabe, Basel, Stuttgart (1966);

Two symposia with numerous articles on immunoglobulin and antibody activity and structure.

Frangione, B. and E. C. Franklin. Structural studies of human immunoglobulins. Differences in the Fd fragments of the heavy chains of G myeloma proteins. Journal of Experimental Medicine **122**; 1 (1965); *evidence from fingerprinting for a variable region in the heavy chain of human* γ*G immunoglobulin.*

Thorpe N. O.,and H. F. Deutsch. Studies on papain produced subunits of γG globulins. II. Structures of peptides related to the genetic Gm activity of γG globulin Fc fragments. Immunochemistry **3**: 329 (1966).

Webb, T. and H. C. Goodman. Structure and function of immunoglobulins. *In* Modern Trends in Immunology. (2d ed.; 1967) (R. Cruickshank, and D. M. Weir, eds.). Butterworth & Co. Publishers Ltd., London; *a survey of biological activities of immunoglobulins.*

Porter, R. R. [Organizer]. A discussion on the chemistry and biology of immunoglobulins. The Royal Society (London), Proceedings, B. **166**; 114-243 (1966); *an important series of papers on the structure, biosynthesis and biological activities of immunoglobulins.*

Utsumi, S. and F. Karush, Peptic fragmentation of rabbit γG-immunoglobulin. Biochemistry **4**: 1766 (1965); *an analysis of the data on the number of disulfide bridges linking the heavy chains of* γ*G immunoglobulin leading to the suggestion that two crossed disulfide bridges are involved.*

Jukes, T. H. Molecules and evolution. Columbia University Press, New York (1966); *a very stimulating presentation of evolution as the consequence of mutational changes in nucleic acids and the resulting differences in structure of proteins.*

Killander, J. [ed.]. Nobel Symposium III Gamma Globulins. Structure and control of biosynthesis. Almqvist and Wiksell, Stockholm (1967).

Cold Spring Harbor Symposia on Quantitative Biology: Antibodies. **32**(1967).

Cohen, S. and C. Milstein. Structure and biological properties of immunoglobulins, Advances in Immunology, **7**: (1967). [Academic Press, New York]; *comprehensive surveys of the most recent developments on the structure of heavy and light chains and of the current status of immunoglobulin and antibody biosynthesis.*

Noelken, M. E., C. A. Nelson, C. E. Buckley, and C. Tanford. Gross conformation of rabbit 7 S γ-immunoglobulin and its papain-cleaved fragments. Journal of Biological chemistry **240**: 218 (1967); *proposes flexibility of Fab relative to Fc fragment from physicochemical considerations.*

Feinstein, A. and A. J. Rowe. Molecular mechanism of formation of an antigen-antibody complex. Nature **205**: 147 (1965).

Valentine, R. C. and N. M. Green. Journal of Molecular Biology **27**: 615 (1967).

Two electron microscopic studies indicating flexibility of Fab relative to Fc fragments in γ*G antibody.*

Lennox, E. S. and M. Cohn. Immunoglobulins. Annual Review of Biochemistry **36**: part 1, 365 (1967).

Smith, D. S. and S. Utsumi. Structure at the hinge region in rabbit immunoglobulin G. Nature **216**: 332 (1967).

10

Where and How Are Antibodies Formed?

Despite our already extensive and rapidly growing knowledge of antibody and immunoglobulin heterogeneity and structure, we do not have anything like comparable insight into how antibodies are formed. Indeed, it is only recently that the question of which cells of the body synthesize antibody has been clarified. The major uncertainty in our knowledge about antibody formation is the role of antigen in the process. This uncertainty exists both at the cellular and at the molecular level. Moreover, we have little concrete information as to the kinds of antibody molecules which can be formed by a single cell.

Antibody formation is essentially a dynamic metabolic process, and techniques must provide evidence of actual synthesis of antibody by a cell rather than merely reveal its presence in a cell. Most reliable for such studies is evidence of net synthesis by the incorporation of labeled amino acids into antibody protein. Another very important method is the Jerne plaque technique for revealing individual cells that can release antibody hemolytic for sheep erythrocytes to the surrounding medium. In principle, a suspension of spleen or lymph node cells is diluted in a semisolid medium such as agar to which sheep erythrocytes have been added, poured into Petri plates, and allowed to harden. After incubation for one hour at 37°C, a solution of guinea pig complement is placed on the agar surface. On further incubation for

30 minutes small plaques or clear areas of hemolysis may be seen on the plate, each generally having a lymphoid cell at its center. An alternate technique uses carboxymethyl cellulose as a thickening agent with sheep red cells and complement. After adding the lymphoid cell suspension, a drop is placed on a microscope slide, covered with a cover slip (the edges sealed with vaseline), incubated, and examined for plaques. The dynamics of the cellular response following injections of sheep red cells into animals is very readily followed by this technique and it has revealed a striking increase in the number of plaque-forming cells in the lymphoid organs during the period of antibody formation. Studies with metabolic inhibitors suggest that some synthesis of antibody by plaque-forming cells is taking place during the *in vitro* incubation and that what is being measured is not merely release of preformed antibody. A typical plaque with a lymphoid cell at the center is seen in Fig. 10.1. These plaques appear to be formed

Fig. 10.1 A lymphoid cell at the center of a hemolytic plaque on an agar plate. (From Jerne, N.K., A.A. Nordin, and C. Henry. *In* Cell-bound Antibodies, Conf. of the National Acad. of Sciences—National Research Council, Wistar Univ. Press, Philadelphia, p. 109. [1963]; by permission of the copyright owner, The Wistar Institute of Anatomy and Biology.)

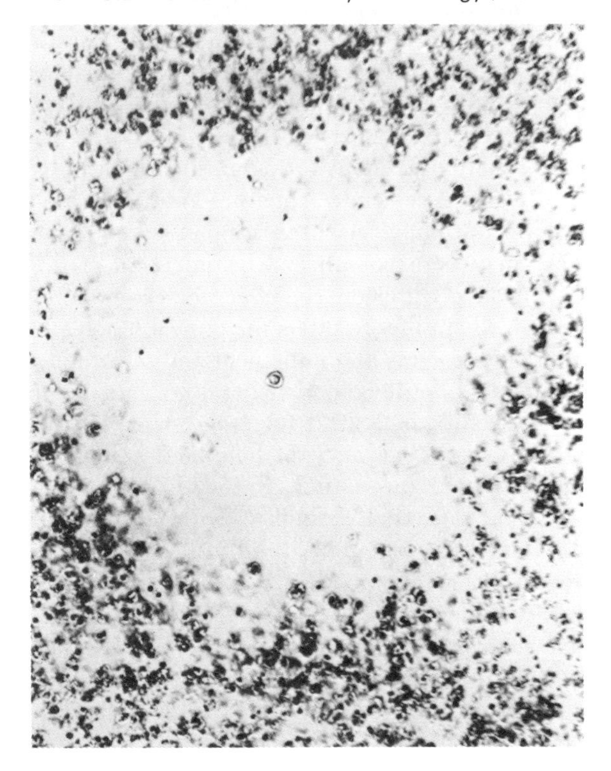

predominantly by γM antibody which is much more potent in hemolyzing red cells than γG antibody (see Chapter 11). Procedures have been developed to extend the scope of the plaque method to reveal cells forming γG antibodies as well as those forming antibodies to antigens which can be absorbed or attached to erythrocytes and which will produce hemolysis in the presence of complement. Studies have also been carried out using individual lymphoid cells isolated in microdroplets; significant results have been obtained, but this procedure is far more time consuming than the plaque technique and permits study of far fewer cells although it may be used to demonstrate antibodies to many types of antigens. Another method used with antibody formation to sheep (or other) erythrocytes is the enumeration of the number of lymphoid cells around which rosettes or clusters of agglutinated sheep cells form when placed in contact with them at 4°C in liquid tissue culture medium. These clusters have been shown not to hemolyze with complement, and the cells producing them may not be the same as those producing plaques. Many more rosette-forming than plaque-forming cells are present. Considerable experimental evidence has been obtained (Fig. 10.5) showing that rosette-forming lymphoid cells of guinea pigs and mice generally do not absorb circulating antibody and that they are themselves engaged in synthesizing antibody. On the other hand macrophages from the same animal could readily be shown to absorb antibody, and mixed rosettes involving macrophages are quite common. Antigen-coated bentonite particles also attach to antibody forming cells.

Other important techniques of demonstrating antibody synthesis involve the introduction of various cells into immature animals or animals whose capacity to form antibody has been suppressed by large doses of x-radiation. This may be accomplished by injection of the cells or by implanting them in a diffusion chamber, for example, in a small chamber having as walls millipore filters impermeable to cells but allowing passage of serum proteins and immunoglobulin. Samples of antiserum may be obtained at various periods and examined for antibody. A special case (see immunological tolerance, Chapter 14) involves the injection into irradiated mice of lymphoid cells from immunized rats; in this instance the actual synthesis of antibody immunoglobulin showing rat specificity might be demonstrated. Similarly, lymph node cells from immunized rabbits continue to synthesize rabbit antibody when implanted into the hamster cheek pouch. Much valuable information has also been obtained by fluorescent and electron microscopy and by various other procedures for detecting antibody in cells and tissues. Fragments of spleen and lymph node from immunized animals may continue to elaborate antibody in tissue culture.

Most sorely needed to resolve problems of antibody heterogeneity in relation to individual cells would be a method of growing cells in tissue culture with retention of antibody forming capacity and the ability to develop mass cultures of antibody forming cells from single cell isolates. To date no such techniques are available, but cell lines have been obtained from normal individuals and from patients with lymphomas and leukemias that produce γG, γM, and γA immunoglobulins; these γG immunoglobulins resembled myeloma globulins in being relatively homogeneous, having a narrow range of mobility and being made up of one type of light and one type of heavy chain. In the electron microscope the cultivated cells of many lines were seen to contain particles resembling herpes virus.

THE DYNAMICS OF ANTIBODY FORMATION

When an animal receives an injection of antigen for the first time, if the dose is sufficient, it may respond by forming antibody. This PRIMARY RESPONSE with many antigens is of short duration, and when the antibody level has fallen the animals will show an enhanced antibody response (SECONDARY or ANAMNESTIC RESPONSE) to a subsequent injection of antigen given some time later. Even when the primary injection does not elicit detectable antibody, the animals will form substantial amounts of circulating antibody when a second injection is given. Such animals are said to be primed, and the enhanced capacity to respond to the second dose of antigen is often spoken of as IMMUNOLOGICAL MEMORY. The response of humans to polysaccharide antigens is quite different, an initial injection producing an antibody response of very long duration with little falling-off in antibody level over many years; this response is not greatly affected by subsequent injections. The human, however, responds in the same fashion as other animals to injections of protein antigens such as diphtheria or tetanus toxoids, with antibody levels that decline sharply in a few months and secondary responses that are readily achieved.

The process of antibody synthesis is extremely rapid, since the incorporation of labeled amino acids into antibody takes place within 20 minutes, both in the animal and in isolated lymph node cells. In addition, histological studies indicate that antibody production, especially in the secondary response, is accompanied by tremendous cellular multiplication in certain tissues and organs; and studies by the plaque technique have shown a rise, after an injection of sheep red cells, in the number of plaque-forming cells per mouse spleen of from 25 on the first day to almost 60,000 on the fourth day. A similar rise in rosette-forming cells also occurs. Cells labeled with a pulse of tritiated thymidine have shown rapid multiplication with division times of 7 to 12 hr. Cells not stimulated with antigen may show longer division times.

The character of the antibody formed during primary and secondary responses may be very different as regards the class of immunoglobulin, the binding affinity of the antibody, and the antigenic determinants of the antigen to which antibody is being formed. These relationships vary from species to species as does the persistence in the serum of the various forms of antibody both with and without repeated antigenic stimulation. It is also often impossible to be certain that a response is truly primary, since absence of prior contact with antigen is difficult to establish.

Numerous observations have been reported which indicate that γM antibody is formed first, followed by γG antibody. In many of these studies, assays—such as passive hemagglutination—were used, which permit the detection of γM antibody at much lower concentrations than γG antibody. Were γG and γM antibody produced in equal amounts and at the same rate, the γG antibody might often be missed. Thus it becomes important for valid interpretations to determine the sensitivity on a weight basis of the techniques used in assaying for both γM and for γG antibody. It does appear that γM antibody often has a relatively transient existence in serum and that a secondary response generally elicits γG antibody. With antibody to blood group A and B substances a considerable proportion of the antibody in man may be of the γM variety and with anti-typhoid O agglutinins all of it may be γM throughout life.

While normal mouse spleen generally contains small numbers of plaque-forming cells, it is not at all clear that these are the progenitors of the cells that appear on antigenic stimulation, since administration of mouse antiserum to sheep red cells reduced the number of plaque-forming cells in immunized mice (see Feedback Inhibition, page 224) without affecting the numbers in normal mice. Germ-free piglets raised on a synthetic diet show no plaque-forming cells or natural antibody, but respond normally to immunization.

TISSUES AND ORGANS CAPABLE OF FORMING ANTIBODY

Early studies established the spleen, bone marrow, lungs, and lymph nodes as important sites of antibody formation. In addition, substantial amounts of antibody have been shown to be formed in local areas where clusters of antibody forming cells come into contact with antigen, as in the granulomata formed by injections of antigen in Freund adjuvants (see Chapter 3) or in depots of intraperitoneal fat-containing cells that have formed around particles of antigen. The spleen, bone marrow, and lungs have been shown to be the most important sites following intravenous injection, while local granulomata and draining lymph nodes are most important following subcutaneous or intraperitoneal injection. The relative importance of these various organs and tissues may differ for different species.

Antibody may also be formed by cells in the intestinal tract, and antibody in feces has long been recognized (COPROANTIBODIES). Evidence also exists that some antibody may be formed within the central nervous system; this is not a property of nerve cells but probably of lymphoid cells in this system.

Many of the early experiments to demonstrate antibody formation by various organs were very ingenious. A classical one involved the injection of two antigens, one into each ear of a mouse; examination of the lymph nodes draining each ear showed the earlier appearance, and the presence in higher concentrations, of agglutinins for the antigen that had been injected into the corresponding ear than for antigen injected into the opposite ear. Explants of splenic red pulp in tissue culture and containing immature plasma cells produced more antibody than similar explants of white pulp.

Incorporation of labeled amino acids into antibody has firmly substantiated the above findings with respect to antibody formation by spleen, liver, bone marrow, granulomata, and draining lymph nodes. Small amounts of antibody formed by organs such as the liver are attributable to small numbers of granuloma-type cells rather than to hepatic cells. In the spleen, antibody formation tends to be concentrated in the red pulp and, in the lymph nodes in the germinal centers, in previously immunized animals given a second injection of antigen (secondary response). During the early stages following an initial injection of antigen, changes generally occur in the lymphoid tissue of the spleen surrounding the small central arteries (white pulp) and in the primary lymph follicles with the formation of large lymphoid cells. During the next several days the cells appear to mature into plasma cells and to migrate to the outer regions of the white pulp and into the red pulp.

Detailed consideration of the structures of various tissues and cells involved in antibody formation is outside the scope of this volume but excellent illustrated descriptions of the histology of the spleen and lymph node as well as other tissues may be found in W. Bloom and D. W. Fawcett, *A Testbook of Histology* (8th ed.; 1966) W. B. Saunders, Philadelphia, Pennsylvania.

THE CELLS INVOLVED IN ANTIBODY FORMATION

For the past 20 years evidence has been accumulating by numerous techniques to indicate that two types of white blood cells are involved in the actual synthesis of antibody. These are cells of the plasmacytic series and cells of the lymphocytic (small, medium, and large lymphocytes) series. Fluorescent localization techniques (Chapter 3) have made it abundantly clear that the plasma cell is of major importance, but it is noteworthy that in single-cell microdroplet studies, one third of the antibody forming cells observed were lymphocytes, the rest being plasma cells. Inbred rats whose lymphocytes had been specifically depleted by drainage through the thoracic duct showed impaired antibody formation; infusion of thoracic duct lymphocytes from other rats of the same line restored capacity to form antibodies. The thoracic duct lymphocyte suspensions were over 99 percent lymphoid cells (small lymphocytes). With the electron microscope, cells at the center of plaques have been found to be of two types, plasma cells and lymphocytes. The chief characteristic in the electron microscope of cells that actively synthesize protein for exogenous purposes is considered to be a rough-surfaced endoplasmic reticulum, and this has been seen in both types of cells, although much less was present in the lymphocytes. Figs. 10.2 and 10.3 show electron micrographs of a plasma cell and a lymphoid cell found at the center of plaques. Plasma cells with similar development of endoplasmic reticulum are seen in Waldenström macroglobulinemia and in mouse and human myeloma. Cells from rabbits immunized with ferritin could be sectioned, allowed to react with ferritin, and examined by electron microscopy; the localization of the ferritin granules within the spaces of the endoplasmic reticulum indicates the location of the specific antiferritin (Fig. 10.4). A similar pattern is seen in the plasma cells of mink with Aleutian disease, a virus infection producing very high levels of serum γG immunoglobulin.

The cells involved in antibody formation are generally not in a static state, but go through a series of differentiations as do all of the white blood cells and cells of the erythrocytic series. These steps have long been recognized by differences in morphology and in staining properties. Immature cells are basophilic, for example, they take up certain basic dyes because of the presence of ribonucleic acid in their cytoplasm. They also show pyroninophilic granules in their cytoplasm. This is associated with active synthesis of protein. Most of the white blood cells during maturation lose the basophilic staining of their cytoplasm, but the plasma cell retains this property even when ma-

Fig. 10.2 Antibody producing plasma cell with well developed endoplasmic reticulum (ER) organized into lamellae. M = mitochondria; NU = nucleus × 17,500. (From Harris, T. N., K. Hummeler, and S. Harris. J. Exp. Med. **123**: 161 [1966]; by permission of The Rockefeller University Press. The photograph here reproduced from printed halftone copy inevitably shows a loss of detail, and the quality of the results is not representative of the original.)

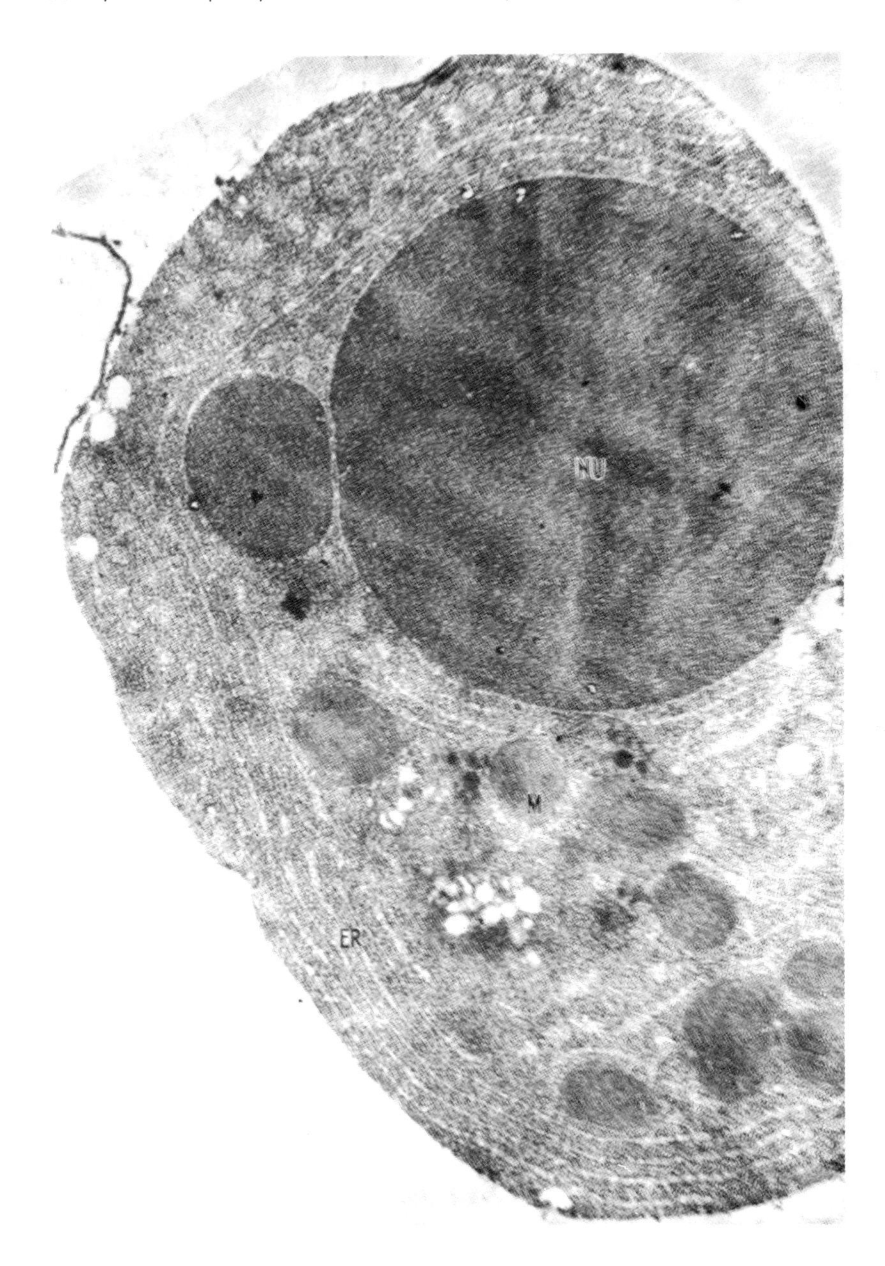

Fig. 10.3 Large antibody producing lymphocyte. Eccentric nucleus (NU) with large nucleolus (NOS). Numerous mitochondria (M) in one cell pole. Many narrow channels of endoplasmic reticulum (ER) which are not organized. × 17,000 (From Harris, T. N., K. Hummeler, and S. Harris. J. Exp. Med. **123**: 161 [1966]; by permission of The Rockefeller University Press. The photograph here reproduced from printed halftone copy inevitably shows a loss of detail, and the quality of the results is not representative of the original.)

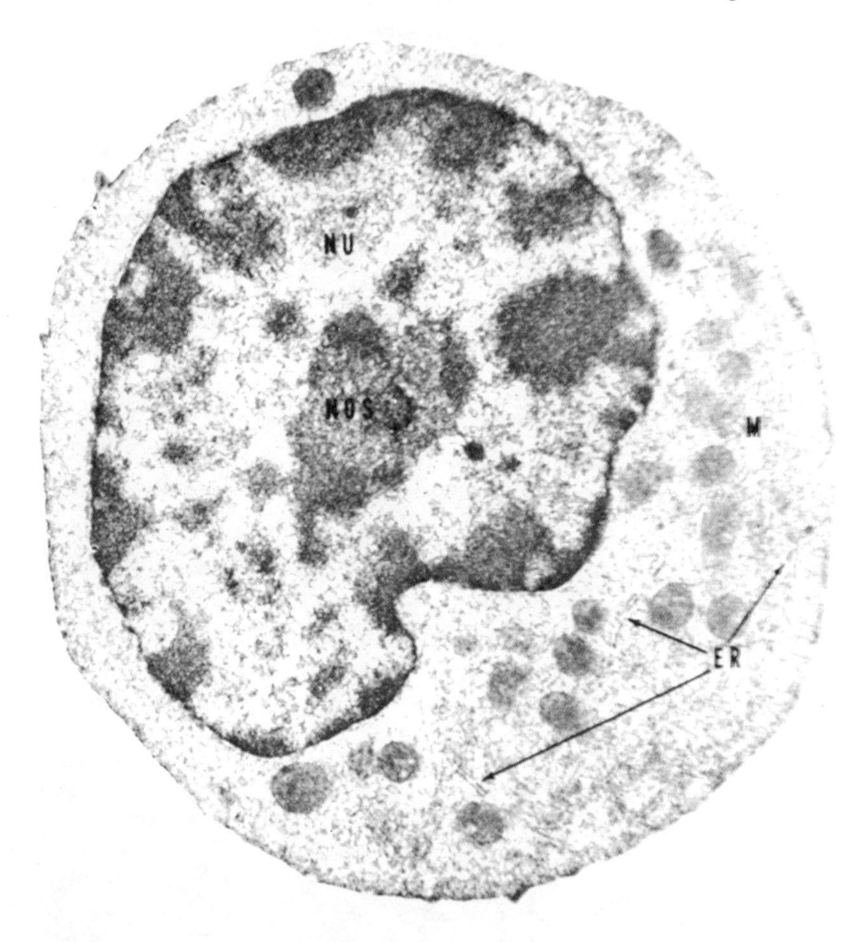

ture. The basophilic staining is a property of the endoplasmic reticulum and its associated ribosomes. Following injection of antigen, the differentiation to mature plasma cells from primitive reticulum cells via several intermediate stages has been found to parallel closely the rise in antibody in the blood.

The process of antibody formation has long been thought to involve the macrophages or phagocytic cells since these cells could

Fig. 10.4 Ferritin particles concentrated in the cisternae of the endoplasmic reticulum and in the perinuclear space indicate the location of antiferritin molecules. A few granules are also present in the outer cell membrane × 70,000. (From de Petris, S., G. Karlsbad, and B. Pernis. J. Exp. Med. **117**: 849 [1963]; by permission of The Rockefeller University Press. The photograph here reproduced from printed halftone copy inevitably shows a loss of detail, and the quality of the results is not representative of the original.)

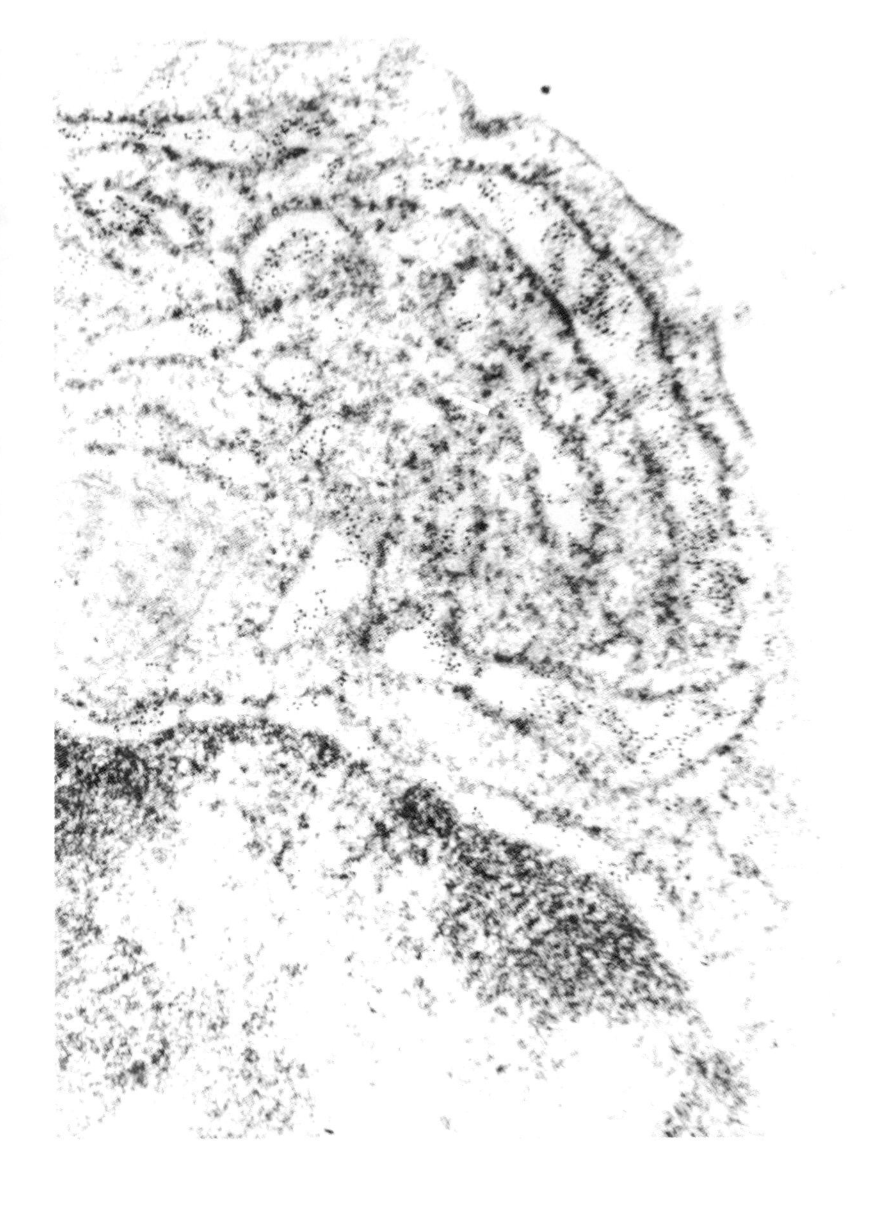

readily be seen to take up antigen, since antibody formation was generally enhanced by the administration of antigens in particulate form, and since blockade or overloading of the phagocytic cells with inert particles diminished antibody formation. Although earlier studies tended to consider the large macrophages as antibody forming cells, modern techniques have not shown them to form antibody even though they generally contain large amounts of antigen and, with many antigens, persistence of the injected material in phagocytic cells may be observed for very long periods. On the other hand the plasma cells and lymphoid cells associated with the active synthesis of antibody generally contain little or no antigen. Establishing the complete absence of antigen from the antibody forming cells is extremely difficult experimentally.

This essentially poses one of the major problems in understanding antibody formation: What role does antigen play in effecting the tremendous increase in antibody forming cells and in antibody synthesis? There are several ways of looking at the data. One is that the bulk of the antigen is not needed for the synthesis of antibody, that the macrophage system essentially is involved in removing the excess, and that only minimal—almost indetectable—amounts are needed and that these somehow get into the antibody forming cells. Lymphoid cells are not actively phagocytic, but may imbibe fluid droplets at their surface by a process called PINOCYTOSIS. An alternate hypothesis is that the macrophage is an important step in processing or modifying the antigen so that it, or its information, can be communicated to the antibody forming cells. This latter hypothesis is extremely attractive and has led to some interesting experimentation.

In one type of study 5×10^6 plaque-forming units of bacteriophage T2 as antigen were mixed with a suspension of 10^9 peritoneal rat macrophages. After 30 minutes the macrophages were centrifuged off, washed, disrupted, and passed through a bacterial filter to eliminate intact cells. Ribonucleic acid (RNA) was then prepared from these extracts and subjected to density gradient centrifugation in sucrose. Fractions were collected from the top, middle, and bottom of the gradient. Each fraction was added to a suspension of rat lymph node cells, placed in a millipore diffusion chamber, and intraperitoneally implanted into x-irradiated rats. Four days later the serum of the rats was examined for neutralizing antibody to bacteriophage; the results can be seen in Table 10.1. RNA from macrophages exposed to T2 and the top sucrose gradient fraction induced the formation of neutralizing antibody, while RNA from macrophages not exposed to T2 did not. The ability to induce an antibody response of the RNA from T2-treated macrophages was destroyed by ribonuclease (RNase). The antibody formed a few days after implantation was of the γM

TABLE 10.1

Serum Antibody to Bacteriophage T2 in Irradiated Rats with Implanted Diffusion Chambers with Macrophage RNA Fractions and Lymph Node Cells

Material Implanted	RNA (μg)	Fraction of Rats with Anti-T2 in Serum at Four Days[a]
Lymph node cells + RNA (M - T2)[b]	150	8/13
Lymph node cells + RNA (M - T2) top layer	190	4/8
Lymph node cells + RNA (M - T2) middle layer	360	1/8
Lymph node cells + RNA (M - T2) middle layer	180	0/9
Lymph node cells + RNA (M - T2) bottom layer	150	0/12
Lymph node cells + RNA (MT - 2) + RNase	150	0/14
Lymph node cells + RNA (M)	200	0/9

Data from M. Fishman and F. L. Adler. J. Exp. Med. **117**: 595 (1963).

[a]A positive result was taken as neutralization of 30 percent of the test dose of bacteriophage (500 pfu) by a 1:4 dilution of serum.

[b](M – T2) indicates macrophages exposed to T2; M indicates untreated macrophages.

variety, but after longer intervals γG antibody was found. Several groups have reported that normal mouse spleen cell suspensions treated with RNA from mice that had been immunized with sheep red cells showed an increased number of cells forming plaques, suggesting conversion of non-antibody forming cells to antibody forming cells by the RNA. This effect was blocked by chloramphenicol and RNase, but not by DNase. It was specific for the antigen used.

This type of experiment is open to several interpretations. One would be of course that the macrophage RNA itself was transmitting information for the synthesis of specific antibody. Another would be that the macrophage was processing the antigen and making it more effective in inducing antibody formation in the lymph node cells. Phage antigens have actually been demonstrated in RNA preparations of the type employed in Table 10.1. Using another antigen, hemocyanin, which had been labeled with I^{131}, the presence of residual antigen in RNA from macrophages exposed to antigen could be demonstrated. The antigen-RNA preparation induced an antibody response in mice previously primed by a small injection of hemocyanin so that they would give an enhanced antibody response. The minimal dose of hemocyanin by itself to give a response in such primed mice was 0.001 μg, which was 20 times more than the hemocyanin in the quantity of antigen-RNA needed. Other workers have also reported the association of RNA with antigen in tissue extracts.

In a subsequent study in rabbits of known allotypic constitution, RNA was prepared from peritoneal macrophages of one allotype that had been exposed for 30 minutes to T2 phage and added to tissue cultures of lymph node fragments from rabbits of a different allotype. The γM antibody produced during the first few days had the antigenic markers of the donor allotype, while the γG antibody formed later was of the recipient allotype. The genetically determined allotypic markers were associated with the light chains of the immunoglobulins of both donor and recipient rabbits.

This experiment is especially hard to interpret except on the hypothesis that the RNA is transmitting information for the synthesis of the γM antibody, since it is very difficult to see how the mere processing of antigen into a more effective form would permit the synthesis of the donor allotypic determinants. Some evidence has been advanced suggesting that there may be two forms of RNA in peritoneal exudate macrophages, one free of antigen and associated with the formation of γM antibody which passes rapidly from diffusion chambers and is very sensitive to ribonuclease, while the other is more resistant to ribonuclease, is present even when no antigen is added, diffuses more slowly, is associated with γG antibody formation, and may form the complexes with antigen reported by other workers. Further studies along these lines are needed.

That some macrophages are not merely removing excess antigen but are actually participating in the process of antibody formation is probable. Macrophages from peritoneal exudates mixed with suspensions of Shigella *in vitro* and inoculated into irradiated animals induce good antibody formation, although the microorganisms themselves do not. If the macrophages are obtained from irradiated donors or if the macrophages are irradiated *in vitro*, antibody formation does not occur; the phagocytic capacities of the irradiated macrophages were unchanged. Many observations have been made indicating that macrophages often are surrounded by clusters of plasma cells and lymphocytes. In lymphoid follicles a fine web of phagocytic reticular cells with dendritic processes is found; the cytoplasmic membrane and dendritic processes of these cells take up and retain antigen, and extensive multiplication of lymphoid cells takes place around them. Cytoplasmic connections between macrophages and the surrounding lymphoid cells in tissues have been reported. In other regions of the lymph nodes, the antigen in macrophages has an entirely different distribution, being located chiefly inside the cell associated with granules and vacuoles. This type of circumstantial evidence for intimate contact between certain types of macrophages and lymphoid cells suggests the participation of both macrophages and lymphoid cells in antibody formation. It is apparently not completely excluded that the reticular phagocytic cells could actually multiply and turn into antibody forming plasma cells and lymphocytic elements. There is still substantial discussion among histologists as to the capacities of various cells to develop into other cells, and detailed consideration of these aspects is outside the scope of this volume. Of special interest are the findings that a portion of the population of small lymphocytes are very long lived — estimates in man of over ten years having been made — while others have a very short lifetime of the order of days. Small lymphocytes from the thoracic duct of an immunized rat when transferred to irradiated rats of the same strain, produced antibody on subsequent injection of antigen into the recipient and thus possess immunological memory. Whether this is associated with the long-lived population remains to be established. It is not known whether other cells may also exhibit immunological memory. Lymphoid cells play an important role in other immunological processes, notably in graft rejection, tolerance, and delayed hypersensitivity (see Chapters 13 and 14).

It should be recognized that histological and electron microscopic observation give no insight whatever into the differences that must exist among the antibody- and immunoglobulin-synthesizing cells and that determine their capacity to produce one or more of the heterogeneous populations of immunoglobulin molecules previously discussed.

BIOSYNTHETIC POTENTIAL OF IMMUNOGLOBULIN AND ANTIBODY SYNTHESIZING CELLS

A very basic question to antibody formation and immunoglobulin synthesis is how many kinds of immunoglobulin or antibody a differentiated cell may form. If a cell can form only one or a limited number of immunoglobulins, how has the process of differentiation accomplished this restriction? Similarly, if a cell has multiple potentialities, what determines which of these will be expressed and under what circumstances? This is another area in which information is sorely needed. Cells that have the potential capacity to form antibody when stimulated by antigen are often called IMMUNOCOMPETENT cells.

Using fluorescent-labeled antisera to K and L light chains and to the μ, α, and γ heavy chains of γM, γA, and γG immunoglobulins, individual cells may be studied in tissue sections for the presence of the various chains. By this technique the immunoglobulin-containing cells are almost exclusively of the plasma cell series, probably because this method is less sensitive than microdroplet assays of phage antibody or immune adherence. The antiserum to one of the chains is labeled with fluorescein, and the antiserum to the other with rhodamine; after staining with both labeled antisera these give green and orange fluorescence, respectively, with cells containing only one chain. If both types of chain are present a yellow fluorescence is observed and a rough indication may be obtained of the relative proportions of each type, depending upon whether the cells were orange-yellow or greenish yellow.

In general, results by this technique indicate that almost all the immunoglobulin-containing cells have only a single type of light chain, either K or L; only 1 or 2 percent of the cells show evidence of both. The ratio of cells containing K to those having L chains was about 60 to 40, closely corresponding with the proportion of molecules with these chains in the serum immunoglobulins.

Most cells also contain but a single type of heavy chain, only about 1 percent of the cells showing both γA and γG heavy chains. In the intestine, most of the immunoglobulin-containing cells showed γA heavy chains.

By contrast, however, a very large proportion of cells showed the presence of both light and heavy chains, indicating that one cell can synthesize a complete immunoglobulin molecule.

Although γM and γG heavy chains usually are found in different cells, in the germinal centers of the lymph follicles of immune animals both occur in the same cells, generally in close proximity to the reticular network of phagocytic cells mentioned earlier. It is not clear that both chains have been formed by the same cell and this is considered by several workers to be an artefact.

Studies of the localization of allotypes of rabbit γG immunoglobulins in lymphoid cells have shown that two allotypes controlled by genes at two different loci could occur in the same cell, while those controlled by allelic genes at a single locus were present in separate cells of heterozygotes, again except in the germinal centers where both were found.

These studies leave completely unsettled the questions of the potentialities for immunoglobulin synthesis by these cells, of whether a given cell can shift from the synthesis of one class of immunoglobulin to another, and of what factors control the expression of the genetic information for immunoglobulin synthesis.

With respect to the synthesis of antibody by single cells, the existing evidence indicates that, when animals are simultaneously immunized with two different antigens, most of the cells form antibody only to one but a percentage form antibody to both. This percentage varies for the different studies, ranging from a few percent to as much as 20 percent. These results have generally been obtained with individual cells in microdroplets, measuring the ability of the droplets to agglutinate bacteria, or observing immune adherence of the bacteria to the cell, or measuring the neutralization of the bacteriophage by the droplet. By the rosette technique, 2-6 percent of the antibody forming lymphoid cells of mice immunized with red cells of two species, for example, sheep + human or sheep + pigeon, formed rosettes containing both types of erythrocytes (Fig. 10.5).

Fig. 10.5 Low-power view showing rosettes formed by adherence of erythrocytes to lymphoid cells from mice immunized with a mixture of sheep (small round) red cells and pigeon (elongated nucleated) red cells. Rosettes containing only a lymphoid cell and a single type of erythrocyte are seen slightly to the left of center (sheep) and at the extreme right (pigeon). In the center is a lymphoid cell rosette formed with both types of erythrocyte. Free erythrocytes of both species and free white blood cells are also evident. Below are shown high power views of rosettes formed by adherence of a single kind of erythrocyte to a lymphoid cell and a mixed rosette formed with both species of erythrocyte. Technique as described in Biozzi, G., C. Stiffel, D. Mouton, M. Liacopoulos-Briot, C. Decreusefond, and Y. Bouthillier. Ann. Inst. Pasteur. **110**:7 (1966). (Courtesy of Dr. Guido Biozzi and with the permission of the Ann. Inst. Pasteur.)

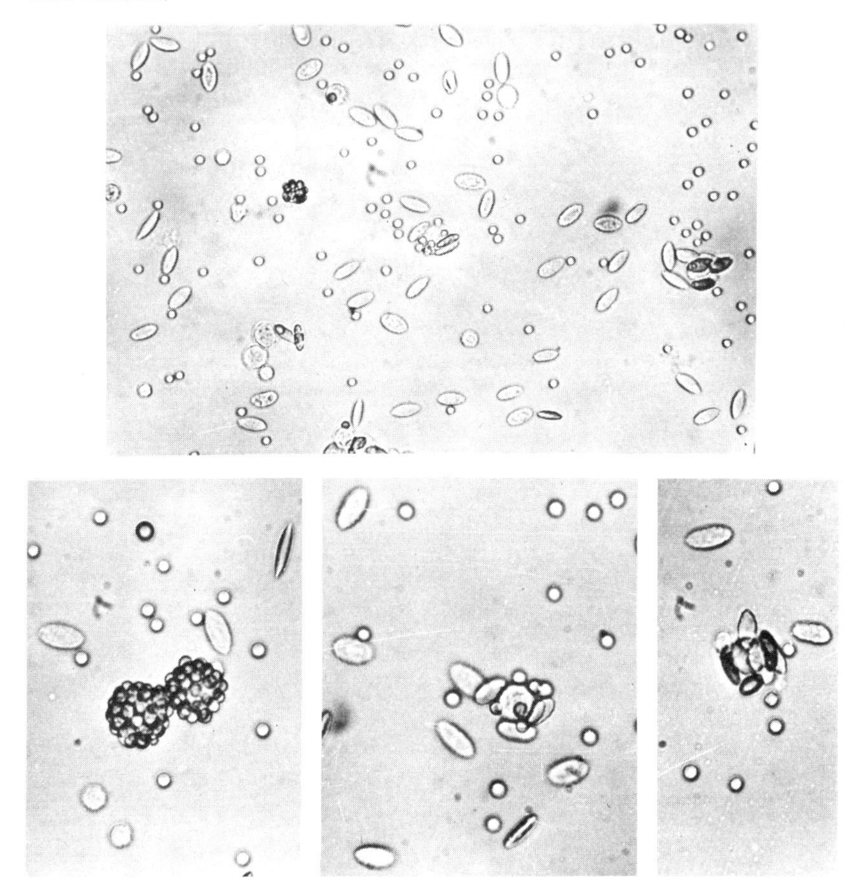

An interesting system involved antibody to two types of antigenic determinants concerned in the neutralization of T5 bacteriophage; one neutralized plaque-forming ability as assayed on *E. coli* B and the other on *E. coli* F. This difference is a consequence of the reactions of antibodies with two antigenic determinants on the bacteriophage. Nineteen of twenty-nine cells formed antibody that neutralized T5 as tested with both strains, while the remaining cells produced antibody that neutralized phage for growth on only one of the two strains. Unless one were to assume the presence of a third distinct kind of antibody capable of neutralizing phage as assayed on both strains, the bulk of the cells were producing two antibodies.

With respect to the heterogeneity of the antibody response, the antibody produced by individual cells from rabbits immunized to phage T6 varied in the ratios of their cross reactivity with phage T4 to T6, but the kinds of antibody produced by a given cell were not established.

Using two types of fluorescent antibody toward determinants on the Fc and Fab fragments of human γG immunoglobulin, one group of investigators reported that 45 percent of cells from the spleens of guinea pigs which had been immunized subcutaneously and intraperitoneally with human γG immunoglobulin in Freund adjuvant formed antibody to two distinct non-cross reacting determinants. However, another study using guinea pig γG immunoglobulin in adjuvants injected into the footpads of rabbits showed that only 3.7 percent of popliteal lymph node cells formed antibody to two non-cross reacting determinants on the Fc and Fab fragments, and this was ascribed to the lack of specificity of the reagents used. The two types of study are very different, and one does not necessarily contradict the other.

With hapten-protein conjugates, individual lymph node cells from rabbits and guinea pigs formed antibody only to the hapten or antibodies to other determinants on the protein; antibodies to both were not seen by fluorescent antibody and by ability to take up radioactive antigen.

In very few areas of immunology has there been so sharp a division, with many investigators finding no cells—or but few—producing more than one antibody while many other workers find a substantial proportion of cells make more than one antibody. The uncertainties are even further compounded, since some investigators whose own data most convincingly show a substantial proportion of cells producing two antibodies favor genetic interpretations that lead them to believe that one cell can produce but a single antibody. Such an interpretation would provide a greatly simplified view of antibody heterogeneity and would fit with much of the data on myeloma globulins.

The study of the myeloma proteins with antibody activity for heterogeneity might help resolve the problem.

At the moment, there is no valid experimental basis for doubting the findings that some cells under certain conditions may produce two antibodies. Further studies are needed to reconcile the areas of disagreement; more sensitive techniques of detecting antibody, as well as dynamic methods that permit study of the specificity of antibody formed by single cells over considerable time intervals, might help resolve the disagreements. It would also be of importance to determine whether the antibody produced by a single cell toward a single determinant is homogeneous with respect to size and conformation of the antibody combining sites.

MOLECULAR ASPECTS OF IMMUNOGLOBULIN BIOSYNTHESIS

The biosynthesis of the heavy and light chains of γG immunoglobulin and antibody has recently been studied in several laboratories. Essentially it appears to be no different than that of other well-studied proteins such as hemoglobin, biosynthesis taking place on polyribosomes held together by a strand of ribonuclease-sensitive material that is messenger RNA (m-RNA). Mouse myeloma tumor cells and lymph nodes and spleen from immunized rats have given essentially similar results. Extracts of these tissues are prepared and subjected to density gradient ultracentrifugation. Two polyribosome peaks are observed and represent clusters of 16 to 20 and 7 to 8 ribosomes in the extracts from tissues of immunized animals; the peaks are much larger than those from nonimmune animals although more ribosomes were used in the gradient from nonimmune lymph node. They disappear on treatment with ribonuclease (Fig. 10.6). The number of ribosomes in the polyribosomes associated with each peak was confirmed by electron microscopy.

When the lymph node was exposed for a short period (1.5 to 2 min) to C^{14}-labeled amino acids, the protein on the polysomes in the process of biosynthesis could be shown to be fully labeled. During this period 10 percent of the injected radioactivity was contained in the node and 20 to 40 percent of this was present in material precipitable by trichloroacetic acid; the polysome supernatant from the density gradient centrifugation could be shown by quantitative precipitin assays to have 30 to 50 percent of its radioactivity in antibody.

Estimates of the size of chain being synthesized by the two types of polysomes are obtained by comparison with polysomes synthesizing hemoglobin. In this system the hemoglobin chain of about 16,000 is made by a polysome with five ribosomes; thus the peak with seven to eight ribosomes could be making a chain of about 25,000, and the sixteen- to twenty-polysome peak would be making a chain of 55,000 to 60,000. These correspond closely to the sizes of the light and heavy chains of γG immunoglobulin.

Myeloma globulin synthesis is also associated with two polysome peaks of about 300 S with twelve to eighteen ribosomes and 120-180 S with five to six ribosomes. The 300 S peak could be shown, by precipitation with antisera to the Fc fragment, to contain nascent

Fig. 10.6 Sucrose density gradients of ovalbumin-immunized rabbit lymph node extract, (*A*) and (*B*) and sucrose density gradients of non-immunized rabbit lymph node extract (*C*) and (*D*) The primary response is shown, the serum titre was 1.16 mg antibody protein per ml. The node had carbon-14 amino-acids injected into it for 1.5 min. (*A*) The untreated extract had antibody that could be detected at the top of the gradient in fractions 25-28 using

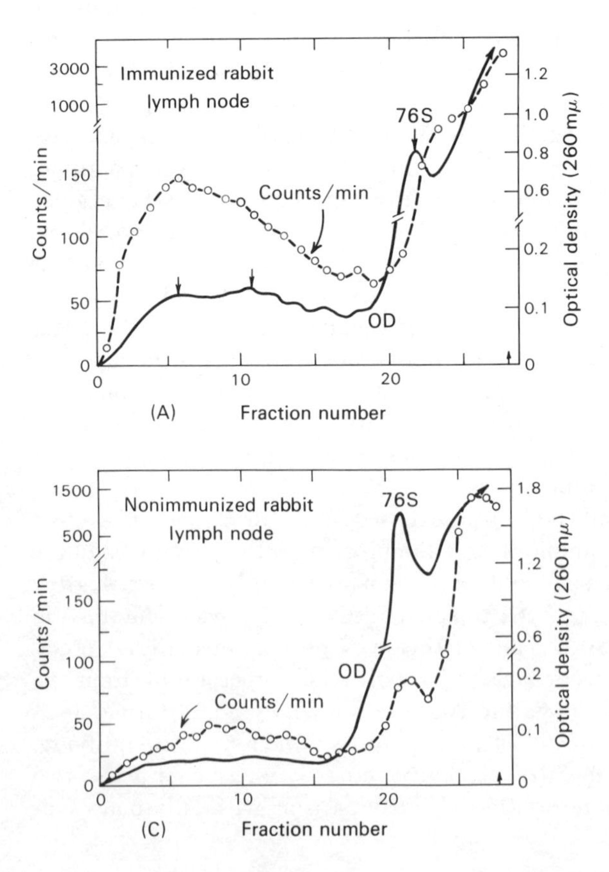

heavy chains. Light-chain determinants appeared to be associated with the 120 to 180 S peak, but showed a lower proportion of precipitable radioactivity with antibody to light chains. The biosynthesis of these chains thus takes place on separate polysomes and involves separate messenger RNAs. Completed light chains were found to be released from the ribosomes and to exist as a small free pool intracellularly. Only intact myeloma globulin, and not free heavy chain, could be found in polysome supernatants, and it is thought that the small pool of free light chains serves to effect release of the heavy chain from the ribosome. No evidence was found to suggest

a modified ring test. (*B*) A portion was incubated with 5 mg per ml of ribonuclease at 0° for 30 min before centrifuging. (*C*) Untreated extract. (*D*) Treated with ribonuclease as in (*B*), (From Becker, M.J., and A. Rich. *Nature* 212: 142 [1966]; by permission of the copyright owner, Macmillan [Journals] Ltd., London.)

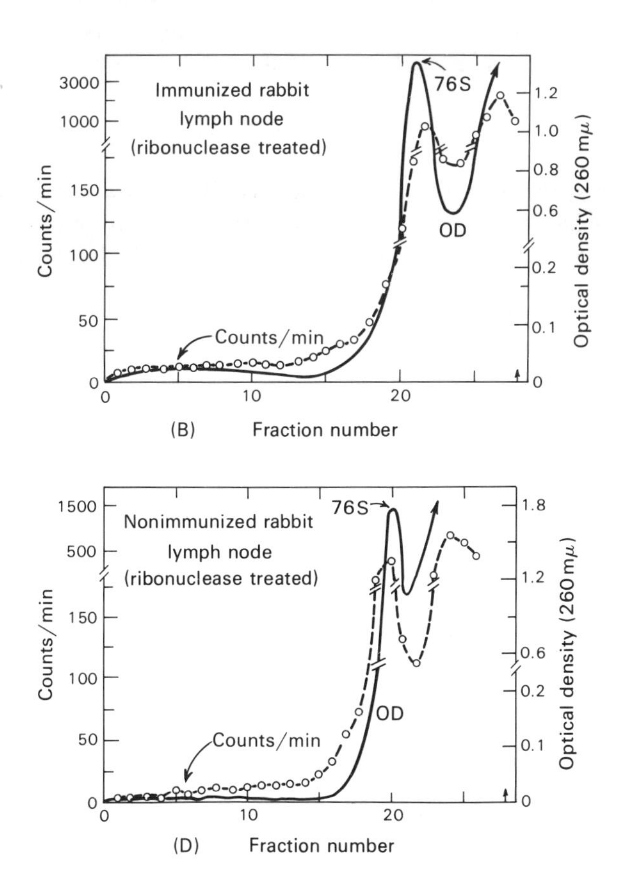

that the variable and constant regions of each chain were separately synthesized.

Accepting these data, the biosynthesis of antibody and of myeloma globulins closely conforms to the accepted mechanisms of synthesis of protein. The major question, however, is how this scheme of biosynthesis permits antigen to play a role. One school favors an instructive theory—for example, that the antigen or antigenic determinant serves as a template for the imparting of antibody specificity—and proposes that the antigenic determinant attaches to the ribosome or to the m-RNA and modifies transcription by causing a conformational change and leading to the incorporation of amino acids that form a complementary pattern over the antigenic determinant with rejection of unsuitable amino acyl-s-RNA molecules that might have been satisfactory if the antigenic determinants were not present. The other school, favoring selection, considers that the information for the synthesis of all possible antibody combining sites is genetically determined and that the antigen stimulates selected cell populations containing receptors complementary to it to multiply and to synthesize increasing amounts of their immunoglobulin that already possesses a particular antibody specificity. Among workers of the latter school there are differences of opinion as to whether there is a separate gene for each antibody specificity, for example, each variable region on the light and heavy chains, or whether this is accomplished by some somatic mutation mechanism. It is impractical to attempt to summarize the various arguments for or against each theory and their modifications; these may be found in the Suggested Readings. It is perhaps most fair to conclude this section by saying that we at present have no idea as to how antigen plays a role in the synthesis of specific antibody.

GENETIC ASPECTS OF ANTIBODY FORMATION

It would be an important step forward if some system could be obtained that would permit analysis of the genetic factors involved in the production of antibody sites specific for a given antigenic determinant. Although the genetics of immunoglobulin synthesis has been well delineated with respect to the Gm and Inv determinants and shown to follow classical Mendelian principles, these essentially describe the genes controlling antigenic specificities of these molecules and tell nothing about the genetic control of antibody specificity. Since immunoglobulin molecules may often have a given antibody specificity—in some instances even to a single antigenic determinant—and yet be different with respect to their various Gm or Inv groups or allotypes, the conferring of antibody specificity is evidently under independent genetic control. The finding that in γG1 heavy chains the Gm (a) and Gm (z) determinants and the Gm (f) and Gm (y) determinants always are found in the myeloma proteins of Caucasians and Negroes as Gm (a+z+) and Gm (f+ y+) indicates that genes Gm^{az} and Gm^{yf} control the biosynthesis of the heavy chains. Since Gm (a) and Gm (f) are found on the Fd while Gm (z) and Gm (y) occur on the Fc fragment (see Fig. 9.10), these two halves of the heavy chain are probably synthesized as a unit in agreement with the biosynthetic findings already considered.

Several groups have obtained lines of animals with good and poor antibody responses to a single antigen by selection and inbreeding. Crosses of heterozygous good responders with homozygous poor responders have given offspring with about 50 percent good and 50 percent poor responders, as would be expected for a single Mendelian dominant gene. The problem of the relation of this gene to the antibody specificity, however, rather than to any of the other factors that influence the antibody response, has not yet been established. In one such study using DNP-polylysine in guinea pigs, lines of responders and nonresponders were readily obtained. However, the gene involved was not influencing the formation of the DNP-antibody combining sites, since specific anti-DNP antibodies were readily produced in nonreponders by mixing the DNP-polylysine with a variety of carriers such as bovine or human serum albumins. Moreover, in nonresponders antibodies to other determinants could not be obtained by coupling them to polylysine. Thus the gene that was being recognized was affecting the ability to respond to the polylysine portion of the DNP-polylysine.

An interesting genetic system was obtained in mice with respect to antibody formation to the polypeptide (T.G)-A -- L (see Chapter 2). One inbred line, C57 responded well and another, CBA, gave a poor antibody response. Crosses of the two lines showed that the antibody response appeared to be under the control of a single dominant gene. If the tyrosine in the antigen was replaced by histidine the CBA mice were good antibody producers and the C57 were poor. If further studies establish the gene in these lines as specific for the formation of the antibody combining site, substantial progress may be made.

FACTORS AFFECTING THE ANTIBODY RESPONSE

The antibody response in an intact animal is subject to many factors that influence it. Among these the most important are the thymus and, in avian species, the bursa of Fabricius, x-irradiation, cortisone, nitrogen mustard, certain vitamin deficiencies, and so forth. In addition levels of immunoglobulin and antibody are apparently subject to regulation by feedback control.

Thymus and Bursa of Fabricius

Phylogenetic studies indicate that the evolution in vertebrates of the antibody forming apparatus was related to the appearance of the thymus and other lymphoid tissues. The hagfish, one of the two groups of cyclostome fishes (the most primitive class of vertebrates), shows no thymus, fails to form antibody, shows no local response to mycobacteria in Freund adjuvants, and does not develop delayed hypersensitivity (see Chapter 13). The other group, the lampreys, showed a few round cells under the gills which may represent a protothymus, and some evidence of weak antibody production was observed. Lampreys produce anti-H on injection of human blood, show delayed hypersensitivity, and reject grafts (see Chapter 14). On the other hand, the next higher group of fishes, the elasmobranchs and the lower bony fishes, show well-developed thymuses and gave definite evidence of antibody production. After injection of hemocyanin in Freund adjuvants, precipitating antibodies were obtained and a severe local reaction occurred at the site of the adjuvant injection; delayed sensitivity also was seen. The immunoglobulin and antibody in elasmobranchs such as the dogfish is exclusively γM, while in an anuran amphibian, the bullfrog, γM and γG immunoglobulins were present and antibodies of these two classes were formed. The two classes of immunoglobulin had their characteristic chain structures and carbohydrate contents (see Chapter 9).

In embryogenesis the thymus is the first organ to show lymphoid elements. In addition the lymphoid tissue of the appendix and, in birds, the bursa of Fabricius, a pear-shaped mass of lymphoid tissue near the anus, may have a separate origin. The lymphoid tissue in other areas, however, is not formed until later, and in some species does not appear until after birth. In some species the rate of production of lymphocytes in the thymus is much higher than in other lymphoid organs if they have not been subjected to antigenic stimulation, and some workers consider that the thymus and the bursa of Fabricius seed lymphoid elements into these other organs during embryonic and early life. Although in mammals thymectomy in adult life has very little effect on immunological processes, thymectomy at birth causes marked decreases in lymphocytes in the blood and in lymphoid tissues excepting bone marrow. It also causes a decrease in antibody formed in mice to some antigens (sheep red cells and Salmonella), but not to others (hemocyanin and type III pneumococcal polysaccharide). γG immunoglobulin levels were somewhat lower during the first weeks of life, but at six weeks of age were comparable in thymectomized and normals; γM immunoglobulin was no different, but thymectomy resulted in increased γA immunoglobulin levels in animals surviving over seven weeks. In the rat, neonatal thymectomy resulted in the disappearance of a particular type of immunoglobulin. Other consequences of neonatal thymectomy were impaired ability to reject skin grafts and failure to develop delayed hypersensitivity (see Chapters 13 and 14).

These latter effects seem to be more clear cut than the effect on antibody production. Restoration of immunological reactivity could be accomplished by thymus grafts or by the injection of spleen or lymph node cells; bone marrow cell suspensions were ineffective, although they contained comparable numbers of small lymphocytes. When neonatal thymic tissue from any of several different strains was placed in millipore diffusion chambers, restoration of immunological reactivity was observed; this could not be done with splenic and lymph node tissue in diffusion chambers. There would thus appear to be some humoral factor elaborated by the thymic cells which regulates immunological competence. Whether this is the sole manner in which the thymus influences immunological competence or whether it also seeds cells into the other organs is not clear. Isolation from thymus of the substance determining immunological competence is a problem of major importance. In the rabbit the appendix also plays a role auxiliary to the thymus.

Several unusual cases have been described of human infants born with no thymic tissue. In such infants lymphocytes have been found; these are undoubtedly derived from tissues other than the thymus. They did not appear to have a high degree of immunological competence; perhaps the thymic humoral factor or circulation through the thymus is essential for immunological competence.

In birds that have a bursa as well as a thymus, it has been possible to differentiate to some extent between the immunological functions controlled by each organ. Removal of the bursa may be surgically carried out or, if eggs are injected with androgens the bursa fails to develop on hatching; the majority of chickens obtained from such eggs show a normal thymus. These animals show an almost complete absence of the plasma cell series, while the cells of lymphoid follicles and the circulating blood lymphocytes are but slightly affected. Thymectomy, however, causes a profound reduction in the lymphoid cells and blood lymphocytes without affecting the plasmacytic series. Surgical bursectomy at less than two weeks of age or hormonal bursectomy resulted in much lower antibody levels on immunization with various antigens, while neonatal thymectomy had little or no effect. On the other hand neonatal thymectomy was associated with reduced ability to reject foreign skin grafts, while bursectomy had no effect. Bursectomy and thymectomy in chickens, as in other species, must be carried out in early life for their effects to be manifest.

Further studies tend to indicate that there may be two primary origins for all lymphoid cells, one thymic and the other corresponding to the bursa although the exact source has not been located in mammalian species. In the chicken, bursal cells have a much larger mean cell volume than thymic cells during embryonic life and posthatching, also suggesting that they represent two distinct populations. There are many additional facets to this subject, which can be found in the Suggested Readings.

X-radiation

The effect of large doses of x-radiation on antibody formation has been known for over 60 years, when it was first shown that irradiation prior to the administration of an initial dose of antigen suppressed the antibody response and that this was accompanied by a reduced rate of elimination of the antigen from the circulation. In such animals a second injection fails to provoke a secondary response, suggesting that the initial irradiation had prevented development of the committed immunocompetent cells required for the secondary response. The effect of radiation depends critically on the time relationship to the primary dose of antigen, it being most effective from shortly before antigen injection up to one day following it and being completely ineffective several days after a primary injection. The secondary response is generally much less sensitive, no effect being obtained with some antigens while with others some reduction in antibody response is seen; the results vary with the antigen, the dose, and the time of administration. X-radiation is considered to affect DNA function. Administration with antigen of enzymatic digests of DNA and RNA containing tissue extracts could prevent the effect of x-radiation, but the mechanism is not clear.

Figure 10.7 shows the disappearance curves of bovine serum albumin when injected intravenously in relation to the appearance of antibody. The upper two curves show the accelerated disappearance of antigen and more rapid appearance of antibody in immunized animals—one having circulating antibody (upper curve) and the other having no circulating antibody (anamnestic)—as compared with a normal animal (middle curve). The lower two curves show the prolonged delay in appearance of antibody, the lower antibody levels

Fig. 10.7 Disappearance of antigen and appearance of complement-fixing antibody in rabbits following an injection of 75 mg I^{131} bovine γ-globulin. Sensitized: Previously immunized with bovine γ-globulin—circulating antibody present. Anamnestic: Previously immunized—no circulating antibody. Control: Normal rabbit; no previous contact with bovine γ-globulin. 200 R: Normal rabbit previously given 200 Röntgens of whole body irradiation. 500 R: Normal rabbit previously given 500 Röntgens whole body irradiation. (From Dixon, F. J., D. W. Talmage, and P. H. Maurer, J. Immunol **68**:693 (1952); by permission of the copyright owner, The Williams & Wilkins Company, Baltimore, Md.)

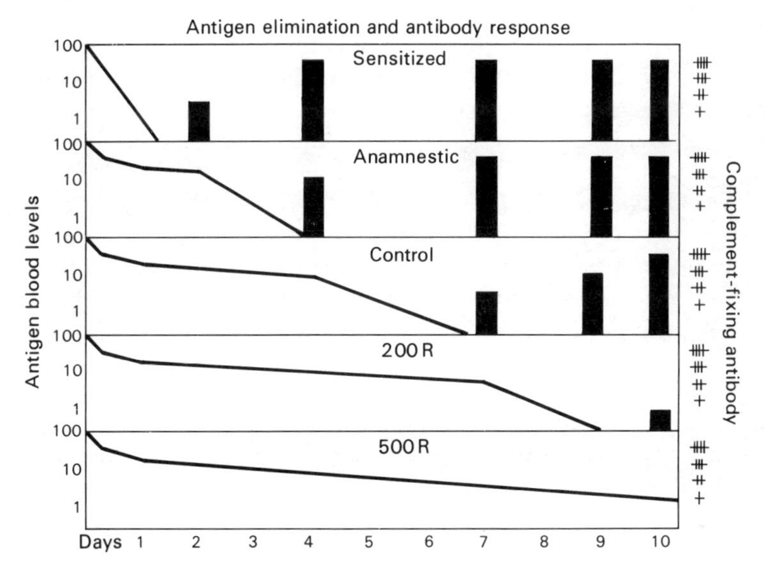

and the persistence of antigen in animals receiving two different doses of x-radiation. Disappearance curves of I^{131}-labeled antigens are very useful for evaluating the immunological status of animals following various treatments provided the antigens are carefully labeled so that denaturation is avoided. Denatured or too heavily labeled proteins are removed very rapidly from the circulation in normal animals; indeed, one test of a satisfactorily labeled plasma protein is that it not be removed more rapidly than the unlabeled protein.

Cortisone

This adrenal hormone and related glucocorticoids in large doses have been found to have a profound effect on lymphoid tissue, causing reduction in the weight of the spleen and thymus and almost complete absence of lymphocytes from lymph follicles. They inhibit granuloma formation to the mycobacteria in Freund adjuvants, reduce the rate of disposal of phagocytized bacteria, and produce a decrease in the rate of antibody synthesis. Cortisone and x-radiation are similar in some ways. Cortisone must be started two days before antigen is administered; it was ineffective if antigen was given first. For maximal effects administration is often continued during the entire study. Its effects on antibody formation are not so striking as those of x-radiation.

Feedback inhibition of antibody formation

In the over-all response of an animal to injection of antigen, what factors affect the kind of antibody produced, and its level and persistence in, or disappearance from the circulation? As yet we have relatively little information about these points, but some evidence is accumulating that circulating antibody inhibits the synthesis of new antibody; for example, the injection of antiserum containing specific antibody to bacteriophage at the time of a primary injection of phage inhibited antibody formation; γG antibodies were more effective than γM antibodies, and the latter could inhibit synthesis of γM antibody only when given at the same time as the antigen. Adequate dosage of γG antibody from hyperimmune animals given three days after antigen prevented a primary γG antibody response and reduced the γM antibody level one week after injection of antigen. This feedback inhibition has been shown to be specific for the antigen and could be produced by pepsin-digested anti-phage from which the Fc′ fragment had been split.

Several studies have indicated that the antimetabolite 6-mercaptopurine (6-MP) prolongs the γM antibody response while it inhibits the γG antibody response. Administration of γG antibody to 6-MP treated animals (as well as to normals) also suppressed γM synthesis. Feedback inhibition as mentioned earlier can be seen by the plaque technique. In small doses 6-MP stimulates antibody formation.

Many facets of feedback inhibition require further study, and numerous other observations are difficult to interpret and have not been presented. Of special interest would be the study of the effects of excess immunoglobulin containing only K or L light chains and only of an individual subgroup, in order to establish whether the feedback inhibition was specific or nonspecific. If it were clearly established whether γM and γG antibodies to a single antigenic determinant may be formed by a single cell or whether different cell populations are involved, the analysis of feedback inhibition might become clearer.

A phenomenon of importance in immunoglobulin synthesis is the specific suppression of the formation of γG immunoglobulin of a given allotype in rabbits by immunization of the mother. Homozygous

A4 A4 female rabbits immunized with rabbit A5 A5 γG immunoglobulin and mated with A5 A5 males gave rise to heterozygous A4 A5 offspring who produced little or no A5 immunoglobulin. This failure of the A5 genetic information to be expressed was of long duration.

This chapter has described important directions which studies on antibody formation are taking; further work along these lines may make clear the basic mechanisms involved.

SUGGESTED READINGS

Schultze, H. E. and J. F. Heremans. Molecular biology of human proteins. (1966) American Elsevier Publishing Company, New York vol. **1**, Sec. 3, Chap. 1; *a good survey of the synthesis of plasma proteins.*

Feldman, J. D. Ultrastructure of immunological processes. Advances in Immunology **4**: 175 (1964). Academic press, New York ; *the intracellular aspects of antibody formation, fate of antigen, and consequences of antigen-antibody reaction as explored with the electron microscope.*

Haurowitz, F. Antibody formation. Physiological Reviews **45**: 1 (1965); *a review of recent theories by a firm advocate of template theories.*

Wolstenholme, G. E. [Ed.]. The immunologically competent cell. Ciba foundation Study Group. No. 16. Little, Brown & Company (1963).

Wolstenholme, G. E. and M. O'Connor. The cellular aspects of immunity. Ciba Foundation Symposium. J. and A. Churchill, London (1960).

Gowans, J. L. and D. D. McGregor. The immunological activities of lymphocytes. Progress in Allergy **9**: 1 (1965). S. Karger AG, Basel, Switzerland.

Thorbecke, G. J. and B. Benacerraf. The reticulo-endothelial system and immunological phenomena. Progress in Allergy **6**: 559 (1962).

Uhr, J. W. and M. S. Finkelstein. The kinetics of antibody formation. Progress in Allergy **10**: 37 (1967).

Symposium on recent advances on the biology and function of the lymphocytes. Federation Proceedings **25**: 1711-1741 (1966);

The above six reviews provide excellent sources of reference material and different viewpoints.

Hiramoto, R. N. and M. Hamlin. Detection of two antibodies in single plasma cells by the paired fluorescence technique. Journal of Immunology **95**: 214 (1965).

Green, I., P. Vasalli, V. Nussenzweig, and B. Benacerraf. Specificity of the antibodies produced by single cells following immunization with antigens bearing two types of antigenic determinants. Journal of Experimental Medicine **125**: 511 (1967);

Two papers with diametrically opposite results, but not carried out under the same conditions.

Williamson, A. R. and B. A. Askonas. Biosynthesis of immunoglobulins: The separate classes of polyribosomes synthesizing heavy and light chains. Journal of Molecular Biology **23**: 201 (1967) and other papers (Nature

211: 369 (1966); The Royal Society (London), Proceedings, B. **166**: 232 (1966)).

Shapiro, A. L., M. D. Scharff, J. V. Maizel, Jr., and J. W. Uhr. Polyribosomal synthesis of the H and L chains of gamma globulin. Proceedings of the National Academy of Sciences **56**: 216 (1966).

Becker, M. J. and A. Rich. Polyribosomes of tissues producing antibodies. Nature **212**: 142 (1966);

The above three papers give the data on the polysomal synthesis of heavy and light chains of myeloma globulin and antibody.

Holborow, C. J. [ed.] Antibodies. British Medical Bulletin **19**: 169-258 (1963).

Symposium on differentiation and growth of hemoglobin and immunoglobulin synthesizing cells. Journal of Cellular Physiology **67** (Suppl. 1): 1-224 (1966).

Porter, R. R. [Organizer] A discussion of the chemistry and biology of Immunoglobulins. The Royal Society (London), Proceedings B. **166**: 114-243 (1966);

These three symposia offer many articles on the structure and biosynthesis of antibodies and on genetic aspects and other factors affecting the antibody response.

Miller, J. F. A. P. The thymus and the development of immunological responsiveness. Science **144**: 1544 (1964).

Warner, N. L. and A. Szenberg. The immunological function of the bursa of Fabricius in the chicken. Annual Review of Microbiology **18**: 253 (1964).

Good, R. A. and A. E. Gabrielson (ed.) The thymus in immunobiology. (1965) Paul B. Hoeber, Inc. New York [Medical Dept. of Harper & Row, Publishers].

Three references summarizing the work on the thymus and bursa of Fabricius.

Sterzl, J. [ed.]. Molecular and cellular basis of antibody formation (1964) Publishing House; Czechoslovak Academy of Science, Prague; *an important collection of papers on this subject.*

Fishman, M., F. L. Adler, and S. Dray. Antibody formation initiated *in vitro*. III. Antibody formation and allotypic specificity directed by ribonucleic acid from peritoneal exudate cells. Journal of Immunology **97**:554 (1966); *data suggesting the transmission of information on RNA in antibody synthesis.*

Schwartz, R. S. Immunosuppressive drugs. Progress in Allergy, **9**: 246 (1965). [S. Karger AG, Basel, Switzerland]; *a good source of information on substances affecting antibody formation.*

Bussard, A. E. and C. Hannoun. Antibody production by cells in tissue culture II. Qualitative and quantitative aspects of antibody production (local hemolysis in gum) by cells obtained from long term tissue culture. Journal of Experimental Medicine **123**: 1047 (1966).

Globerson, A. and R. Auerbach. Primary antibody response in organ cultures. Journal of Experimental Medicine **124**: 1001 (1966).

Two recent approaches to the study of antibody production in organ cultures.

Samter, M. [ed.]. Immunological diseases (1965) Little, Brown & Company. Boston; *for further information on the histological aspects of antibody formation, on the function of the thymus, and on other aspects of antibody formation.*

Gallily, R. and M. Feldman. The role of macrophages in the induction of antibody in irradiated animals. Immunology **12**: 197 (1967); *evidence for a role of the macrophage in antibody formation.*

Lischner, H. W., H. H. Punnett, and A. M. DiGeorge. Lymphocytes in congenital absence of the thymus. Nature **214**: 580 (1967).

11

Antigen-Antibody Interactions with Complement and Their Effects on Cells

Probably the most widely studied interaction of antigen and antibody with a cell in the presence of complement (C′) is the lysis of the erythrocyte. In this instance the antigen is a portion of the red cell membrane; the antibody is usually from rabbits immunized with sheep erythrocytes, or with boiled sheep stromata (anti-Forssman antibody); and the C′ is fresh guinea pig or human serum.

This is a prototype for many related interactions of these substances with bacterial or tissue cells to cause bacteriocidal, cytocidal, bacteriolytic and cytolytic effects, immune adherence and phagocytosis.

The analysis of the mechanisms by which antibody and C′ bring about these effects has been one of the major accomplishments in immunology during the past two decades, although evidence for the multicomponent nature of complement goes back about sixty years. It is impossible to outline all the developments that led to the present scheme for the lysis of the erythrocytes by antibody and C′. In principle, the general reaction of the sheep erythrocyte (E) or a site (S) on an erythrocyte with antibody (Ab) to form sensitized erythrocytes (EAb) and C′ leads to the formation of one or more lesions on the erythrocyte membrane (E*) and to hemolysis. The reaction

$$\mathrm{E + Ab} \rightleftarrows \mathrm{EAb + C'} \longrightarrow \mathrm{E^*} \longrightarrow \text{hemolysis} \tag{11-1}$$

has been separated into more and more intermediate steps as chemical procedures yielded fractions none of which alone could substitute for whole C′ in causing hemolysis, but which were effective when recombined.

Thus four distinct complement components termed C′1, C′2, C′3, and C′4 could be recognized in guinea pig and human serum by the various procedures and tests shown in Fig. 11.1. For instance, whole C′ could be separated on dilution with water and dialysis into water-soluble (pseudoglobulin) and insoluble (euglobulin) fractions; these showed no C′ activity by themselves, but when recombined gave hemolysis. Heating at 56°C, or treatment with yeast or an insoluble carbohydrate from yeast called zymosan, or treatment with ammonia (or hydrazine) inactivated C′, but evidently in different ways

Fig. 11.1 Interrelations of complement and its components. Combinations giving hemolysis are denoted by an H. (From M. M. Mayer *in* Kabat and Mayer's *Experimental immunochemistry* [2d ed.; 1961] Chas C. Thomas, Publisher, Springfield, Ill.)

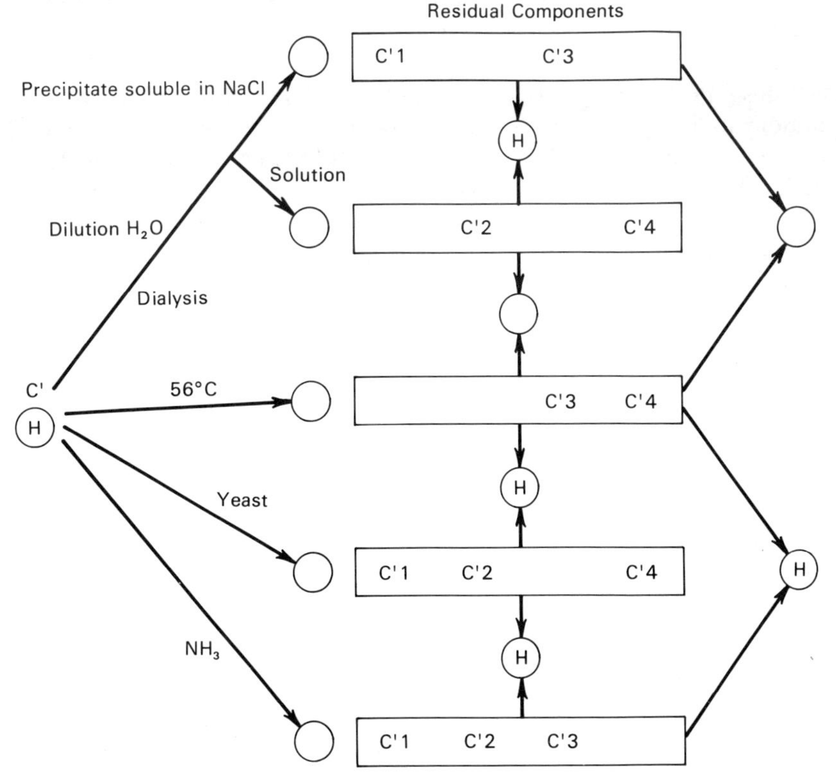

since heated C′, which could not restore C′ activity to either dialysis fraction, could reactivate the yeast- or ammonia-treated serum. At least four components were necessary to account for the experimental findings, and the compositions of the various fractions are evident from Fig. 11.1. Fractions or combinations of fractions containing any three of the components may serve as reagents for the detection of the component they lack.

Further progress has come (1) from the use of chromatographic methods of fractionation which have permitted the isolation of additional components; (2) from the use of precise kinetic methods of assay; (3) from assuming immune hemolysis to be a one-hit process, which postulates that a single lesion S* on a red cell is sufficient to cause lysis; and (4) from studies with specific antisera to various components of C′ and their effects. The sequence of action of the various components is rigidly determined and was shown to be in order EAbC′1; EAbC′1,4; EAbC′1,4,2. Since C′ and some of its components are very labile, fractionations of components are rapidly carried out, always with the temperature maintained at close to 0°C.

The reaction EAb with C′1 involves three factors: A euglobulin fraction of human serum containing C′1, in the presence of trisodium ethylenediaminetetraacetate (EDTA) a chelating agent that binds divalent cations, could be separated into three peaks on DEAE-cellulose, designated C′1q, C′1r, and C′1s. The three fractions are present in human serum as a macromolecular complex held together by Ca^{++} and dissociated by chelation with EDTA. C′1q is an 11 S molecule, C′1r a 7 S; and C′1s a 4 S proesterase. To form EAbC′1, and for the activation of the proesterase to an esterase, the three components must be recombined in solution with Ca^{++} before adding to the EAb as follows

$$\text{EAb} + (\text{C}'1\text{q} + \text{C}'1\text{r} + \text{C}'1\text{s}) \underset{}{\overset{Ca^{++}}{\rightleftharpoons}} \text{EAbC}'1 \longrightarrow \underset{\text{active esterase}}{\text{EAbC}'1\text{a}} \quad (11\text{-}2)$$

The esterase of EAbC′1a can be dissociated by EDTA

$$\text{EAbC}'1\text{a} \underset{Ca^{++}}{\overset{\text{EDTA}}{\rightleftharpoons}} \text{EAb} + \text{C}'1\text{a- esterase} \quad (11\text{-}3)$$

and the esterase could be obtained in purified form by chromatography on DEAE-cellulose. It is not clear whether C′1q is eluted from the complex in Eq. (11-3). The esterase was first recognized by its ability to split the synthetic amino acid esters *p*-toluenesulfonyl-L-arginine methyl ester (TAME) and *N*-acetyl-L-tyrosine ethyl ester (ATEe). Polyinosinic acid has been shown to inactivate C′1q at a concentration of 10^{-3} M; as a double helix with polyadenylic acid it has no effect. Polyadenylic acid may be used to stop the reaction.

Normal serum contains an inhibitor of C′1a which inhibits its esterase action on TAME. This inhibitor has been shown to be very low, or lacking, in patients with a disease called hereditary angioneurotic edema which is characterized by localized noninflammatory areas of swelling. The inhibitor is an acid labile α_2-glycoprotein, and levels may be measured by inhibition of enzyme activity as well as immunochemically. From such studies two types of genetic defect have been recognized: (1) a failure to synthesize the inhibitor and (2) the synthesis of an enzymatically inactive protein that reacts with antiserum to the esterase inhibitor.

In the next step the activated esterase complex combines with C′4 to form a stable complex

$$\text{EAbC}'1\text{a} + \text{C}'4 \longrightarrow \underset{\text{stable}}{\text{EAbC}'1\text{a}, 4} \qquad (11\text{-}4)$$

C′4 is a β_1 globulin in immunoelectrophoresis and has been designated β_1E. It was purified from the pseudoglobulin of human serum by chromatography on TEAE-cellulose, by electrophoresis on a pevikon block, and by rechromatography. It gave a single component in the β_1 region on immunoelectrophoresis with rabbit antibody to whole human serum, was ultracentrifugally homogeneous, and had a sedimentation constant of 10 S.

Purified C′4 was taken up only by the active EAbC′la; if the EAbC′1a were inactivated by diisopropylfluorophosphate (DFP), an esterase inhibitor, reaction (11-4) did not occur. C′1 esterase, when dissociated [Eq. (11-3)] from the EAbC′1a complex, inactivated purified C′4 in solution so that it was no longer capable of reacting in Eq. (11-4) and, as in whole serum, it was also inactivated by hydrazine. Many proteolytic enzymes have esterase activity, and it is possible that C′1 esterase could be acting proteolytically. Polyinosinic acid in the presence of C′1 and Ca^{++} inactivated C′4. Changes in electrophoretic mobility of the β_1E globulin occur on inactivation. The enzymic action of C′1a is thought to expose a site on the C′4 by which it attaches to a receptor on the cell surface. This attachment must take place rapidly, or the site on the C′4 becomes inactive (C′4i). Thus the nonproductive side reaction

$$\text{C}'4 \xrightarrow[\text{EAbC}'1\text{a}]{} \text{C}'4\text{i} \qquad (11\text{-}5)$$

is probably taking place simultaneously with reaction (11-4). This receptor site on the erythrocyte need not involve antibody, since unsensitized erythrocytes could be shown to take up C′4 in the presence of C′1a in solution and these EC′4 could participate in further reactions.

The next step involving addition of C′2 is the most complicated one in the sequence of reactions, since it leads to the formation of an intermediate that is necessary for the further steps, but which is unstable and decays back to the original EAbC′1a , 4. The reaction considering individual sites on the erythrocyte is:

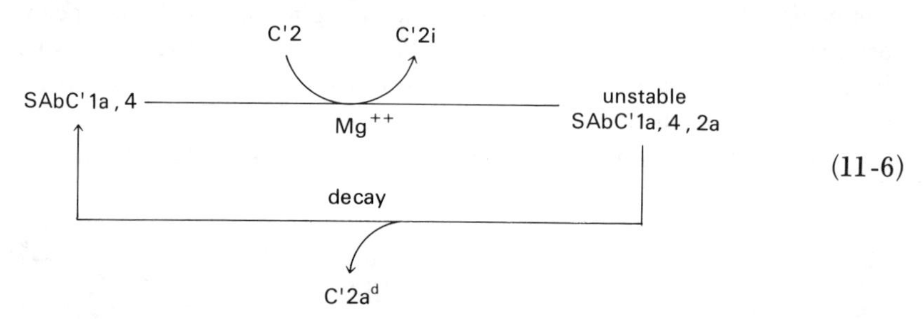

(11-6)

C′2 adsorbs to SAbC′1a,4 to form SAbC′1a,4,2; and the enzymatic action of the bound C′1a irreversibly converts it to SAbC′1a,4,2a. At the same time some C′2 is inactivated to C′2i at the cell surface; C′2i can also be formed from C′2 by C′1a in solution. Formation both of SAbC′1a , 4 , 2a and of C′2i is blocked by the enzyme inhibitor diisopropylfluorophosphate (DFP), as was found with Reaction (11-4), which suggests that both involve the esterase action of C′1a. This is also supported by the finding that TAME, a synthetic substrate for C′1a, competitively inhibits the formation of SAbC′1a,4,2a. Reaction (11-6) is further complicated by the reversible dissociation of SAbC′1a, 4 and of SAbC′1a,4,2a into SAbC′4 and SAbC′4,2a, respectively, and by the decay of SAbC′4,2a to SAbC′4. Thus the over-all series of reactions involved in the formation of a site capable of going on to hemolysis–that is SAbC′1,4,2a or SAbC′4,2a –is as follows:

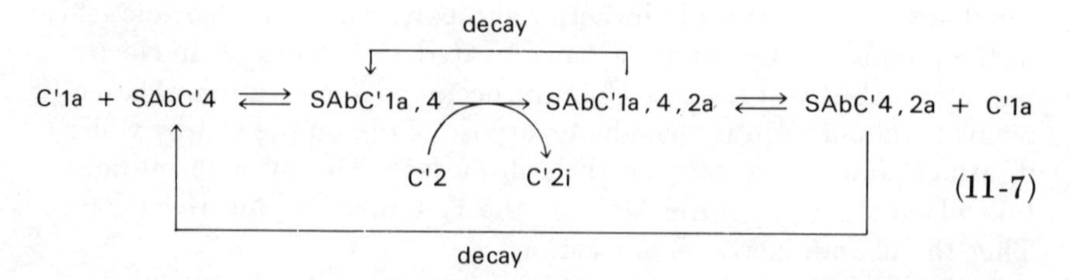

(11-7)

In the presence of a sufficient excess of C′2 a steady state may be obtained in which the concentration of SAbC′1a,4,2a + SAbC′4,2a is constant. With the use of a specific antiserum to guinea pig C′2 it could be shown that C′2 is actually taken up by EAbC′1a,4 to yield EAbC′1a,4,2a. Decay has also been shown to be accompanied by release of an inactive component ($C'2a^{d}$) which reacts with anti-C′2. This decomposition product $C'2a^{d}$ could be shown to differ from C′2 in molecular weight, and the two could be separated from one another on G-100 Sephadex. Of special interest in this system is that 10^{-4} M iodine increases the degree of hemolysis between sixfold and tenfold and the half-life of EAbC′1a,4,2a from 8 to 120 min, which materially simplifies the use of this complex. A hereditary defect in C′2 has been found in certain individuals whose serum fails to show whole C′ activity; the C′2 level is less than 5 percent of the normal value.

For further steps leading to hemolysis C′1a is no longer needed, and EAbC′4, 2a and EAbC′1a, 4, 2a cells can both go on to hemolysis. EDTA will remove the C′1a from the EAbC′1a,4,2a cell as in reaction (11-3).

The next component involved, C′3 or C′3c in human and guinea pig respectively, is a β_1C globulin in immunoelectrophoresis. It may be recognized as such in fresh serum, but in aged sera it is changed into a rapidly moving inactive β_1A globulin. Highly purified C′3 was unaffected by incubation with EAbC′1a,4 cells, but was converted by EAbC′1a, 4, 2a cells (Fig. 11.2) into a more rapidly migrating protein that was no longer effective as C′3 (C′3i). C′3i was not identical with β_1A globulin. Many times more I^{131}-labeled C′3 were taken up by cells if C′2a was present on them. The reaction is enzymatic in nature, since about three hundred C′3 molecules were taken up per

Fig. 11.2 Immunoelectrophoretic demonstration of the conversion of highly purified C'3 to C'3i by EAbC'1a, 4, 2a cells. Upper pattern: C'3 after incubation at 37°C for 15 min with EAbC'1a, 4, 2a. Lower pattern: C'3 after incubation under the same conditions with EAbC'1a, 4. Anode was at the right; pattern was developed with rabbit anti-C'3. (From Müller-Eberhard, H. J., A. P. Dalmasso, and M. A. Calcott. J. Exp. Med. **123**:33 [1966]; by permission of The Rockefeller University Press.

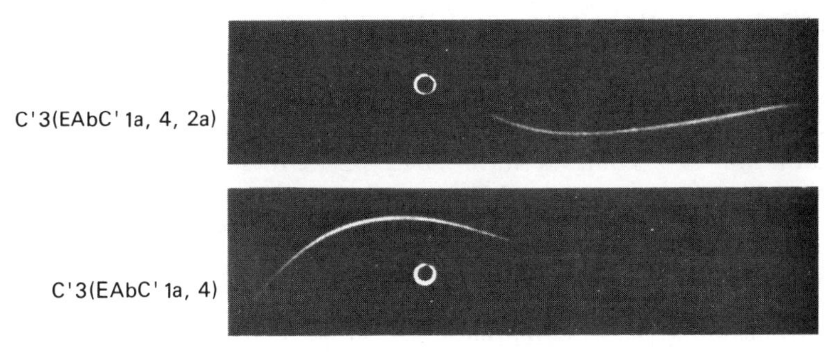

red cell for each SAbC′4,2a site if excess C′3 was present. The large number of C′3 molecules taken up indicates that there must be many receptors on the erythrocyte membrane and that interaction is not restricted to the EAbC′4,2a sites. The reaction is thus best represented considering the erythrocyte

$$\text{EAbC'4, 2a} \xrightarrow[\text{C'3} \;\curvearrowright\; \text{C'3i}]{} \text{EAbC'4, 2a, 3} \tag{11-8}$$

Antibody to the sheep erythrocyte is unnecessary for reaction (11-8), since erythrocytes in the form EC′4,2a could be shown to take up C′3. Reaction (11-8) is inhibited by the glycoside phloridzin.

Step (11-8) is a very important one, for at this stage erythrocytes show immune adherence. Between 170 and 500 molecules of C′3 per erythrocyte were required for detectable immune adherence, while several thousand molecules were needed for maximum effects. The only inhibitor affecting immune adherence is 0.04 M NaCN.

The complex formed in Eq. (11-8) also exhibits CONGLUTINATION. Conglutinin is a term used to describe a substance in normal bovine serum which produced agglutination of antigen-antibody-complement complexes in the presence of Ca^{++}. Conglutinin will not react with C′ in solution, but only when it is complexed with antibody. The immunization of animals with antigen-antibody-complement complexes gives rise to IMMUNOCONGLUTININ, which reacts with EAbC′1a,4,2a,3 complexes and does not require Ca^{++}.

It is also a crucial reaction for hemolysis, since the attachment of many C′3 molecules was important for effecting hemolysis by subsequent steps. There is a reciprocal relationship between the number of C′4 and the number of C′3 molecules bound and the degree of hemolysis. With 154 molecules of C′4 per erythrocyte, 5500 C′3 molecules were needed for 23 percent lysis; while with 1020 molecules of C′4, 1333 molecules of C′3 gave the same degree of hemolysis. The complex EAbC′4,2a,3 also undergoes erythrophagocytosis.

The complex with C′3 in reaction (11-8) decays in solution at 37°C, to inactive EAbC′4,3 or EAbC′1a,4,3 as in reaction (11-7) and can be maintained by excess C′2.

The next steps in the sequence leading to hemolysis may be divided into two stages. The first requires three steps and leads to the formation of a complex stable at 37°C (EAbC′4,2a,3,5,6,7) and the second requires two steps (C′8 and C′9) to the final stage of formation of a damaged site S* giving a damaged cell E*.

The number of components in this first stage is now known to be three; they are numbered in the order in which they act. Other designations are given in parenthesis.

EAbC′1a ,4 ,2a ,3 or EAbC′4 ,2a ,3 react in sequence with C′5 (C′3b or β_{1F}), with C′6 (C′3e), and with C′7 (C′3f). The first two of these complexes continue to decay fairly rapidly; the half times for the C′5-containing complex being sixteen min at 30°C, for the C′6 seventy-five min, and for the C 7 three hundred thirty min; this final complex is stable for several weeks in the cold. The nature of the decay of the complexes with C′5 and with C′6 is not understood.

C′5 is of special interest. An allotypic determinant in mice MuBl—first recognized by the immunization of mice of one strain with the sera of other inbred strains - the inheritance of which involved a single gene, correlated with the absence of hemolytic C′ in the various inbred mouse strains. An antigen analogous to MuBl is present in a large number of mammalian species, including man and guinea pig. MuBl is C′5. It is moderately heat stable and is inactivated at low pH. MuBl levels in adult males are higher than in females; gonadectomized males have values identical with those of females. Administration of testosterone propionate restores the concentration in the male and raises it in the female. MuBl levels are twice as high in homozygous animals as in heterozygous ones. The release of histamine from mast cells and for liberation of anaphylatoxin (see Chapter 13) requires the participation of all components through C′5.

C′6 is a macroglobulin with a half-life of 41 min at 56° C and is inactivated by ammonia and hydrazine. A strain of rabbits genetically deficient in C′6 has been found. EAbC′ complexes or antigen-antibody-C′ aggregates brought to the state at which both C′5 and C′6 had reacted, showed chemotactic properties; that is, they could stimulate the migration of polymorphonuclear leucocytes toward them. This phenomenon of chemotaxis is extremely important in the inflammatory response of tissues. Assay of chemotaxis is carried out using a diffusion chamber with two compartments separated by a millipore filter and with glass cover slips as walls. The substance to be tested is placed in one compartment, and the leucocytes are placed in the other. If the material possesses chemotactic properties the leucocytes can be observed to migrate through the millipore filter; the number of leucocytes which have migrated to the side with the material is counted as compared with controls. Addition of the serum from the C′-deficient strain of rabbits to antigen-antibody-C′ complexes containing components up to and including C′5 did not result in chemotaxis, but when human or rabbit C′6 was added high chemotactic activity was found. The chemotactic effect can be obtained by C′5 + C′6 alone provided the C′5 has been activated by exposure to antigen-antibody complexes containing the earlier-reacting C′ components and is then dissociated from them. Table 11.1 summarizes data on the biological effects of the various complexes.

TABLE 11.1
Composition of Various C' Complexes and Their Biological Effects

Biological Effect	Complex Necessary
Hemolysis	EAbC'1a, 4, 2a, 3, 5, 6, 7, 8, 9 or EAbC' 4, 2a, 3, 5, 6, 7, 8, 9
Immune adherence Conglutination Erythrophagocytosis and Bacterial phagocytosis	EAbC'1a, 4, 2a, 3 or EAbC' 4, 2a, 3
Anaphylatoxin and histamine release from mast cells	EAbC'1a, 4, 2a, 3, 5 or EAbC' 4, 2a, 3, 5
Chemotactic property	EAbC'1a, 4, 2a, 3, 5, 6 or EAbC' 4, 2a, 3, 5, 6

C′7 appears to be a molecule of about 5 S which has a half life of 23 min at 56°C. It is inactivated by trypsin, but not by ammonia or phloridzin. Apart from being essential for ultimate hemolysis, no other known function has been found for it. It is possible that it may participate in chemotaxis.

The final stages of the hemolytic reaction involve the formation of at least one damaged site S* on the membrane, which renders the erythrocyte in the stage E*.

$$\text{SAbC}'4,2a,3,5,6,7 + \text{C}'8 + \text{C}'9 \longrightarrow \text{S}^* \ (\text{E}^*) \qquad (11\text{-}9)$$

C′8 (C′3a) from guinea pig serum is heat labile but relatively stable to low pH, while C′9 (C′3d) is heat labile, sensitive to low pH, unaffected by hydrazine, and present in human saliva and in bovine serum in high concentrations. Their function is unknown.

The reaction

$$\text{E}^* \longrightarrow \text{stroma} + \text{hemogloblin} \qquad (11\text{-}10)$$

has also been shown to be complex.

$$\underset{\text{(precursor)}}{\text{E}^*} \xrightarrow[\text{dependent}]{\text{Temperature}} \underset{\text{(activated)}}{\text{E}^*} \xrightarrow{\text{Blocked by 0.09 M EDTA}} \underset{\text{(damaged)}}{\text{E}^*} \xrightarrow{\text{Blocked by 25 percent bovine serum albumin}} \text{stroma} + \text{hemoglobin} \qquad (11\text{-}11)$$

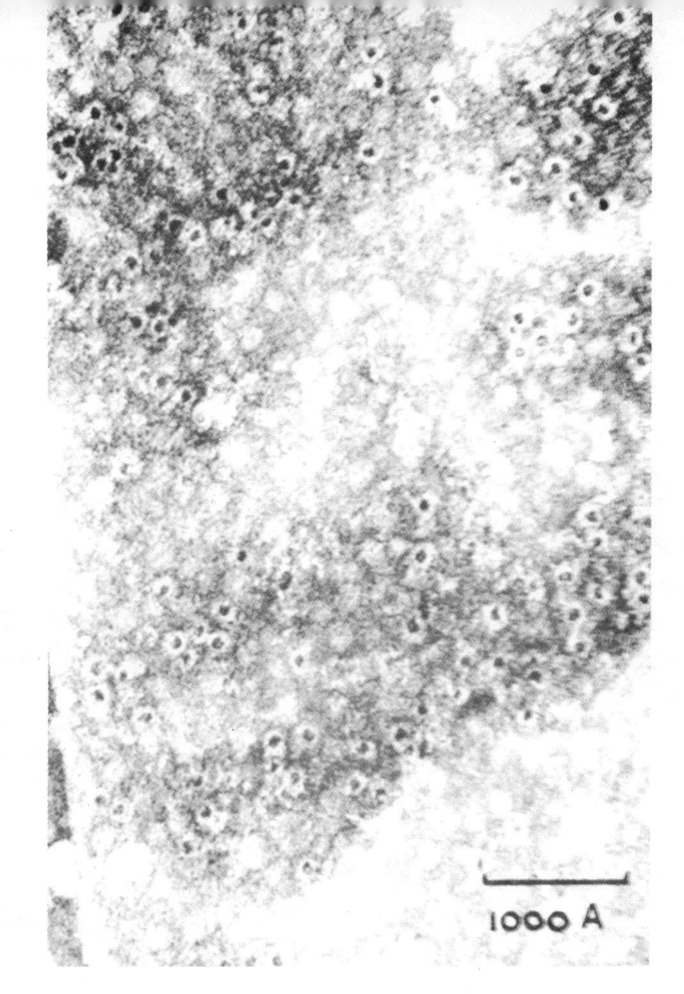

Fig. 11.3 Electron micrograph of part of the membrane of a sheep erythrocyte lysed with Forssman antibody and guinea pig complement. Large numbers of holes are seen on the surface of the membrane, each hole being surrounded by a clear ring. (From Humphrey, J.H., and R. R. Dourmashkin. Ciba Foundation Conf. on Complement, p. 175 (1965); by permission of the Ciba Foundation, London.)

The first step (E* precursor $\longrightarrow$ E* activated) was recognized by a change in reaction kinetics if the cells were given a prior incubation at 30°C, as a consequence of which the lysis became essentially independent of temperature. The second step is blocked by EDTA, and the final step by a high concentration of bovine plasma albumin which is thought to act by stabilizing osmotic effects on both sides of the cell membrane, although a terminal component C′T has been reported to be involved -- whose action it might be blocking.

Electron microscopic study of erythrocytes lysed by antibody and C′ showed that holes were formed in the erythrocyte membrane (Figs. 11.3 and 11.4). Similar holes have been found in ascites tumor cells lysed and *E. coli* cells killed by the same mechanism. They have also been found after lysis of sheep erythrocytes coated with the O

Fig. 11.4 A single hole from an experiment similar to that illustrated in Fig. 11.3: the clear ring around the hole is surrounded by small projections. (From Humphrey, J. H., and R. R. Dourmashkin. Ciba Foundation Conf. on Complement, p. 175 [1965]; by permission of The Ciba Foundation, London.)

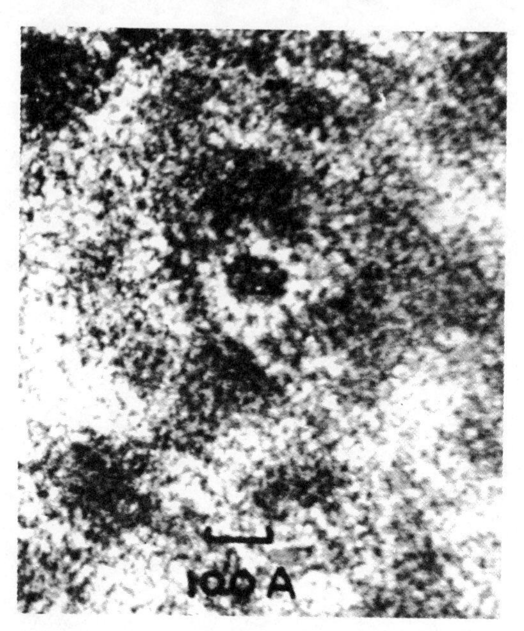

antigen of the Shiga dysentery bacillus and lysed by anti-Shiga O antibody and C′. It is of interest that if EDTA-treated complement were used to lyse cells in the EAbC′1a,4,2a state [Eq. (11-6)], the holes were very hard to visualize or were not present. This would fit well with the observation that EDTA inhibited a terminal stage in the lysis of E*.

The number of antibody molecules required to make one hole in the erythrocyte membrane was estimated in two ways:

1. With the use of I^{125}-labeled antibody, the number of molecules required to lyse 50 percent of a known number of erythrocytes could be calculated. Assuming a lysed cell to have at least one hole and an unlysed cell to have none, at 50 percent lysis there should theoretically be an average of 0.69 holes per cell.

2. Erythrocytes could be lysed with known numbers of antibody molecules and the number of holes per erythrocyte counted.

By both methods using purified γM antibody, two to three molecules were found per hole, while with γG antibody about two thousand to three thousand molecules were needed. With labeled γM and γG antibody, estimates of 90,000 and 600,000 antigenic sites per erythrocyte were obtained. Since only two to three molecules of γM antibody sufficed to produce one hole, it is extremely unlikely that more than one was attached to a single receptor site with 90,000 available, and thus one γM molecule per hole is probably the true value under ideal experimental conditions. The two thousand to three thousand molecules needed with γG antibody might indicate that two molecules were required to attach to a single antigenic site for the sequence of C′ reactions to occur. Many of the γG molecules are ineffective for the hemolytic reaction, since in the guinea pig two types of γG antibody have been found, of which only the slower-moving γ_2 globulin molecules were found to fix C′. Moreover, the γG anti-sheep RBC antibodies of the Forssman type are probably mixtures with specificities for different antigenic determinants, or with combining sites of various sizes not all of which might show equal hemolytic potency.

The relative inefficiency of γG as compared with γM molecules in the hemolytic reaction is of great importance in the plaque test in which the plaques represent exclusively γM-forming cells. It also often leads to erroneous interpretations in studies of antibody synthesis, since if both γM and γG antibody were formed at the same rate on a weight basis, the γM antibody would reach detectable levels long before the γG antibody and would appear to have been formed first. The same criticism often applies to other reactions of antibody and C′ in which γM antibody may be more effective than γG antibody.

The sequence outlined above of the steps leading to hemolysis must not be considered as final. The system is obviously sufficiently complex so that other steps may still be discovered. In addition, there are certain difficulties to be considered. Of these the most important is that certain relationships in the sequence are more readily established with human C′, while others are more definitely worked out with guinea pig C′. Although in many steps the two are interchangeable, in others the optimum conditions for reaction of the components hypothesized to be identical may be quite different. The interchangeability of components is best considered as a very productive working hypothesis. The nine-component sequence has thus far been established only for guinea pig complement.

BACTERIOCIDAL AND BACTERIOLYTIC EFFECTS

While the action of C′ with antibody on various Gram-negative bacteria kills the bacteria and causes holes similar to those seen in the erythrocyte membrane, bacteriolysis does not generally occur. Microorganisms of the species *Vibrio* are a notable exception, and bacteriolysis by antibody and C′ was first demonstrated with *Vibrio cholera*. As far as is known, all the steps for hemolysis are required for bacteriolysis. The other Gram-negative organisms killed by antibody and complement are lysed if the enzyme lysozyme is added to the system. If hypertonic sucrose is present when the lysozyme is added, lysis does not occur and spheroplasts are formed. The Ab + C′ appears to produce lesions; but in the presence of a cell wall such as is found in bacteria, lysis does not occur. The action of lysozyme on the cell wall then results in lysis.

Complement does not exhibit bacteriocidal effects on Gram-positive bacteria. Gram-positive microorganisms coated with, or agglutinated by, antibodies that fix very little C′ are readily phagocyted. Thus, type-specific pneumococci treated with horse antipolysaccharide antibody of the same type undergo rapid phagocytosis *in vitro* and *in vivo*. Whether C′ or some of its components are involved has never been clearly established.

Complement and its components are involved in many other reactions, some of which are less clearly worked out. Certain of these will be mentioned in subsequent chapters. Others may be found in the Suggested Readings.

SUGGESTED READINGS

Wolstenholme, G. E. W. Ciba Foundation Symposium. Complement. (1965) J. and A. Churchill, London; *a very recent comprehensive survey of complement action.*

Mayer, M. M. *in* Kabat and Mayer's Experimental immunochemistry. (2d ed.; 1961) Charles C. Thomas, Publisher, Springfield, Ill. [Chapter 4]; *for details of methodology and for early studies on complement.*

Nelson, R. A. The role of complement in immune phenomena. *In* The inflammatory process. (1965) (B. W. Zweifach, R. T. McCluskey, and L. H. Grant [Academic Press, New York].

Rosen, F. S., P. Charache, J. Pensky, and V. Donaldson. Hereditary angioneurotic edema: Two genetic variants. Science **148**: 957 (1965); *genetic defect in an inhibitor of the esterase activity of complement component C′*1a.

Rapp, H. J. and T. Borsos. Complement research. Journal of the American Medical Association **198**: 1347 (1966).

12

Effects of Antigen-Antibody Interaction In Vivo: Protection

The reactions of antigen with antibody and complement are of profound importance to the organism when they occur *in vivo*. The consequences of antibody-antigen interaction *in vivo* may be broadly divided into two major categories: protective and allergic. In the first of these, the antigens are of exogenous origin and the antibodies are either formed by an animal in response to contact with antigen (active immunization) or may be produced by another animal and introduced into the recipient (passive immunization). In the second group the antigen may be exogenous or endogenous (AUTOALLERGY), and the antibody is either introduced from an exogenous source or may be produced as an autoantibody. The allergic reaction may be evanescent and not lead to tissue damage, or injury may result from the attachment of antibody to tissue cells and the subsequent reaction with homologous exogenous antigen—as well as from the converse in which antigen or hapten is taken up by cells, which are then damaged by reaction with antibody. The present chapter will consider only those antigen-antibody interactions leading to protection of the host.

The protective effects of antibody may be of two general types. The first is by direct combination with the toxic material or infectious agent to prevent it from combining with the host tissue cells and exerting its effect. Neutralization of toxins, snake venoms, and viruses are the most notable examples of this type of action. Since these antigens usually contain many antigenic determinants and elicit very heterogeneous populations of antibody molecules, it is not suprising that not all of the antibodies formed to these substances show protective power. Thus, even after more than sixty years of intensive research since the pioneering studies of Paul Ehrlich introduced *in vivo* methods of standardizing diphtheria antitoxins, the heterogeneity of the antibodies formed to diphtheria toxin has not been sufficiently resolved to give a clear idea of the antigenic determinants that give rise to neutralizing antibody and those which react with the antigen and produce only flocculation. At the molecular level one would hypothesize that the neutralizing antibodies react with the region of the toxin molecule which is responsible for the toxic activity or sufficiently close to it to block it sterically, or–in terms of modern findings with enzymes–conceivably by an allosteric effect remote from the site of action, which nevertheless inhibits attachment to cells or possibly toxicity. The heterogeneity of the antibody response has greatly complicated the assay of the antitoxins used therapeutically and has necessitated final assay of potency solely by *in vivo* methods. The α-toxin of the anaerobic microorganism *Clostridium perfringens* which causes gas gangrene has been shown to possess a lecithinase activity by which it may be assayed. This is usually measured by its capacity to cause opalescence of egg lecithovitellin, or of normal serum, by the splitting of lecithin into phosphoryl choline and a diglyceride. This enzymatic activity is inhibited by antibody to the α-toxin, but no analysis of the heterogeneous antibody populations has been made.

With equine diphtheria antitoxin it has been known for many years that the ratio of neutralizing power to flocculating ability varied greatly for the flocculating γG(T) and for the γG types of antitoxin, the γG(T) antitoxin being much more effective in neutralization per flocculating unit or per unit weight. One cannot conclude, however, that this is necessarily an intrinsic property of the γG(T) antibody, since much of the γG antibody might be directed toward antigenic determinants in the toxin which are unrelated to its toxicity while most of the γG(T) antitoxin could be specific for determinants close to the site determining toxicity. In a study of human diphtheria antitoxin, the γM antibodies were less effective in neutralization of toxicity than the γG antibodies, but the same uncertainty exists and it cannot be inferred that γM antibodies would necessarily be less efficient in neutralizing toxin if equal amounts of both with specificity for the same determinant were assayed.

Similar considerations apply to the neutralization of viruses by antibody, and a definite evaluation of the mechanism of such neutralization will depend on the isolation of those antibodies directly involved in the neutralization rather than from studies on the entire spectrum of antibodies. Dissociation of complexes of poliomyelitis virus and rabbit antibody by increasing acidity show the presence of two types of γM antibody as well as of several γG antibodies with different neutralizing capacities. The proportion of each changed during immunization and was accompanied by changes in the electrophoretic mobility of the antibodies.

Both with diphtheria toxin and with viruses (bacteriophage, polio, and type-V adenovirus) some data, largely with rabbit antibodies, indicate that bivalent fragments $F(ab')_2$ obtained by peptic digestion (Chapter 9) show some reduction in neutralizing potency as compared with the intact antibody and that the monovalent Fab or Fab′ fragments are even less active. With α- and ϵ-toxins of *Cl. perfringens*, the $F(ab')_2$ fragments were not of lower neutralizing activity but the Fab fragments showed as much as 50 percent loss in potency. The activity of the Fab fragments could be increased by sheep antibody to rabbit γG globulin which would attach to the Fab fragment and aggregate the toxin-Fab fragments, suggesting that steric factors or state of aggregation might be important. Also, the relative diphtheria antitoxic activity and capacity to inhibit hemagglutination by antitoxin of tanned erythrocytes coated with toxin was different for the two Fab fragments I and II (see Chapter 9). Fab fragments of anti-polio and anti-western equine encephalitis virus could neutralize the cytotoxic action of the viruses in tissue culture, but could not neutralize virus infectivity for the mouse.

In many ways the reactions of antibodies to enzymes may offer a model for neutralization which may prove applicable to toxins and viruses. Thus, in studies of antibodies to hen and duck lysozymes, two polypeptides were obtained by peptic digestion which would inhibit the lysozyme anti-lysozyme precipitin reaction but which did not affect neutralization. Evidence for both neutralizing and nonneutralizing antibodies were obtained. With ribonuclease, antibodies that inhibited the action of the enzyme and those which had no neutralizing effect were found; the latter could block the action of the neutralizing antibody. These studies are most simply interpreted on the hypothesis that the neutralizing potency is associated with antibodies that neutralize the active site or that sterically prevent access of the substrate to the active site. The blocking effect of the nonneutralizing antibodies might be exerted by their attaching at a site somewhat further from the active region, sufficiently close to prevent the neutralizing antibody from reacting, but not close enough to interfere with combination with substrate. These inferences are further strengthened by studies on the Fab fragments which showed greater potency in inhibiting the action of ribonuclease on a substrate of high molecular weight such as nucleic acid, than on one of low molecular weight such as cyclic 2′,3′-cytidylic acid, the latter being able to reach the catalytic site despite the presence of Fab fragment. By equilibrium dialysis measurements with ribonuclease and with ribonuclease partially neutralized by Fab fragment using a competitive inhibitor of ribonuclease (2′-cytidylic acid), the number of molecules bound corresponded to the number of sites which had not been neutralized by Fab fragments. Antibody to Fab fragment increased its neutralizing potency; and the Fab_I and Fab_{II} fragments from the same pool of antibody were different, findings corresponding closely to those for diphtheria antitoxin mentioned above.

Another interesting system involves the enzyme penicillinase from *B. cereus*. Antisera prepared to the soluble enzyme neutralize the enzyme activity, and antisera produced to washed *B. cereus* do not. The antisera to the washed organisms inhibited neutralization by the neutralizing antibody, probably by a mechanism similar to that proposed above. Some antibodies to penicillinase actually enhanced the enzymatic activity.

Little is known of the sequences of amino acids in various toxins or of the groupings that are responsible for their toxic effects. Antisera to the venoms of poisonous snakes are among the most effective in neutralizing the toxic effects of the specific venoms, and large quantities are widely used therapeutically in regions of the world where such snakes are common–Brazil, India, and Thailand, for instance. Purification and study of the venoms and of their specific neutralizing and non-neutralizing antibodies may substantially contribute to our understanding of neutralization mechanisms.

The second type of protective action of antibody results from the enhancement of phagocytosis (OPSONIC ACTION) and subsequent interactions with components of complement to produce bacteriocidal and bacteriolytic effects, immune adherence, and so forth as outlined in the previous chapter. All these reactions may aid in the destruction and elimination of invading microorganisms and influence the outcome of infection.

The antibodies formed to most of the antigens of microorganisms, such as the pneumococcus, have no capacity to protect against infection. By assaying antisera for their initial protective capacity and after removing portions of the total antibody with individual purified antigens obtained from pneumococci, with suspensions of pneumococci of other types, or with rough variants derived from the same strain of pneumococcus but which lack the type-specific capsular polysaccharide, protective capacity can readily be shown to be a property of antibody to the type-specific capsular polysaccharide. Other antigens of the pneumococcus, such as the proteins or the group specific C carbohydrate, do not induce the formation of antibody that protects against infection. The primary effect of the type-specific anti-polysaccharide is to facilitate phagocytosis of the microorganisms, since Gram-positive organisms are neither killed nor lysed by antibody even if complement is present. The capsular polysaccharide endows the microorganisms with virulence in that they multiply freely and are not readily disposed of by phagocytosis, while rough forms lacking capsular polysaccharide are readily phagocyted. Capsular polysaccharides are responsible for the virulence of other kinds of microorganisms such as *Hemophilus influenzae* and meningococci of certain types, both of which cause meningitis.

In other microorganisms, virulence may be associated with other kinds of antigens. In the hemolytic streptococcus, a protein called the M protein is responsible for virulence; it is also type specific, and hemolytic streptococci have been classified into some forty or more types with specific anti-M sera. The M protein also confers virulence in that the organisms containing it may survive inside phagocytes, be ejected, and continue to multiply. Antibody to a given type of M protein protects by stimulating phagocytosis and permitting destruction inside the phagocyte. The effectiveness of M protein as an immunizing agent in man is being evaluated.

The protective antigens of Gram-negative organisms–such as Shigella and Salmonella–are the specific lipopolysaccharide O antigens, their type specificity depending upon the specific oligosaccharide determinants discussed in Chapter 7. Protective effects that involve complement result not only from enhanced phagocytosis and intracellular destruction of the microorganisms but also from bacteriocidal action. For many other species of pathogenic microorganisms the relation between virulence and antigenic structure may be much more complicated.

With respect to their capacity to confer protection against infection, antibodies to a given protective antigen show their usual heterogeneity. γM antibodies to several kinds of Salmonella were more effective than γG antibodies in their opsonizing action. It was estimated for antibody to the O lipopolysaccharide of S. *adelaide*, that only 8 molecules of γM antibody as compared with 2200 molecules of γG antibody were needed per microoorganism for phagocytosis.

With S. *typhimurium*, γM antibody was 22 times more effective than γG antibody in agglutination as compared with 120 and 500 to 1000 times more active in bacteriocidal and opsonic assays respectively. With S. *typhimurium*, between 132 and 367 molecules of γG antibody per bacterium were needed for 50 percent immobilization;

the Fab′ fragment was much less effective, about 130,000 molecules per bacterium being needed. The amount of γG antibody for 50 percent immobilization per bacterium was much less than the 19,500 molecules of γG antibody per erythrocyte required for hemagglutination at the 50 percent end point.

With respect to antipneumococcal horse antibodies that were undoubtedly mixtures of γG, γM, and γA immunoglobulins, fractions were isolated many years ago which showed marked differences in their protective power per milligram of antibody N as assayed in mice. With rabbit antipneumococcal antibodies that were almost exclusively γG globulins, partial absorption of antibody with specific polysaccharide also clearly demonstrated that these were not uniform but varied in protective power per unit weight.

Several years ago a type of antibody (termed CYTOPHILIC ANTIBODY) was described which was taken up by macrophages; antigen would then adhere specifically to the macrophages; the reaction does not depend on C′. The term "cytophilic antibody" is used in a very restricted sense, since many antibodies can attach to other kinds of cells (see Chapter 13). These cytophilic antibodies have been shown to be γ_2 immunoglobulins in the guinea pig. They were not absorbed by guinea pig lymphocytes or polymorphonuclear leucocytes. Treatment with reagents blocking SH groups or SH and NH_2 groups or with oxidizing agents destroyed the cytophilic property. Cytophilic antibody by binding antigen to the macrophage would facilitate phagocytosis of its antigen.

The evaluation of the role of antibodies in protection against infection and in neutralization of toxic proteins is of great importance for medical microbiology and immunology, and details and references to many fascinating aspects of this subject may be found in the Suggested Readings.

SUGGESTED READINGS

Humphrey, J. H. and R. G. White, Immunology for students of medicine. (1963). F. A. Davis Company, Philadelphia, Pa.; *for additional information on the mechanism of protection against infection.*

Rowley, D. and K. J. Turner. Number of molecules of antibody required to promote phagocytosis of one bacterium. Nature **210**: 496 (1966).

Cinader, B. and K. J. Lafferty. Mechanism of enzyme inhibition by antibody. A study of the neutralization of ribonuclease. Immunology **7**: 342 (1964); *a comprehensive study of the effects of various antibodies and antibody fragments on ribonuclease.*

Cinader, B. (ed.) Antibodies to enzymes. A three component system. New York Academy of Science, Annals, **103**: 493-1154 (1963); *a symposium. Numerous papers on antibodies to enzymes.*

van Heyningen, W. E. Bacterial Toxins. (1950) Blackwell, Oxford.

Raynaud, M. Heterogeneity of diphtheria antibodies. *In* Antibodies to biologically active molecules. (1966) Pergamon Press, Oxford, **1**: 197; *the current status of diphtheria toxin and its antigenic determinants and the various populations of antibodies formed to them, including precipitating non-neutralizing antibodies.*

Sorkin, E. On the cellular fixation of cytophilic antibody. International Archives of Allergy and Applied Immunology **25**: 129 (1964).

Howard, J. G. and B. Benacerraf. Properties of macrophage receptors for cytophilic antibodies. British Journal of Experimental Pathology **47**: 193 (1966).

Two papers on cytophilic antibody and its properties.

Webb, T. and H. C. Goodman. Structure and function of immunoglobulins. *In* Modern Trends in Immunology, (2d ed. 1967) R. Cruickshank and D. M. Weir, [eds.] Butterworth & Co. (Publishers) Ltd., London.

13

Effects of Antigen-Antibody Interaction In Vivo: Allergy and Tissue Damage

Immunological phenomena, while of major importance in protection and recovery from infectious disease, also can be responsible for many reactions deleterious to man and animals. One well-known group of such effects are the allergic reactions, familiar to the layman from common diseases like hay fever, asthma, and poison ivy sensitivity. The term ALLERGY or HYPERSENSITIVITY denotes an altered immunological reactivity, generally to an innocuous substance, by which the substance may become harmful to the recipient. Such altered reactivity may occur after contact with an antigen (INDUCED HYPERSENSITIVITY or allergy), or it may appear in the absence of any known contact (SPONTANEOUS ALLERGY).

Allergic reactions may further be classified into two large groups. One of these is associated with antibodies that may often be present in the serum of individuals or animals with induced or spontaneous allergies and is termed allergy of the IMMEDIATE TYPE. These allergies are more clearly understood, largely because they have been susceptible to quantitative study since they may be produced with serum containing antibodies. The second group, termed allergy of the DELAYED TYPE, has not been shown to be associated with antibodies that can be found in the serum but is intimately associated with cells showing altered reactivity (SENSITIZED CELLS). The terms "immediate" and "delayed" were originally based on the time necessary for the two kinds of reaction to become apparent, but the determining criterion is now whether they can be passively induced in a recipient with serum from a sensitized animal or human. The various types of manifestations of immediate and delayed allergy are listed in Table 13.1. As will become evident, heterogeneity of antibodies is associated with differences in the capacities of various antibodies to elicit immediate-type allergic reactions in homologous and heterologous species.

ANAPHYLAXIS

Active Anaphylaxis

If a guinea pig receives an initial injection of an antigen such as crystalline egg albumin, no adverse effects are noted. However, a second injection given intravenously after an interval of ten days or more causes a characteristic sequence of signs and symptoms called anaphylactic shock, including restlessness, chewing, rubbing of the nose, dyspnea (labored respiration), convulsive movements, and convulsions – often terminating fatally within a few minutes. The reaction was first observed in dogs early in this century by Portier and Richet. The initial harmless injection is called the SENSITIZING INJECTION, and the second injection the SHOCKING DOSE. The time interval that must elapse is the period during which the animal formed antibody to the initial injection of antigen. Thus, anaphylaxis is a consequence of the combination *in vivo* of antigen with antibody. This triggers the release of pharmacologically active substances that cause the contraction of smooth muscle throughout the body. In a guinea pig this contraction constricts the bronchioles and bronchi so that

TABLE 13.1
Classification of Allergic Reactions

Immediate	Delayed
Anaphylaxis	Tuberculin sensitivity
Arthus Reaction	Contact sensitivity
Serum Sickness	to simple chemicals
Wheal and Erythema type Allergies	Allergies of infection
Pollen allergies	Some drug allergies
Hay fever	
Angioedema	
Some drug allergies	
Some gastrointestinal allergies	

the animal continues to inspire, but cannot expel the air. This results in such a tremendous dilatation of the lung alveoli (emphysema) that the lungs fill the entire pleural cavity with asphyxia, and death results (Fig. 13.1). Many of the symptoms of anaphylactic shock may be produced by an injection of histamine;

$$\text{H—N} \underset{\text{imidazole ring}}{\bigcirc} \text{N} \quad -CH_2CH_2NH_2$$

and histamine has been shown to be liberated *in vitro* by pieces of lung, intestine, uterine muscle, or other tissues from a sensitized guinea pig on contact with antigen.

Sensitized strips of intestine or of uterine muscle, placed in a bath containing a balanced electrolyte solution and oxygenated, contract upon the addition of antigen to the bath (SCHULTZE-DALE reaction). Histamine also causes a marked increase in capillary permeability, especially in man and the guinea pig, and an intracutaneous injection in man produces a local reaction resembling a mosquito bite that is called a WHEAL and ERYTHEMA reaction and is characterized by

Fig. 13.1 Systemic Anaphylaxis: Heart, lungs, and trachea of a normal guinea pig (left) and of a guinea pig that died in anaphylactic shock (right). (From Doerr, R. in Kolle, Kraus and Uhlenhuth Handbuch. G. Fischer, Jena)

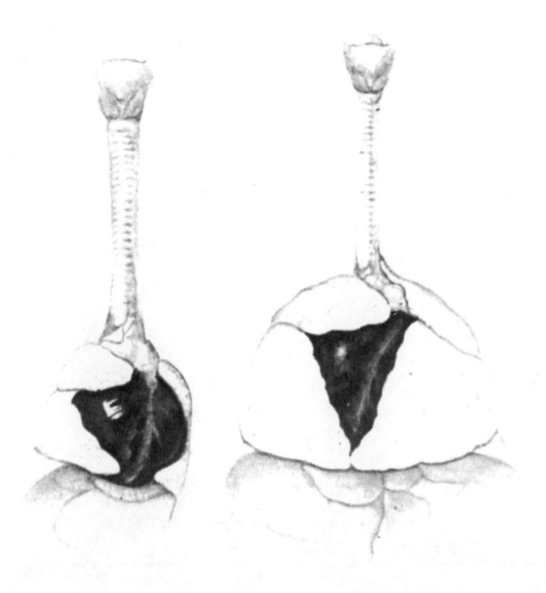

a small area of swelling–due to increased fluid–with a surrounding area of redness (Fig. 13.2). Such a local reaction (CUTANEOUS ANAPHYLAXIS) occurs in a sensitized guinea pig or in humans sensitive to pollens, trees, grasses, and so forth if the antigen is injected intracutaneously. In the guinea pig this local reaction is best revealed by giving the animal an intravenous injection of a dye such as Evans blue shortly before the intracutaneous injection of antigen; the increased permeability resulting from the local antigen-antibody reaction, or from histamine, causes the passage of fluid containing the dye into the site, giving a well-circumscribed blue spot. Anaphylactic reactions show the same specificity relationships as the other immunological reactions, and cross reactions may be demonstrated by anaphylactic as well as by precipitin tests.

Anaphylactic reactions vary in different animal species, and some may be quite resistant to histamine. Three other pharmacologically active substances have been implicated to varying degrees in anaphylactic reactions in different species. They are serotonin, 5-hydroxytryptamine

HO $CH_2CH_2NH_2$
N
|
H

Fig. 13.2 Wheal and erythema reaction to dextran in human skin.

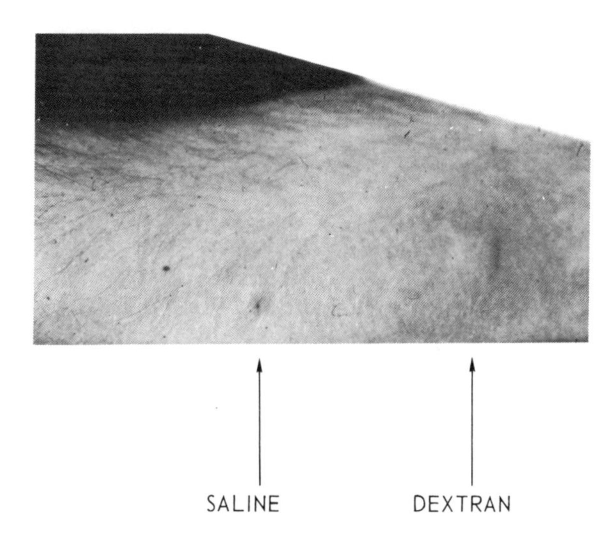

SRS-A or slow-reacting substance, a lipid or lipoprotein of unknown structure; and bradykinin, the nonapeptide

L-Arg-L-Pro-L-Pro-Gly-L-Phe-L-Ser-L-Pro-L-Phe-L-Arg

which has been synthesized. These substances all cause smooth muscle contraction and increased capillary permeability, the last two acting somewhat more slowly. SRS-A is important in producing some of the protracted effects of anaphylaxis and of asthma in man, while the exact role of bradykinin in anaphylaxis is not clear. Another pharmacologically active substance is called ANAPHYLATOXIN; it has the capacity to release histamine from mast cells. Anaphylatoxin is formed when fresh rat or guinea pig serum is incubated *in vitro* with antigen-antibody aggregates or with kaolin, agar, starch, inulin, and so forth. As noted in Chapter 11 complement components through C′5 are required. Anaphylatoxin probably does not play a direct role as a mediator in anaphylaxis.

Passive Anaphylaxis

The injection of suitable amounts of antiserum from a sensitized or from a hyperimmunized animal into a normal one, followed by an intravenous injection of antigen after a suitable time interval, during which the antibody is thought to be fixed to tissue cells (LATENT PERIOD), causes typical anaphylactic shock. This offers the tremendous advantages that it makes possible the use of known quantities of various kinds of antibody for sensitization and permits delineation of the role of antibody heterogeneity and the comparison of antibodies from heterologous as well as from the homologous species in producing anaphylactic sensitization. Such studies have now been carried out in several species. Systemic anaphylaxis may be used, but in recent years passive cutaneous anaphylaxis (PCA)* has largely supplanted it because it permits comparisons of different antibodies, or of varying quantities of antibody, in a single animal. PCA is performed by giving a series of intracutaneous injections of suitable amounts of antibody, followed after a latent period—which for different antibodies and different species may be from 0.5 to 48 hours—by an intravenous injection of antigen mixed with Evans blue. Within a few minutes blue spots appear at the sites of antigen-antibody interaction and reach a maximum after 15 to 30 min. They are most readily seen by sacrificing the animals and examining the under-surface of the skin (Fig. 13.3). The results obtained by passive systemic and passive cutaneous anaphylaxis have been in excellent agreement in almost all instances in which comparisons have been made. Another technique is the

*The same symbol is also used for pyrollidone carboxylic acid as the amino terminal residue on immunoglobulin chains, but is not likely to cause confusion.

Fig. 13.3 Passive cutaneous anaphylaxis in the guinea pig. Sensitization with 0.1 ml dilution anti-egg albumin intracutaneously (left) 0.6 μg AbN, (center) 0.06 μg AbN, (right) 0.006 μg AbN. 0.5 mg of egg albumin in 1 ml 0.5 per-cent Evans blue injected intravenously after a latent period of 3 hr. (Courtesy Dr. Zoltan Ovary).

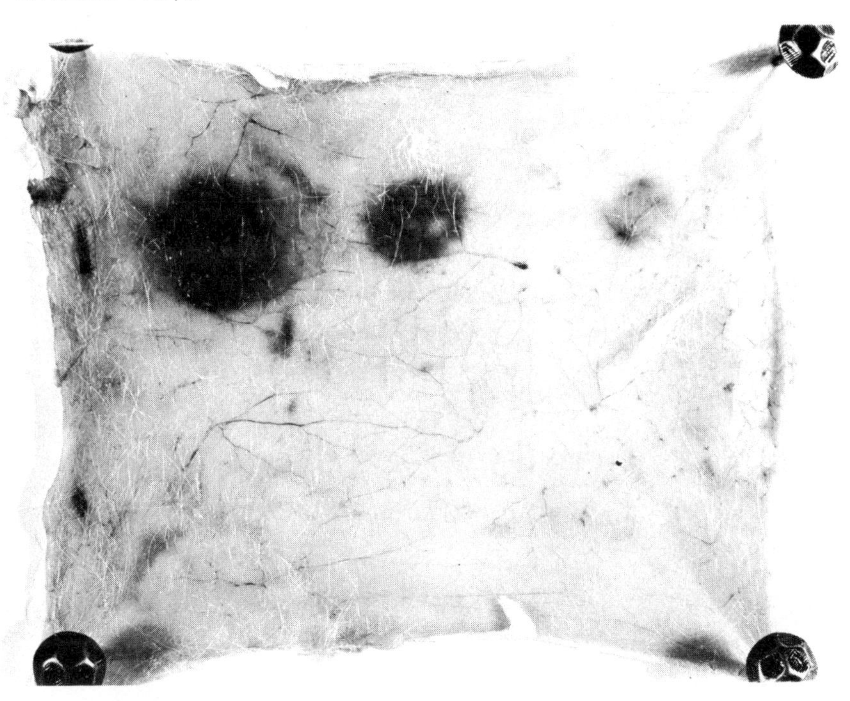

passive sensitization of intestinal or uterine muscle strips *in vitro* by incubating them with antibody and subsequently testing them by the addition of antigen in a Schultze-Dale bath (Fig. 13.4) or by the re-lease of histamine into the surrounding fluid. Another technique in-volves assay of the disruption or degranulation of mast cells from sensitized animals on exposure to antigen. Mast cells are large baso-philic staining cells found in connective tissue which contain large numbers of metachromatic granules; mesentery is very rich in mast cells; upon disruption or degranulation, heparin and histamine are released. Histamine is also released from blood platelets. The basophil cells in blood on exposure *in vitro* to antibody and antigen also show degranulation.

Patients with pollen allergies of the wheal and erythema type have circulating antibody that may be demonstrated by the so-called Prausnitz-Küstner (PK) technique. Serum from a sensitive person is intracutaneously injected into a normal subject, and after a latent period a small amount of antigen injected into the same site causes a wheal and erythema (see Fig. 13.2). This type of antibody, which is

Fig. 13.4 Contractions induced by dextran and rabbit antihuman-globulin in an intestinal strip sensitized *in vitro* with purified human antidextran. Second additions of dextran and antihuman-globulin produced no effect. Sizes of contractions may be compared with those resulting from indicated amounts of histimine added to the bath fluid. (From Kabat, E. A., P. Liacopoulos, M. Liacopoulos-Briot, B. N. Halpern, and E. H. Relyveld. *J. Immunol.* **90**: 810 [1963]; by permission of the copyright owner, The Williams & Wilkins Company, Baltimore, Md.)

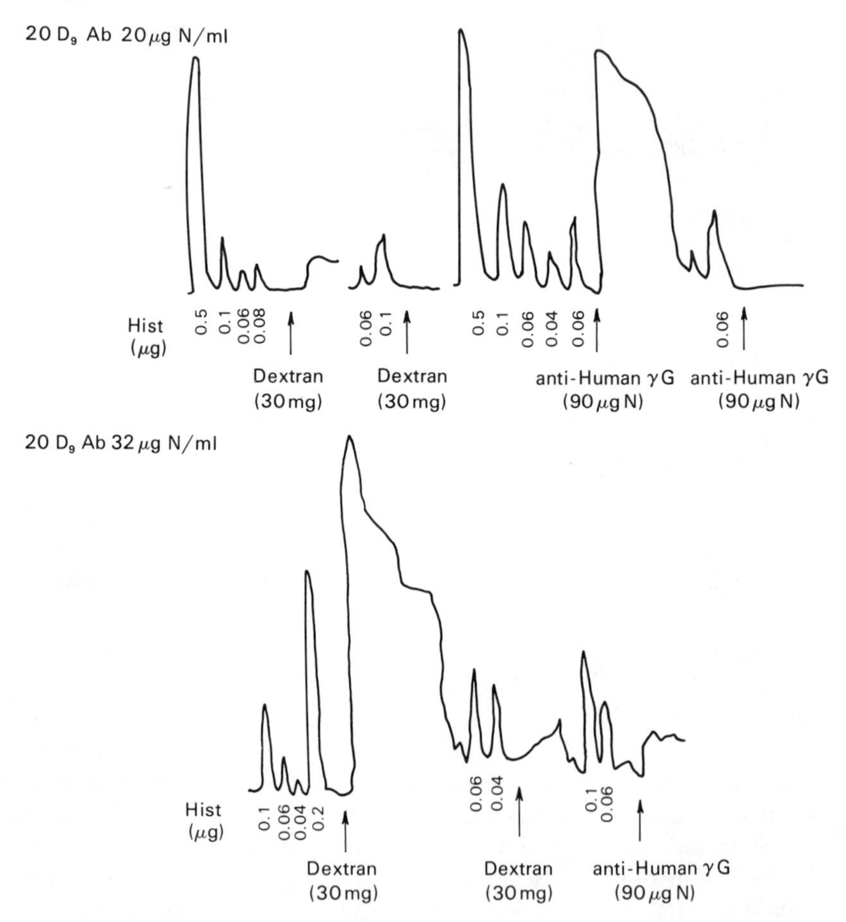

present in quantities too small to measure by other methods, is often called REAGINIC ANTIBODY. The PK reaction in man is essentially the analogue of homologous PCA in animals. Washed leucocyte suspensions from sensitive individuals release histamine on contact with antigen, and normal leucocytes may be sensitized with serum containing reaginic antibody and will liberate histamine on contact with antigen.

Antibody Heterogeneity And Anaphylactic Sensitization

It has only recently become possible to make some systematic classification of antibodies with respect to their ability to sensitize homologous and heterologous species. For many years it had been recognized that human reaginic antibodies would not sensitize the guinea pig, but could be studied in human skin and, more recently, in the skin of other primates. Real insight into the basis of this difference was gained when two groups of what are termed ANAPHYLACTIC ANTIBODIES were recognized in several animal species that were generally capable only of giving passive sensitization of their own species and not of heterologous species.

One kind formed by the guinea pig and mouse in large amounts is the γ_1 type of γG immunoglobulin (see Chapter 9). The second, the reaginic type, is present in the rat, dog, rabbit, and in man. They have been produced only in trace quantities in their respective species and often are present only for a short period after immunization. Properties of these anaphylactic antibodies are given in Table 13.2.

The γ_1 antibody resists 56°C, has a relatively short latent period and persists at the site of injection only briefly (up to two days), does not fix C′, and is formed in large amounts on immunization. The reaginic antibody moves in the fast γ or slow β region in electrophoresis, occurs in such small amounts that it can be assayed only in homologous skin, is inactivated at 56°C, persists at the site of injection for several weeks or more, and is inactivated by reduction with sulfhydryl reagents; it appears to sediment between the 7 S and 19 S immunoglobulins.

Human reaginic antibody may sensitize the skin of primates including chimpanzees and various species of monkey (Fig. 13.5). Monkey ileum and lung may also be sensitized, which indicates that homologous species is not an absolute requirement. This will substantially facilitate studies on human reaginic antibodies. Similarly, guinea pig γ_1 antibody gave PCA in the rat.

Human reaginic antibody has been extensively studied in efforts to characterize it more adequately chemically. This has proved extremely difficult because of the minute quantities present in serum. Although various investigators have reported it to be a γA or γG immunoglobulin, it has now been shown by Ishizaka to belong to a new class called γE and a γE myeloma globulin has been found. An individual who had no γA immunoglobulin was shown to produce reaginic antibody.

Antibodies belonging to the γA or γM immunoglobulins, although studied only to a limited extent, have not been found to give passive anaphylactic sensitization of homologous or heterologous species.

TABLE 13.2

Properties of Mammalian Anaphylactic Antibodies

Species	Immunoglobulin	Electrophoretic Mobility	Sedimentation Constant	Sensitivity to 56°C	Inactivation by Sulfhydryl Reagent	Latent Period of PCA Sensitization	Persistence in passively Sensitized Homologous Animals	Antibody Level[a] Obtainable in Serum
Guinea pig	γ_1	Fast γ	7 S	Resistant	Slightly	3 to 5 hr	2 days	mg per ml
Mouse	γ_1	Fast γ	7 S	Resistant	Partially	0.5 to 1 hr	Several hrs	mg per ml
Rat	"Reaginic type"	Fast γ Slow β	>7 S <19 S	Inactivated	Inactivated	24 to 48 hr	30 days	Trace[b]
Dog	"Reaginic type"	Slow β	Not done	Inactivated	Inactivated	24 hr	14 days	Trace
Rabbit	"Reaginic type"	Fast γ	>7 S <19 S	Inactivated	Inactivated	24 hr	17 days	Trace
Man	"Reaginic type"	Fast γ Slow β	>7 S <19 S	Inactivated	Inactivated	24 to 48 hr	28 days	Trace

Data: B. Benacerraf. Proc. Symposium Immunopharmacology; Third Pharmacology Conference Sao Paulo, Brazil (1966)

K. J. Bloch. The anaphylactic antibodies of mammals including man. Progress in Allergy. **10**: 84 (1967). [S. Karger, Basel.]

[a] After specific immunization.

[b] Trace-too little to measure except by PCA. Maximum PCA titers to protein antigens 1/80-1/100.

Fig. 13.5 Passive cutaneous anaphylaxis with human reaginic antibody in *Macacus iris* monkey. Skin sites sensitized with serum of patient violently allergic to pencillin. After a latent period, Evans Blue was given intravenously, and the reaction was obtained 5 min after oral administration of penicillin. (From Layton, L. L., E. Yamanaki, F. C. Greene, and F. Perlman. Int. Arch. Allergy, **23**: 87 [Karger, Basel/New York 1963].

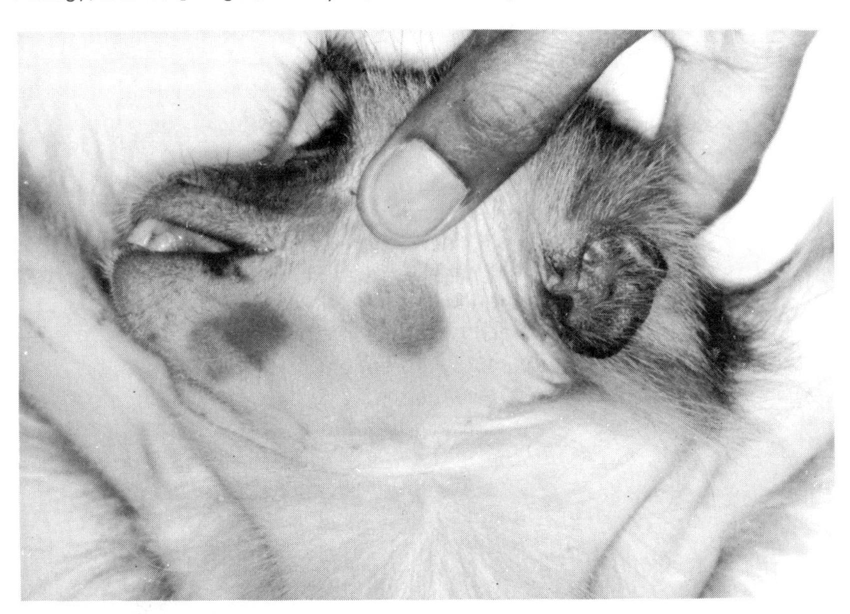

The best-studied class of antibodies to well-defined antigens, the γG immunoglobulins from several species—especially rabbit, man, dog, and monkey—and γ_2 antibodies in the guinea pig and mouse, are generally characterized by their ability to sensitize heterologous species. Thus γ_2 mouse antibody will sensitize the guinea pig but not the mouse; of the two subclasses only mouse γ_2a antibody was effective.

The sensitizing capacity of these antibodies is associated with their ability to attach to guinea pig or other heterologous skin, a property possessed not only by antibody γG immunoglobulins of a given species but also by non-antibody γG and γ_2 immunoglobulins of the same species. This may readily be demonstrated by a technique called REVERSE PCA (RPCA); skin sites are sensitized with normal γG immunoglobulin as antigen, and after a latent period PCA may be elicited by intravenous injection of Evans blue plus rabbit antibody to the γG immunoglobulin. It is called reverse PCA because the antigen rather than the antibody is injected first—the reverse of the usual procedure.

Antisera of known antibody content have been used to determine the minimum quantities of antibody N needed for passive systemic anaphylaxis or for PCA; such assays are generally carried out with dilutions or whole antiserum made in saline. With rabbit antibody, which is generally almost exclusively γG immunoglobulin, about 30 μg of AbN was needed to sensitize a 250 gram guinea pig so that uniformly fatal anaphylaxis would result on intravenous injection of a suitable quantity of antigen 48 hr later; 0.003 μg of AbN was the least amount giving detectable PCA. A strip of intestinal muscle could be sensitized by placing it for 1 hr in a solution containing about 0.01 μg of AbN per ml of rabbit antibody. These values were about the same with antisera to several antigens. With rabbit antisera the latent period for passive systemic and passive cutaneous anaphylaxis could be shown to be dependent on the sensitizing dose of antibody, larger quantities shortening the interval required between sensitization and shock.

The reproducibility of the findings with rabbit antisera does not indicate an intrinsic homogeneity of these antibodies, but merely that the antisera tend to be rather uniform within the limits of the quantitative anaphylactic assays. With antisera of other species considerable variation in the amount of antibody needed for sensitization was found from one serum to another with various antigens. Human antisera to diphtheria toxin varied as much as 100-fold in the amount of antibody needed to sensitize uterine muscle *in vitro*. Even with purified human antidextran very large quantities were required to sensitize. These variations were explained by the finding that human γG2 immunoglobulin was incapable of attaching to guinea pig skin, while γG1 and γG3 were (as demonstrated by reverse PCA with myeloma globulins). The purified human antidextrans were found to be predominantly of γG2 heavy chain subgroup and thus would not bind to skin and give PCA. The variation in the sensitizing power of guinea pig antibodies for the guinea pig is attributable to the varying proportions of the sensitizing γ_1 anaphylactic antibodies and the nonsensitizing γ_2 antibodies present in sera from individual animals.

The ability to sensitize guinea pig skin is not possessed by all species of γG antibody. Horse, chicken, goat, and sheep antibodies do not give PCA. It is hypothesized that the immunoglobulins of those species that sensitize possess some specific site for attachment to guinea pig skin, while the others do not. Some light is shed on the location of this receptor by the finding that pepsin-digested antibodies in which the Fc fragment is destroyed (see Chapter 9) no longer can sensitize the guinea pig for PCA. Moreover the subgroups of γG immunoglobulin differ in the Fc fragment of their heavy chains, and presumably the γG2 heavy chain lacks this receptor. Since the γ_1 and γ_2 varieties of guinea pig antibodies differ in their Fc fragments, this region is probably involved in the attachment to homologous as well as heterologous skin. Rabbit Fc from papain digests can attach to guinea pig skin and sensitize for reverse PCA as could human Fc from γG1 and γG3 but Fc from γG2 could not. Separated light and heavy chains from rabbit antibody did not give RPCA. With purified anti-DNP antibodies the threshold quantities for PCA in the guinea pig of the anaphylactic γ_1 guinea pig antibody could be compared with heterologous γG rabbit and monkey antibody. Values were:

guinea pig γ_1	0.011-0.015 μg AbN
rabbit γG	0.013-0.015 μg AbN
monkey γG	0.045-0.052 μg AbN

for the minimum quantities needed for a PCA reaction (Fig. 13.3) in guinea pig skin.

A variety of reactions have been described in which PCA may be inhibited. These are often useful in identifying antibodies that do not give PCA and immunoglobulins that attach to skin. These are of two general types:

1. An antibody that does not sensitize is mixed with a known amount of a sensitizing antibody and injected into a skin site; when antigen is injected it is bound preferentially by the nonsensitizing antibody so that it does not react with the sensitizing antibody.
2. Non-antibody immunoglobulin that can bind to skin, if added in sufficient quantity to a known amount of skin-sensitizing antibody, will saturate the available receptors at the skin site and prevent attachment of the antibody.

The first type of reaction is widely used as an assay in human pollen allergy. A fairly effective widely used treatment consists of a series of small increasing injections of extracts of the offending allergen. This is accompanied by the appearance of antibody that does not give a PK reaction in human skin, but which when added in suitable proportions to reaginic antibody to the same allergen can inhibit the PK reaction at that site; this blocking antibody appears to be a γG immunoglobulin. Its relation to clinical improvement is not clear. γ_1 anaphylactic guinea pig antibody has also been inhibited by addition of large quantities of γ_2 antibody, about 100 times as much being required. Similarly, papain Fab fragments can compete for antigen with intact antibody and inhibit skin sensitization.

The second type of inhibition is useful in showing that Fc fragment or normal γG immunoglobulin will bind to cells and prevent attachment of intact antibody.

The mechanism by which antigen-antibody interaction causes the release of pharmacologically active substances is not clear. Recent studies with hybrid molecules prepared by recombining half-molecules of antibody (Chapter 9) and half-molecules of normal γG immunoglobulin showed that these monovalent antibody hybrids were as effective in giving PCA as bivalent antibody. PCA, however, can be elicited only by bivalent or multivalent antigens or haptens, and not by monovalent haptens; and it is inferred that the interaction of a single combining site on each of two antibody molecules bound to cells with one antigen molecule is essential.

ARTHUS REACTION

The Arthus reaction, named after its discoverer Maurice Arthus, is an allergic reaction involving severe tissue damage caused by the formation and deposition of antigen-antibody aggregates or complexes in tissues. As with anaphylaxis, it was observed that after repeated injections of an antigen into the skin, inflammation, hemorrhage, and necrosis developed at the sites of later injections although the earlier injections had been completely innocuous. A typical severe Arthus reaction is seen in Fig. 13.6. Although these reactions are most generally studied in skin, they may be produced in any organ. They may be passively elicited with antibody and are characteristically associated with precipitating antibodies—and this is independent of the capacity of such antibodies to induce anaphylaxis. The amounts of antibody N required are many times greater than are needed for PCA; no latent period is needed, and unlike anaphylaxis the Arthus reaction is not inhibited by antihistamines. Soluble complexes of precipitating antibody with excess antigen injected directly into the skin cause Arthus reactions, possibly because the excess antigen diffuses away and an antigen-antibody complex deposits at the site. About 10 μg of precipitating rabbit or guinea pig antibody N gave a minimal Arthus reaction in guinea pig or rat skin and about 25 μg of AbN was needed in rabbit skin. The migration of polymorphonuclear leucocytes to the site of the reaction is important in the development of an Arthus reaction and in its resolution by catabolizing the antigen-antibody precipitate; nitrogen mustard, which causes depletion of circulating polymorphonuclear leucocytes, prevents the appearance of a lesion even though the antigen-antibody complexes are present in the blood vessel walls. The tissue damage is a consequence of the liberation from the polymorphonuclear leucocytes of a cationic protein and of the proteolytic enzymes, cathepsins D and E, which attack the walls of blood vessels and thereby lead to hemorrhage and edema; some increase in

Fig. 13.6 Passive Arthus reactions in the guinea pig: (Right) Direct Arthus 0.90 mg anti-egg albumin N intravenously followed by 0.10 mg egg albumin N intracutaneously 1 min later. (Left) Reverse Arthus 0.50 mg egg albumin N intravenously followed 1 min later by 0.20 mg anti-egg albumin N intracutaneously. Reactions were those seen in 4 hr.

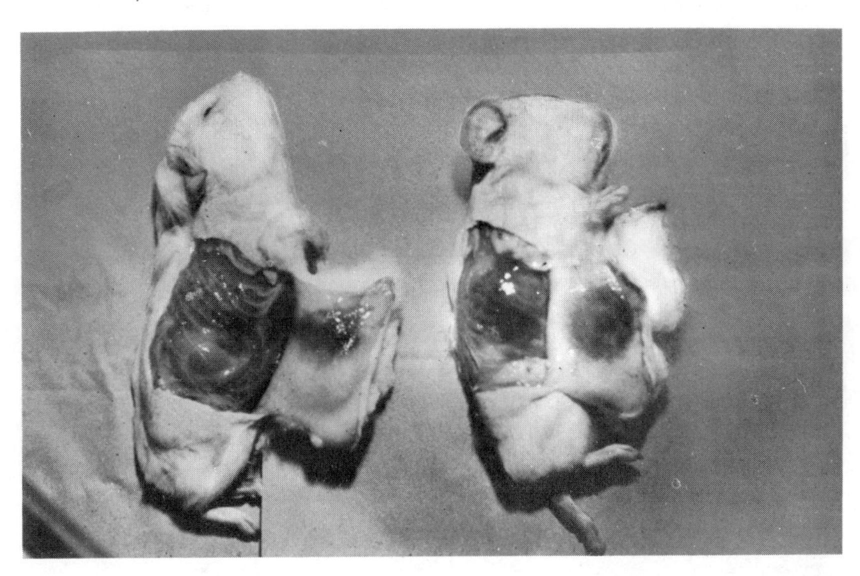

vascular permeability is also seen. The cationic protein and the two cathepsins occur in the lysosomes of the polymorphonuclear leucocytes.

Complement-depleted rats and guinea pigs failed to develop Arthus reactions, although antigen and antibody reacted in vessel walls. This was attributed to the role of C′5,6,7, which would be bound to the Ag-Ab complexes and attract leucocytes to the area.

SERUM SICKNESS

Serum sickness is essentially a man-made disease, since it originated with the therapeutic use of horse antitoxins and other horse antibodies. Seven to twelve days after injection of a large volume of serum or of a purified foreign protein, recipients may show swelling of the lymph nodes, urticarial wheals, and erythematous (reddish) areas with itching and often edema (swelling) of the eyelids, face, and ankles followed by joint pains and fever. These symptoms appear at a time when an antibody response or active sensitization to antigen takes place. The symptoms are a consequence of the interaction of antibody as it is being formed with the excess free antigen in the tissue fluids and blood. With a single antigen the symptoms generally disappear at a time when free antibody appears in the blood; with mixtures of antigens this relationship may be less clear cut. Certain of the manifestations, such as joint pains, resemble the Arthus type of reaction and probably result from the deposition of antigen-antibody aggregates in the joints, blood vessels, and so forth, while others—such as the wheal and erythema and edema—are anaphylactic in character. Indeed, recovery from serum sickness is generally followed by a heightened degree of sensitivity, and fatal systemic anaphylactic shock may occur in individuals who have previously had serum sickness if the same

Fig. 13.7 Relation of time of occurrence of tissue lesions to blood clearance of antigen and development of antibody. The curve showing the median blood clearance of antigen and the appearance of circulating antibody is represented by the thick solid line and refers to the ordinate on the left. Values after the thirteenth day represent antibody. The thin solid line projected from the antigen clearance curve at the sixth day shows the course the antigen would follow in the absence of an increased elimination of antigen by antibody. The incidence of splenic lesions at various times is represented by the broken line, and the incidence of arteritis and glomerulonephritis by the thin solid lines. These values refer to the ordinate at the right of the figure. (From Germuth, F. G., Jr., J. Exp. Med. **97**: 257 [1953]; by permission of The Rockefeller University Press.)

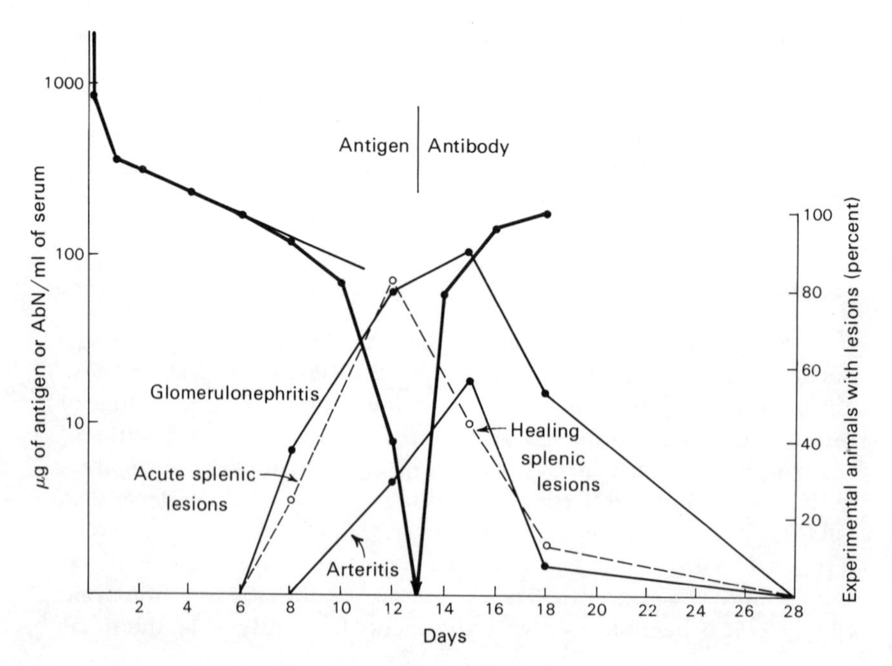

antigen is readministered. For this reason and since some individuals show spontaneous sensitivity to horse proteins, a skin test with a small quantity of the serum to be used for therapeutic purposes is absolutely mandatory. Sensitive individuals develop a wheal and erythema reaction within 15 to 30 min, which indicates that a larger dose intravenously would prove dangerous. Even a skin test may involve some hazard, and these are generally performed on the forearm so that a tourniquet may be used to prevent systemic manifestations if necessary and adrenaline must be available for immediate use.

Serum sickness may also be experimentally produced in animals. Histological examination of the tissues of such animals at various stages during the course of the disease shows the presence of inflammatory changes in the glomeruli of the kidneys (glomerulonephritis) and in the arteries (arteritis) and also of granulomatous changes in the spleen. A graph of the time course of serum sickness and the relationship of the lesions to the removal of antigen from the blood and the appearance of circulating antibody is given in Fig. 13.7.

The relationship between the various antibodies formed in man and the individual manifestations of the disease are not absolutely determined. The Arthus-type lesions are most probably associated with the precipitating antibody of the γG variety, which has been shown to give PCA in the guinea pig. The anaphylactic-type symptoms in man are probably the result of the formation of a separate anaphylactic antibody of the reaginic type, but this has not yet been explicitly established.

DRUG ALLERGY

Sensitivity of various kinds occurs generally in a small proportion of people treated with various drugs or repeatedly exposed to certain chemicals. These substances, usually of low molecular weight, are not antigenic per se, but they or their metabolic products may react with tissue proteins of the recipient to form complete antigens. For example, dinitrofluorobenzene, which reacts with the free amino and other groups of proteins (see Chapter 2), can induce sensitivity on being applied to the skin one or more times. Such sensitivity is most often of the delayed type, but may also be of the immediate type.

Perhaps the most important example of drug allergy is allergy to penicillin, which results from its widespread use in human and veterinary medicine. Thus milk from cows treated with penicillin often contains the drug in low concentration for considerable periods after its administration. The major antigenic determinant formed is the penicilloyl derivative, usually of benzylpenicillin with the ϵ-amino groups of lysine (see Chapter 2). The sulfur-containing penicillin ring may also open to give a free SH group that can react with other SH groups on proteins, but this has been shown to be a minor factor in penicillin allergy.

Antibody response to penicillin, both in animals and in man, is extremely heterogeneous, even when only the benzylpenicilloyl determinant is considered. By passive hemagglutination with erythrocytes that had been treated with penicillin so as to attach α-D-stereospecific or a mixture of stereospecific penicilloyl groups as well as by hapten inhibition studies, evidence for the formation of several stereospecific antipenicilloyl antibodies in human and rabbit sera comparable to those to α- and β-teichoic acids in human sera (see Chapter 7) was found. Most of the antibodies were α-D-stereospecific. γM and γG antibodies of each type were present, the proportions varying for different sera. Both γM and γG antibodies were detectable by passive hemagglutination; and the latter could also be detected by PCA, which, appeared much less sensitive, however. γG antipenicilloyl antibodies from rabbits immunized with penicillin-treated rabbit serum showed two lines in agar diffusion with penicilloyl human γG globulin, both of which had penicilloyl specificity. The finding that γG antipenicilloyl antibodies give very good passive hemagglutination titers is surprising, since with most antigens γG antibodies are not nearly so readily detectable; titrations in this system are carried out in a diluent of 2 percent dextran + normal rabbit serum diluted 1 to 75 in Tris buffer pH 8.2, and antibody was reported to be detectable at a concentration of 0.0001 μg of N per ml; about 200 times more was needed for PCA.

In addition to the above varieties of antibody, a reaginic type of antipenicillin antibody occurs in humans, and this is most probably responsible for the anaphylactic reactions to penicillin. A small proportion of people who experience severe immediate-type reactions upon the administration of penicillin give a direct wheal and erythema reaction when tested directly with penicillin, but a much larger proportion react to penicilloylpolylysine. This latter test is very useful in detecting individuals who might get anaphylactic reactions. These reaginic antibodies may be demonstrated by passive transfer in humans or monkeys (Fig. 13.5). It has been suggested that the individuals who give wheal and erythema reactions to penicillin itself are sensitive to contaminants or to minor antigenic determinants in the penicillin. The γG antibodies seem to be a blocking type of antibody in that they will combine with antigen to prevent it from reacting with skin-sensitizing antibodies. γG antibodies to penicillin have been responsible for a case of hemolytic anemia; after a large dose of penicillin, the red cells reacted with or adsorbed penicillin, which then took up the γG antibody. Such red cells coated with γG antibody are rapidly removed from the blood stream and destroyed with resulting hemolysis and anemia. This is another type of tissue damage caused by antibody.

DELAYED ALLERGY

The sequence of steps leading to the development of delayed allergy, often called tuberculin-type allergy or hypersensitivity, is essentially no different from that associated with the formation of the usual types of antibody and immediate hypersensitivity. Thus in both types initial contact with the antigen is required to sensitize, the response is specific for the antigen, and a response can be elicited in sensitized animals on subsequent contact with antigen. Initial sensitization for both delayed and immediate sensitivity as well as a primary antibody response can be inhibited by x-radiation, although the delayed reactions are less affected; by cortisone to which delayed reactions are more susceptible than are the others; and by antilymphocytic serum. Both delayed and immediate-type reactions are often produced after contact with antigen, and the sorting out of which manifestations are a consequence of delayed hypersensitivity and which are associated with the various kinds of antibody is difficult. Delayed hypersensitivity occurs during or after infections, including bacterial, fungal, and viral infections—especially those of a more chronic type such as tuberculosis—and after contact with certain chemicals or natural products such as dinitrochlorobenzene, penicillin, poison ivy, and so forth. It is readily induced to various antigens by incorporating them with the Freund adjuvants; the use of very minute quantities of antigen or of antigen-antibody precipitates formed in the region of excess antibody tends to produce delayed sensitivity from a few days to perhaps two weeks before detectable antibodies appear in the serum or immediate-type sensitivity is seen. Recognition of delayed sensitivity is by intracutaneous injection of antigen or by applying it to a cleansed area of skin. A positive reaction does not appear for some hours and reaches maximum intensity after 24 to 48 hours. It differs from the wheal and erythema and Arthus reactions and is generally a pinkish or pinkish-brown hardened lump that may vary from a few millimeters to several centimeters in diameter (Fig. 13.8). Histologically the reaction is produced by the accumulation of dense masses of large mononuclear cells, macrophages, and lymphocytes derived largely from the blood, while the wheal and erythema reaction is essentially a deposition of fluid at the site. The Arthus reaction may sometimes be difficult to distinguish microscopically from the delayed reaction, especially in the early stages when both contain many polymorphonuclear leucocytes. If precipitating

Fig. 13.8 A skin reaction of the delayed type in an individual sensitized to ethylene oxide treated human serum. (From Maurer, P. H. J. Exp. Med **113**: 1029 [1961]; by permission of The Rockefeller University Press. The photograph here reproduced from printed halftone copy inevitably shows a loss of detail, and the quality of the results is not representative of the original.)

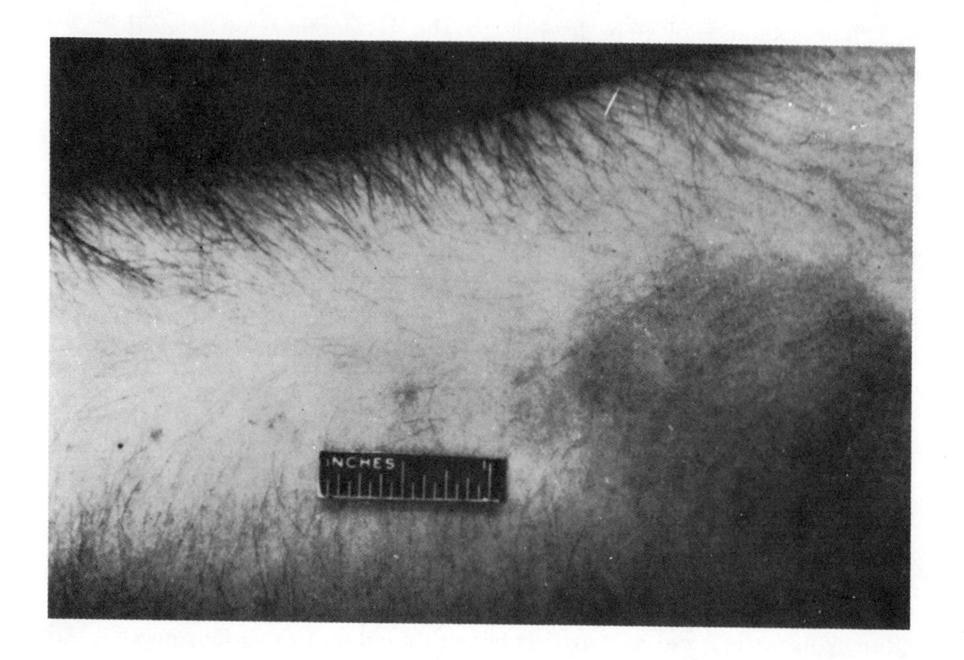

antibodies are present both reactions may occur at a single site. In the early stages of delayed sensitivity some increase in fluid at the injection site also is seen.

Delayed hypersensitivity is differentiated from the immediate-type allergies by its inability to be transferred passively to normal recipients with serum from persons or animals with delayed sensitivity. It can, however, be transferred to normal recipients by lymphoid cells from tuberculin-type sensitive donors; such transfer is not the definitive criterion, since the usual types of antibody may also be elaborated by cells (see Chapter 10). Indeed, antibody can be produced in normal recipients by the transfer of cells from immunized animals who do not show delayed hypersensitivity; and cells from anaphylactically sensitized animals injected into the skin of a recipient may synthesize antibody, producing wheal- and erythema-type sensitivity at the site.

A major continuing obstacle to the understanding of delayed hypersensitivity is the difference between the findings in animals and in man. While in all species including man the transfer of delayed allergy can be accomplished with living lymphoid cells, extracts of disrupted cells have been found to transfer delayed sensitivity in man. Several investigators have reported such transfer with various antigens. The active principle in these extracts, which has been called "transfer factor", is resistant to DNase, RNase, and trypsin; dialyzes freely through cellophane; and emerges as the first peak on Sephadex G-25, indicating a molecular weight of less than 10,000. The sensitivity transferred in humans by cells or cell extracts persists at least for months and even as long as two years. "Transfer factor" is released into solution by the exposure of sensitized cells to antigen, and the cells lose their capacity to transfer delayed sensitivity. On the other hand, efforts to demonstrate transfer of delayed hypersensitivity in guinea pigs with disrupted or nonliving cells have been uniformly unsuccessful when properly controlled. Contact of living cells with antigen does not affect their capacity to transfer delayed hypersensitivity; and the sensitivity transferred is of very short duration, being limited to the life of the transfused cells. Indeed guinea pig cells incubated *in vitro* with mitomycin C, which blocks RNA and protein synthesis, and with actinomycin D, which blocks DNA-dependent RNA synthesis and thus ultimately protein synthesis, no longer transferred sensitivity although they were still viable. The difficulty of carrying out experiments in humans seriously hampers resolution of the problem. In rabbits a nondialyzable fraction from frozen and thawed alveolar macrophages or from serum has been reported to transfer delayed sensitivity; the amounts of fraction needed corresponded to 7.5 ml of packed alveolar macrophages or 100 ml of serum. This material does not resemble the human transfer factor.

A variety of tests for detecting delayed-type allergy through the use of cell suspensions have been performed. One of the most interesting is the inhibition of leucocyte migration. Peritoneal exudate cells from tuberculin-sensitive guinea pigs placed in a capillary tube in small tissue culture chambers migrate out of the capillary and form a large flowery area around the tube in 24-48 hr. Such migration is strikingly inhibited by contact of the cells with specific antigen; cells from nonsensitive animals were unaffected (Fig. 13.9). If a few exudate cells from sensitive animals were added to normal macrophages the sensitivity to antigen could be transferred. The phenomenon required living cells—extracts were ineffective—and the exudate cells had to be capable of protein synthesis to transfer the effect to normal cells, since it was inhibited by mitomycin C. The active cell responsible for this transfer of sensitivity to the macrophage was shown to be the lymphocyte, with the macrophage being merely an indicator cell. The inhibiting effect was not transferable by serum from the sensitized animals and was specific for the antigen. Lymphocytes from guinea pigs immunized to antigens such as ovalbumin, bovine serum albumin, or tuberculoprotein under conditions that did not result in delayed hypersensitivity—for example, using for immunization, anti-

Fig. 13.9 Effect of ovalbumin and diphtheria toxoid on the migration of peritoneal cells from guinea pigs exhibiting delayed hypersensitivity to ovalbumin or diphtheria toxoid. Photographs were taken after 24 hr of incubation. (a) Normal cells without antigen, (b) Normal cells in presence of ovalbumin, (c) Normal cells in presence of toxoid, (d) Ovalbumin-sensitive cells without antigen, (e) Ovalbumin-sensitive cells in presence of ovalbumin, migration is inhibited, (f) Ovalbumin-sensitive cells in presence of diphtheria toxoid, (g) Toxoid-sensitive cells without antigen, (h) Toxoid-sensitive cells in presence of ovalbumin, (I) Toxoid-sensitive cells in presence of toxoid. Migration is inhibited. (From David, J. R., S. Al-Askari, H. S. Lawrence, and L. Thomas. J. Immunol. **93**: 264 [1964]; by permission of the copyright owner, The Williams & Wilkins Company, Baltimore, Md.)

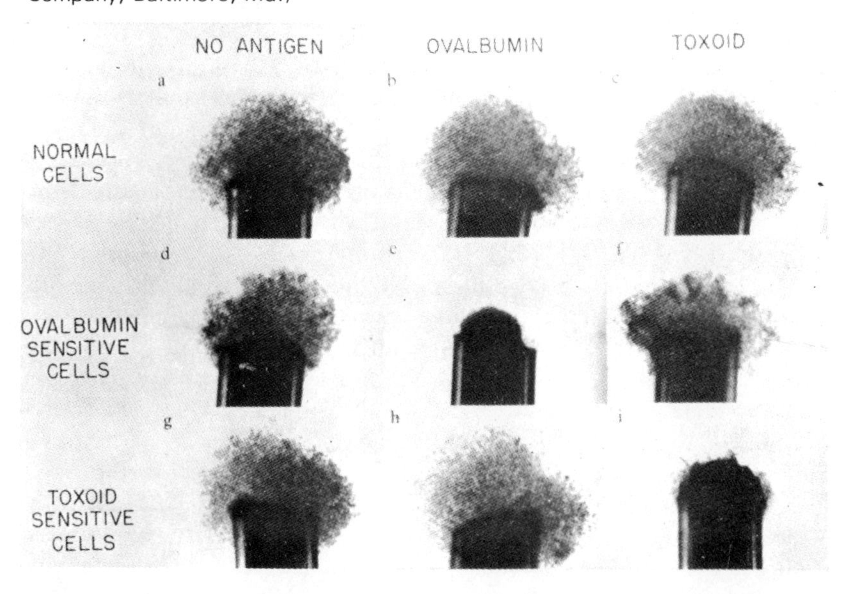

gens adsorbed on alum instead of the Freund adjuvants—did not tranfer to macrophages the sensitivity to antigen. While all these findings tend to associate this reaction with delayed allergy, some investigators (but not others) nevertheless find it possible to inhibit migration by suspending macrophages in culture medium to which precipitating antibody to the above three antigens and the homologous antigen had been added - a finding which could compromise the interpretation that this is exclusively a test for delayed hypersensitvity.

Apart from this latter reservation it appears that viable lymphocytes from animals with delayed hypersensitivity are capable of transferring something to macrophages which on contact with specific antigen inhibits their migration.

In searching to account for the differences between delayed- and immediate-type allergies, several interesting lines of investigation have been developed. One concerns the nature of the antigenic determinants involved in delayed allergy as contrasted with those producing immediate hypersensitivity. Some of the determinants of delayed sensitivity may differ from those involved in immediate hypersensitivity, since upon injection of small amounts of hapten-heterologous protein conjugates one can readily demonstrate delayed hypersensitivity to the original unconjugated protein, but only immediate hypersensitivity to the haptenic group. Similarly denatured proteins induced delayed sensitivity to groupings that are also present on the native protein. Delayed hypersensitivity to haptenic groups can also be obtained with hapten conjugates to homologous proteins. With known haptenic groups, the determinants capable of inducing delayed sensitivity cover a broad range of size, from a relatively small determinant formed by coupling *p*-azobenzenearsonate to tyrosine, to haptenic groups introduced onto proteins in which a portion of the carrier of undetermined length plus the hapten could be shown to be involved. The synthetic polypeptide *p*-(Tyr-Glu)-*p*-Ala-*p*--Lys which gave rise to precipitins in rabbits (see Chapter 2) readily induced delayed hypersensitivity in guinea pigs, while precipitating antibodies were formed only after prolonged immunization. The size range encompassed is thus not very different from that for antibody combining sites (see Chapter 6), although many workers have tended to be impressed by the role of the carrier in delayed reactions and to attribute the major difference between delayed and immediate reactions to the greater contribution of the carrier to the determinant (CARRIER SPECIFICITY) in delayed than in immediate sensitivity.

An important new perspective comes from the finding that relatively small molecules can be immunogenic with respect to inducing delayed hypersensitivity and that such immunogenicity may be essential to the induction of a delayed reaction. Two systems have been studied in different laboratories, and the two are fairly close to the extreme ranges in size for antigenic determinants.

In one of these a series of oligo-L-lysines containing a single dinitrophenyl group linked to the terminal α-amino group of the various oligolysines was studied, as well as the same series but having a butylamide residue substituted on the terminal COOH. The smallest immunogenic compounds were the DNP-hepta- and DNP-octalysines or their amides, and these compounds gave rise to both Arthus and delayed hypersensitivity. The unique finding was that in such actively immunized guinea pigs, compounds smaller than the heptamer which were nonimmunogenic elicited only Arthus reactions when used directly or when conjugated to bovine albumin, while the immunogenic heptamer, octamer, and nonamer gave both immediate and delayed reactions. The DNP group was immunodominant for both types of sensitivity, since the oligolysines themselves gave no reaction.

In the second system it was found that the low molecular weight conjugate of *p*-azobenzenearsonate with D- or L-*N*-acetyltyrosine was immunogenic in guinea pigs which had been injected with the Freund adjuvants and gave rise to delayed hypersensitivity. The delayed reaction, however, could be elicited only with multivalent polymers containing the *p*-azobenzenearsonate conjugated with tyrosine containing polypeptides made up of L-amino acids and could not be elicited with polymers of identical composition but which contained exclusively D-amino acids, the D-polymers generally being non-antigenic while the L-polymers were good antigens.

The requirement in both systems that the material used to provoke the delayed reaction be immunogenic suggests that delayed reactions may require active stimulation of sensitized cells to produce cell-bound or free antibody locally during the time needed for the reaction to become visible. In this sense a delayed reaction has been considered analogous to a rapid local secondary or anamnestic response. This interpretation would appear to account satisfactorily for earlier findings attributing differences between immediate and delayed reactions to "carrier" specificity.

It is of special interest that the α-DNP-heptalysine and higher oligomers gave rise to circulating antibodies of the usual type and that maximum inhibition on a molar basis was achieved with the heptamer (see Chapter 6).

Many hypotheses have been advanced to account for the differences between delayed sensitivity and reactions mediated by circulating antibody. These include (1) the suggestion that delayed hypersensitivity is entirely cellular, being an intrinsic property of a sensitized cell; (2) that delayed hypersensitivity is mediated by an antibody which has a high affinity for tissue cells so that it does not usually exist free in the circulation; (3) that it is associated with minute amounts of circulating antibody having a very high binding affinity for antigen with further synthesis during the time needed for the reaction to develop; (4) that some sort of transfer factor is involved; and (5) that delayed hypersensitivity is an early stage in the formation of circulating antibody of the usual types.

These hypotheses are viewed with varying degrees of enthusiasm by different workers in the field. The chemically oriented workers favor those which involve some sort of antibody, while many other workers consider delayed hypersensitivity as a phenomenon ascribable to cell sensitization. The difficulties with respect to transfer factor have previously been considered. It appears unlikely that the fifth hypothesis is correct, both from the data on the thymus and the bursa of Fabricius (see Chapter 10) as well as from the finding of a patient with a thymoma and a cryptococcus (yeast) meningitis who had no capacity to develop delayed allergy yet readily produced circulating antibody. The other hypotheses are stimulating much work, and eventually some or all of them may have to be modified or discarded. If ultimately delayed allergy is shown to be caused by another type of antibody, a unified concept of allergy could emerge.

TISSUE DAMAGE

As with the various allergic reactions, other immunological phenomena involving cell or tissue damage may be divided into two classes: those in which the damage is directly caused by the interaction of a humoral antibody with the antigen on or in a tissue cell, and those in which tissue damage results from a sequence of events similar to those leading to antibody formation but in which no antibody has as yet been implicated.

In the first group one may include:

1. *Transfusion reactions* in which antibody in the recipient reacts with antigen on the transfused incompatible donor erythrocytes–or vice versa–leading to massive hemagglutination, hemolysis, and erythrophagocytosis *in vivo* with destruction of the erythrocytes, accumulation of masses of red cells, or cell debris in glomeruli of kidneys with anuria (failure to produce urine).
2. *Erythroblastosis fetalis* in which antibody formed in the mother to an antigen present in the fetus passes through the placenta to react with antigen on the fetal red cell, causing destruction of fetal red cells by mechanisms similar to those in transfusion reactions but ususally of a more prolonged nature.
3. *Hemolytic anemia* in which autoantibodies are formed by some unknown mechanism to antigens of an individual's erythrocytes and which react with them and lead to accelerated destruction. Cases of hemolytic anemia due to drugs such as penicillin, quinidine, and so forth appear to involve antibody formation to the drug and accelerated red cell destruction from the interaction of antibody with the drug attached to the red cell surface.

In these cases antibody can be demonstrated on the surface of the erythrocytes, and experimental studies have shown that erythrocytes coated with antibody undergo erythrophagocytosis, hemagglutination, and hemolysis and are rapidly removed from the blood stream. Antibodies to leucocytes and platelets have also been shown to cause accelerated destruction of these tissue elements. Complement components (see Chapter 11) undoubtedly play a role in some of these phenomena. Heterogeneity of antibodies is involved in maternal-fetal antibody-antigen interactions, since γM and γA antibodies are unable to pass through the placenta and perhaps other heterogeneities may prove important.

The second group of diseases, generally termed AUTOIMMUNE DISEASES, occurs naturally in man and a laboratory model usually exists in animals which permits their investigation under controlled conditions. As with delayed hypersensitivity, their production experimentally involves methods similar to those used to obtain antibody and the response is generally specific and often accompanied by circulating antibody, although in no case has passively transferred circulating antibody produced the lesions. The antigens involved are usually constituents of an individual's own tissue—hence the designation as autoimmune—or may be obtained from comparable tissues of other individuals or species that show cross reactivity in the usual immunological tests. They are often called ORGAN SPECIFIC antigens. In most instances the disease is produced rapidly and in high incidence by injection into the experimental animal of whole tissue or tissue fractions as an emulsion with the complete Freund adjuvants. Delayed allergy frequently develops to the tissue antigen, and several of the diseases have been passively transferred with living cells, which leads many investigators to consider that delayed-type allergy is involved in their causation. In no instance has the mechanism involved in any autoimmune disease been completely clarified. Only a few examples can be given, which illustrate the current status of the problem.

Allergic encephalomyelitis Allergic encephalomyelitis is a disease of the central nervous system occurring in man following a variety of infections and occasionally as a consequence of the Pasteur treatment for rabies, in which vaccines containing central nervous tissue are used. It has been produced experimentally in many species including the monkey, guinea pig, rabbit, rat, mouse, and chicken by the injection of emulsions of brain tissue with the complete Freund adjuvants. The disease is characterized by many small areas of cellular infiltration and of destruction of myelin (the lipoprotein covering of the nerve axones); and these pathological changes generally take place around small blood vessels, especially venules, and are scattered throughout the brain and spinal cord. The lesions grossly and histologically resemble multiple sclerosis in man, which has led to the inference that the latter, too, is an autoimmune disease. It has been produced in individual monkeys to their own brain by surgically removing a piece of their frontal lobe and injecting it subcutaneously into them as an emulsion with adjuvants. Although much classical circulating antibody is formed to the various antigens in the brain tissue, attempts at producing the disease with serum have not been successful. Transfer of the disease with lymphoid cells has been accomplished in several species, most effectively by using inbred lines of rats and guinea pigs so that the donor cells were not rejected by the recipient in rats made tolerant to donor cells (see Chapter 14) or in irradiated rabbits; in each instance cells and recipient were of the same species. The failure to transfer the disease with serum in this instance does not provide as strong evidence that allergic encephalomyelitis involves delayed hypersensitivity, since the massive amounts of central nervous tissue of the recipient could be removing antibody as rapidly as it was formed. Sera of animals with the disease have been shown to have a toxic effect on myelin in tissue cultiures. Glial cells (connective tissue elements of the central nervous system) have been shown specifically to attract lymph node cells from rats with allergic encephalomyelitis. The lymph node cells formed patterns in tissue culture around glial cells which resembled agglutination (called CONTACTUAL AGGLUTINATION) and the glial cells degenerated; some evidence was obtained for involvement of a circulating antibody in this system as well. Lymphoid cells from animals with allergic encephalomyelitis also will sensitize macrophages *in vitro* and will inhibit migration on contact with adult brain antigens, but not with fetal brain that lacks myelin. The antigen in central nervous tissue appears to be a basic protein from myelin, and there is evidence that large amounts of serum from diseased animals prevent the development of the disease in animals given central nervous tissue with adjuvants. This system provides one of the most accessible and reproducible models for the study of autoimmune disease, and the mechanisms involved should ultimately become clear.

Chronic thyroiditis Chronic thyroiditis, often called HASHIMOTO'S DISEASE, as well as a number of other thyroid diseases such as goiter, hypothyroidism, and so forth in man are accompanied in a high proportion of cases by the presence of circulating antibodies to constituents in extracts of the thyroid gland. Antibodies to four antigens have been recognized: thyroglobulin, an unidentified antigen present in the colloid of the gland, an antigen in the microsomes of the cells of the thyroid, and an antigen whose homologous antibodies are cytotoxic. Antibodies to thyroglobulin may be detected by precipitation (see Figs. 4.2 and 4.3) and by tanned cell hemagglutination, gel diffusion, and immunofluorescence but they react weakly or not at all by complement fixation. Both antibody to thyroglobulin and antibody to the other colloid antigen could be demonstrated by immunofluorescence in sections of thyroid gland. The microsomal antigen is demonstrated by complement fixation and is located in the cytoplasm of the thyroid cell. Cytotoxic antibodies when mixed with living thyroid cells prevent them from attaching to glass and forming a viable monolayer of cells. The antithyroglobulin antibodies were most often γG immunoglobulins, but γM and γA also occur. Antinuclear antibodies are sometimes present.

Chronic thyroiditis is readily produced in rabbits, guinea pigs, rats, and monkeys with homologous thyroid extracts or with thyroglobulin emulsified in Freund adjuvants; and the disease has been produced in partially thyroidectomized animals with emulsions of their own thyroid. Delayed hypersensitivity and circulating antibody are simultaneously produced. Histologically a normal thyroid consists of an epithelial network forming sacs containing a uniformly staining eosinophilic material called colloid in which thyroglobulin is stored. In chronic thyroiditis there is massive infiltration of lymphoid cells which fill the colloid sacs, often obliterating them almost completely. As with encephalomyelitis the disease cannot be passively transferred with serum from animals with thyroiditis, although such sera contain large amounts of antibody. In monkeys with thyroiditis, cytotoxic antibodies as well as antibodies to the microsomal antigen and to thyroglobulin were found. It appears that neither the delayed hypersensitivity nor the humoral antibody is responsible for the lesions. Thus 6-mercaptopurine, which reduced the circulating antibody response and did not affect delayed sensitivity, prevented thyroid lesions, while a picrylated thyroglobulin gave diminished circulating antibody but delayed sensitivity and pathological changes were unimpaired. Transfer of thyroiditis with cells has been reported, but is apparently more difficult than with allergic encephalomyelitis. Antibodies to thyroid have been reported in high incidence in the mothers of children with certain chromosomal abnormalities, and an association between thyroid disease and chromosomal abnormalities has been noted. The basis of this relationship is not understood.

Rheumatoid arthritis Rhematoid arthritis, an inflammatory disease of the joints and synovial membranes of unknown etiology, is generally accompanied by the presence of antibodies (RHEUMATOID FACTOR) that agglutinate erythrocytes coated with rabbit or human γG immunoglobulin and precipitate with γG immunoglobulin aggregated by heating.

The antibodies are often directed against antigenic determinants exposed by enzymatic digestion of the γG immunoglobulin. In some instances the rheumatoid factors are specific for one or another Gm factor. Most rheumatoid factors are γM, but some have been reported to be γG immunoglobulins. In addition to the 19 S peak of rheumatoid factor, the serum of patients with rheumatoid arthritis frequently shows a 22 S peak that is considered to be a complex of 7S γG immunoglobulin with rheumatoid factor. Rheumatoid factor does not appear to be responsible for the pathological changes in rheumatoid arthritis; it is not infrequently present in other diseases and occasionally occurs in large amounts in individuals without evidence of disease. In addition, rheumatoid arthritis without rheumatoid factor is seen in children with acquired agammaglobulinemia.

Lupus erythematosus Lupus erythematosus is another connective tissue disease of unknown etiology which shows a substantial predilection for young females. It is frequently fatal, death being a consequence of kidney failure. It is characterized by an extreme augmentation of antibody forming capacity, many of the very rare blood group antibodies having been found in such patients. Their sera generally contain antibody to DNA, to nucleoprotein, to histone, to cytoplasmic constituents, and so forth which are demonstrable by complement fixation or precipitation. Sera of patients contain an antibody called the LE factor which reacts with cell nuclei to produce swollen structureless masses that are phagocyted by leucocytes. The unusual microscopic appearance of such leucocytes is of value in diagnosis and is called the LE phenomenon.

The antibodies to DNA in individual cases have been extensively studied; some react better with denatured than with native DNA; others react equally with both, while still others react more strongly with native DNA. Fluorescent antibody staining shows localization in nuclei and in connective tissue. $C'3(\beta_1 c)$ is also found together with γG immunoglobulin in the glomeruli of kidneys of patients with the disease. Complement levels in serum are generally low, but rise after treatment with corticosteroids, which sometimes produce remissions of the disease. As in other autoimmune diseases the role of antibody in etiology is not clear. There is no analogous disease in experimental animals.

Glomerulonephritis Glomerulonephritis, a disease characterized by pathological changes in the basement membrane of the kidney glomeruli in man, often follows an infection with the hemolytic streptococcus and is generally limited to only a few types 12, 4, and 1; more than 80 percent of the cases follow infection with streptococci of type 12 with respect to their M protein. Two types of mechanism are involved. In one antibody reacts with an antigen on or in the glomerulus and in the second antigen-antibody complexes unrelated immunologically to the glomerulus are deposited in the glomeruli. By immunofluorescence and electron microscopy, the former type shows a very uniform distribution of antibody and complement on the glomerular basement membranes while in the latter a patchy distribution of antigen-antibody-complement complexes is seen.

With the respect to the first type of mechanism, injection of heterologous kidney tissue into animals has been known for many years to yield an antiserum which when inoculated into animals of the species which provided the kidney would produce glomerulonephritis. In certain species the kidneys of the animals used to provide the antiserum showed glomerulonephritic changes. Usually, in humans with glomerulonephritis circulating antibody to glomerular basement membrane antigen is not seen, but recently, in several instances Dixon found that bilateral removal of the kidneys prior to transplantation of a normal kidney was followed by the appearance of circulating antibody. Evidently, in patients with glomerulonephritis the antibody is constantly being removed by their kidneys as fast as it is being formed, since it disappeared 24 hours after transplantation of the normal kidney. These data provide very firm evidence for an autoantibody in human glomerulonephritis.

There are several other experimental models which involve the first type of mechanism. One of these, termed the MASUGI TYPE, is produced in animals by injecting them with antisera to kidney formed in a heterologous species. In the original studies, ducks were immunized with rabbit kidney. The duck antisera injected into rabbits caused the appearance of protein in the urine and other changes characteristic of glomerulonephritis, and the antibody could be demonstrated on the glomerular basement membrane. One theory postulates that during the seven to ten days following injection of the duck antiserum, antibodies are formed by the rabbit to the heterologous duck immunoglobulins and that these react with the duck antibody already on the glomeruli to produce antigen-antibody complexes to which complement is fixed, thereby causing the disease. If peptic digests of the nephrotoxic antibody are used the disease is not produced, again suggesting that complement is involved.

The second type of mechanism in which antigen-antibody-complement complexes deposit in kidney with the production of glomerulonephritis has been described under serum sickness (Fig. 13.7) and other types of antigen-antibody complexes may also deposit in glomeruli to produce the disease.

Another interesting experimental model exists in a strain of mice NZB/B1 which spontaneously develop a hemolytic anemia and also often die of a chronic glomulerulonephritis that generally develops when the mice are more than seven months of age and has never been seen in mice less than five months old. Injection of living spleen cells from adult mice with glomerulonephritis into four-week-old mice resulted in glomerulonephritis within an additional four to nine weeks. Recent studies have shown that many of the manifestations of the disease, including the glomerulonephritis, may be produced by injecting filtrates of tissue extracts into preweanling mice. Viruslike particles that resemble other oncogenic viruses have been seen in the electron microscope. While the exact role of these viruslike particles in the hemolytic anemia is not clear, it raises the possibility of a viral etiology for an autoimmune disease. The distribution of the antigen-antibody-complement complexes indicates a mechanism of the second type and the antigen in the complexes appears to be DNA. Injection of complexes of DNA with methylated BSA at four months of age results in a rapidly developing glomerulonephritis before the spontaneous disease usually appears.

There are numerous other diseases in which autoantibodies are found such as Addison's disease, myasthenia gravis, ulcerative colitis, and so forth. Many other autoantibodies to tissue constituents may occur in healthy individuals; the role or function of these various antibodies and the nature of the antigens involved is an important area for study.

SUGGESTED READINGS

Humphrey, J. H. and R. G. White. Immunology for students of medicine. (2d ed.; 1964) F. A. Davis Company, Philadelphia. Pa.

Kabat, E. A. Kabat and Mayer's Experimental immunochemistry. (2d ed.; 1961) Charles C. Thomas, Publisher, Springfield, Ill. [Chapter 6].

Ackroyd, J. F. Immunological methods. (1964) Blackwell, Oxford.

Descriptions of methods of passive cutaneous anaphylaxis and of the Schultz-*Dale reaction and anaphylactic histamine release.*

Ovary, Z. PCA reaction and its elicitation by specific immunoglobulin species and fragments.Federation Proceedings **24**: 94 (1965).

Bloch, K. S. The anaphylactic antibodies of mammals including man. Progress in Allergy **10**: 84 (1966). [S. Karger, Basel].

Stanworth, D. R. Reaginic antibodies. Advances in Immunology **3**: 181 (1963) [Academic Press, New York].

Siegel, B. B. Hidden contacts with penicillin. Bulletin of the World Health Organization **21**: 703 (1959); *detective story relating the tracing of allergy to penicillin from milk, contaminated syringes, and the inhalation of traces.*

Bloom, B. R. and M. W. Chase. Transfer of delayed-type hypersensitivity. Progress in Allergy, **10**: 151(1967). [S. Karger AG, Basel]; *an excellent critical survey of the literature and an analysis of the problems with respect to transfer of delayed hypersensitivity in animals and man.*

Uhr. J. W. Delayed hypersensitivity. Physiological Reviews **46**: 359 (1966).

Schlossman, S. F., S. Ben-Efraim, A. Yaron, and H. A. Sober. Immunochemical studies on the antigenic determinants required to elicit delayed and immediate hypersensitivity. Journal of Experimental Medicine **123**: 1083 (1966).

Schlossman, S. F. and H. Levine, Immunochemical studies on delayed and Arthus type hypersensitivity. I. The relationship between antigenic determinant site size and antibody combining site size. Journal of Immunology **98**: 211 (1967).

Leskowitz, S. Mechanism of delayed reactions. Science **155**: 350 (1967).

Wolstenholme, G. E. W. and M. O'Connor. Cellular aspects of immunity. Ciba Foundation Symposium. (1966) J. and A. Churchill, London; *a comprehensive review of the cells mediating various immunological and allergic reactions. Gives nomenclature and descriptions of cells involved in various immunological reactions.*

Raffel, S. [Guest ed.] Basic and clinical immunology. Medical Clinics of North America **49**; 1487-1768; *a series of surveys of more medical aspects of immunology including allergy and autoimmune disease.*

Turk, J. L. [Scientific ed.] Delayed Hypersensitivity. Specific cell-mediated hypersensitivity. British Medical Bulletin **23**: 1-97 (1967); *a symposium covering many facets of delayed hypersensitivity.*

Patterson, P. Y. Experimental allergy encephalomyelitis and autoimmune disease. Advances in Immunology **5**: 131 (1966). [Academic Press, New York]; *a very recent comprehensive review.*

Samter, M. (ed.) Immunological diseases. (1966) Little, Brown & Company, Boston.

Kunkel, H. G. and E. M. Tan, Autoantibodies and Disease. Advances in Immunology **4**: 351 (1964).

Miescher, P. and P. Grabar. [Ed.] Fifth International Symposium on Immunopathology. B. Schwabe and Co. Verlag Basel (1967); *for the most recent findings on glomerulonephritis.*

14

Immunological Tolerance

Although we have seen in the previous chapter that autoimmune responses by the host to its own tissue antigens can result in serious damage, autoimmune diseases are relatively rare and their low frequency raises the fundamental question of why there is usually no reaction to antigens in an individual's own tissue.

Several lines of evidence have contributed to our present ideas on the subject. Perhaps the most important, both conceptually and experimentally, is the evidence based on the acceptance or rejection of tissue grafts.

IMMUNOLOGICAL BASIS OF TISSUE TRANSPLANTATION

Tissue transplantation studies in man and in animals have resulted in findings essentially interpretable on an immunological basis. It was readily established that skin grafts from one part of the body to another (AUTOGRAFTS) were readily accepted and survived indefinitely. Similar grafts made from one unrelated individual to another (HOMOGRAFTS) generally survive for periods ranging from seven to ten days with initial development of a blood supply; but then become inflamed and infiltrated with lymphocytes and monocytes, become necrotic, and are sloughed from the skin. Homografts made between identical twins or between animals of a given inbred line survived indefinitely, as if they were autografts. Inbred lines are derived by repeated brother-sister matings until they are relatively homogeneous genetically. The striking similarity of experiments with skin grafts and other immunological phenomena was the finding that an animal who had rejected a skin graft from a given donor would reject a second graft from that donor more quickly. This accelerated rejection was specific in that an initial graft from a new donor made simultaneously would survive for the usual time. The sequence of events leading to the rejection of an initial skin graft between unrelated individuals is called a FIRST SET, and the accelerated response following a second graft from the donor is termed a SECOND SET response. Under some circumstances second or subsequent grafts are rejected and never even go through the early stages of developing a blood supply; these are termed WHITE GRAFTS.

Graft rejection is accepted as being the consequence of an immune response to genetically determined isoantigens in the tissues of the donors which are lacking in the recipient. These isoantigens are called HISTOCOMPATIBILITY (H) antigens, and large numbers of them have been recognized in many species; with inbred lines of mice the genetic control of the histocompatibility antigens has been carefully mapped. Thirteen loci have been identified, two of which are associated with the X and Y chromosomes; the others are numbered H1 to H11, and one locus termed the H2 locus is of predominant importance in mice. Many of the H antigens in mice are present on red cells as well as in other tissues and may be detected by hemagglutination. Tumor transplantation in inbred lines has also established the importance of H antigen compatibility in successful transplants. The H2 locus governs many antigens that are transmitted on the same chromosome, by a series of closely linked genes. Among different inbred lines, first-set graft survival is related to the degree of histocompatibility, being longer if differences do not involve the H2 locus.

In man extensive studies on the isoantigens of leucocytes are being carried out in the hope that selection of more compatible donors will result in prolonged graft survival.

The immunological nature of graft rejection is further strengthened by findings which indicate that lymphoid cells are of primary importance in the process. Thymectomy at birth in mice unlike bursectomy in chickens results in the animals' failure to reject homografts. If a lymph node from a mouse of strain (A) which has rejected a graft of skin from an unrelated donor (D) is implanted into a normal mouse of strain A, the normal mouse will acquire the capacity to reject D skin at an accelerated rate—this is called ADOPTIVELY ACQUIRED IMMUNITY and involves the transfer of immunologically primed living cells that recognize the donor histocompatibility antigens. Such an adoptively immunized mouse would show normal first-set rejection patterns toward skin containing H antigens other than those in donor D.

There is substantial disagreement as to whether graft rejection is exclusively a cellular process or whether circulating antibody plays a role. Lymphoid cells from mice which had rejected skin homografts when introduced in millipore diffusion chambers into recipients of the same strain have given accelerated graft rejection for some investigators; but others have failed to find such an effect. In other studies in humans, however, immunization of blood group O recipients with A red cells caused a substantial decrease in the time of rejection of skin homografts from incompatible A donors as compared with those of compatible O donors, but the rises in circulating anti-A level were small and it is not excluded that cellular responses could have been responsible.

IMMUNOLOGICAL TOLERANCE OF GRAFTS

The preceding outline of the fundamental rules governing tissue transplantation was found to hold generally for many species. One dramatic exception, however, yielded the clue that led to an understanding of immunological tolerance. Nonidentical bovine twins, having different genetic compositions, were found to have two kinds of red cells, one with blood group antigens corresponding to its own genetic make up, the other to that of its co-twin. These two types of red cells persist throughout the entire life of the animals; such animals are called CHIMERAS. The basis for this chimerism was found by Owen to be the exchange from one twin to the other of primitive blood-forming cells *in utero* by the means of anastomoses (connections) between their placental blood vessels. The foreign cells survived in each twin and continued to produce erythrocytes of their genetically determined isoantigenic composition side by side with the twin's own erythrocytes. Several sets of red cell chimeras have now been found among human twins. The bovine chimeras were unique not only in having two types of blood but also in that one twin was able to tolerate a skin graft from its co-twin indefinitely while rejecting grafts from other siblings in the usual fashion.

This tolerance to skin homografts in bovine chimeras as an "experiment of nature" suggested that contact with antigen at an early age permitted the antigen to be recognized as self by an individual, so that antibody formation or other immunological reactions to it would not take place. It was possible for Medawar to produce such tolerance experimentally in mice by injecting the fetuses while *in utero* with living spleen cells, leucocytes, whole blood, or suspensions of other tissues from donors of an incompatible strain. When these injected animals were delivered and grew to maturity they became tolerant to skin grafts from the strain of mouse that had provided the cells for the *in utero* injection. This has been termed ACTIVELY ACQUIRED TOLERANCE.

A typical set of experiments is shown in Fig. 14.1, using two inbred lines of mice, a brown (agouti) mouse (strain CBA) and a white mouse (strain A).These two strains have incompatibilities in at least 15 transplantation antigens including those involving the H2 locus. Initial skin homografts from A mice into CBA mice were rejected with a median survival time of 11.0 ± 1.1 (s.d.) days while CBA skin in A mice had a mean survival time of 10.2 ± 0.9 days. The first photo (A) shows the injection of CBA fetuses with a suspension of A tissue cells; (B) shows the appearance of a control graft of A skin into a normal CBA mouse after 11 days; breakdown is complete. Photo (C) shows the healthy white hair growing at the site of the A skin grafts in four CBA mice that had received the donor A cells while *in utero*. In each case the graft on the left had been made 83 days before and that on the right, 33 days earlier. Photo (D) shows the specificity of the tolerance for A cells, the two white patches being healthy grafts that had survived 48 and 98 days, respectively, while between them is a graft from an unrelated AU strain donor which was placed 13 days earlier, but has been totally destroyed. The tolerance to A skin [Fig. 14.1 (C)] could be abolished, and the graft destroyed by adoptive transfer of a lymph node from normal adult CBA mice that had been immunized with A strain skin; Photos 14.1 (E) and (F) show the breakdown of an A skin graft that had been tolerated for 77 days, 8 and 12 days after such a lymph node implantation. A lymph node from a normal nonimmunized CBA mouse would also cause breakdown of the tolerated A graft, but generally only after a longer interval–the difference presumably reflecting the time for the normal CBA node to respond immunologically to the A graft antigens. The same set of observations could be made using A recipients and CBA donors.

Fig. 14.1 Production of actively acquired tolerance to skin homografts in mice and its abolition. (A) Injection of living spleen cells of inbred strain A into 17-day-old fetuses of strain CBA. (B) A control initial graft of A skin into a CBA mouse. Complete breakdown and scab formation at 11 days. (C) Healthy homografts of A skin growing white hair in four tolerant CBA mice that had been injected with strain A spleen cells while *in utero*. Grafts on left had been placed 83 days, those on the right 33 days earlier. (D) Rejection of AU skin in 13 days by a CBA mouse tolerant of A skin. The AU homograft has been destroyed while the two white patches of A skin have survived 48 and 98 days. (E) Loss of tolerance by implantation of lymph node cells from a CBA mouse that had been actively immunized by homografts of A cells which they had rejected. Loss of hair and inflammation at 8 days. (F) Same mouse as (E) complete breakdown of graft at 12 days. (From Billingham, R. E., L. Brent and P. B. Medawar. Phil. Trans. Roy. Soc., (London), Ser. B. **239**: 357 [1956]; by permission of the copyright owner.)

Similar findings may also be made in chickens. While the eggs may be injected with cells, a simpler technique [Fig. 14.2 (A)] is to join two eggs from different lines of chicken by a technique called PARABIOSIS ,as studied by Hasek in which cross circulation of blood between the two eggs is achieved. The two bared areas are placed face to face and connected by a disc of clotted plasma; after a few days blood vessels form in the plasma clot connecting the two circulations. When such eggs hatch the chickens accept skin grafts from eachother. Fig. 14.2 (B) and (C) show such reciprocal grafts from a Rhode Island red to a White Leghorn, and from the White Leghorn to the Rhode

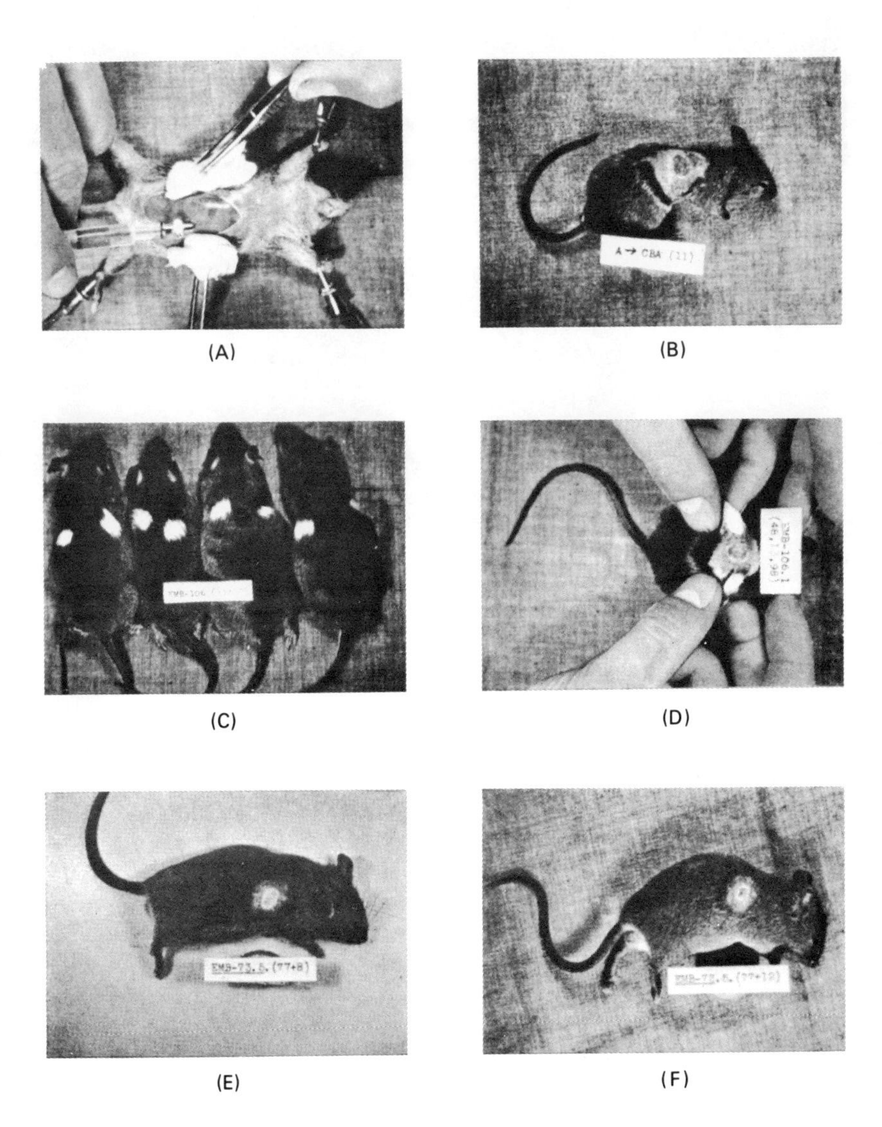

Fig. 14.2 (A) Technic of parabiosis of two 11-day-old chick embryos to effect cross circulation (B) A Rhode Island Red graft 282 days after transplantation to its 6-day-old parabiotic partner. (C) A White Leghorn graft 240 days after transplantation to its newly hatched Rhode Island Red parabiotic partner. (From Billingham, R. E., L. Brent, and P. B. Medawar. Phil. Trans. Roy. Soc. [London], Ser. B. **239**: 357 [1956]; by permission of the copyright owner.)

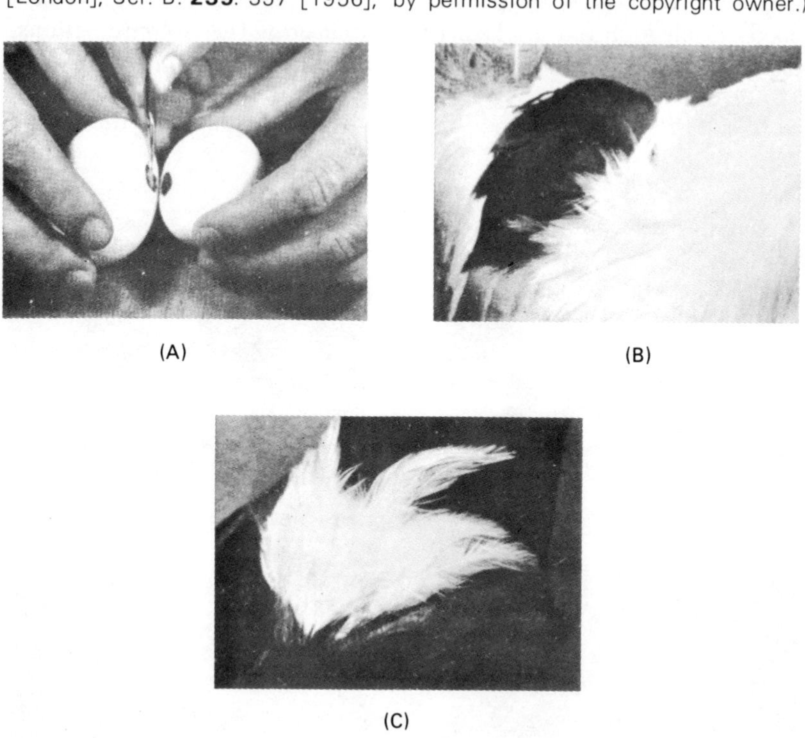

(A) (B) (C)

Island red after grafts had survived 282 and 240 days respectively. Tolerance between heterologous species was also readily produced by parabiosis of hen and turkey or hen and duck eggs.

Thus the introduction of antigen into fetal animals had resulted in a failure of the host to recognize them as foreign, with the result that they were treated as "self." In this instance, since the cells were living they continued to survive and produce antigen throughout the lifetime of the host; and any subsequent contact with cells of the same genetic and antigenic composition—for example, the skin graft—would also be treated as self and tolerated.

The age at which tolerance can be induced with living cells varies with different species. In some species it may be induced shortly after birth or hatching, in others only while *in utero*.

It has been suggested that the failure of the fetuses or newborn animals to reject the initially introduced foreign cells is caused by the undeveloped state of its own immunological apparatus. In support of this hypothesis it has been possible to produce chimeras experimentally in adult animals by destroying their immunological reactivity by a lethal dose of irradiation and then giving them an injection of bone marrow or spleen cell suspensions from another strain. These living bone marrow cells take root in the recipient's blood-forming organs and continue to multiply and produce mature red and white blood cells. In this instance also, species barriers may be crossed; and chimeras have been produced with rat blood cells in irradiated mice.

The role of age in the problem of tolerance is far from clear. The fetal lamb with a gestation period of 150 days could be shown to produce antibodies within 6 days to bacteriophage ϕX 174 injected at 35 days of gestation; capacity to form antibodies to other antigens developed at different stages of gestation—antiferritin not being formed until 15 days after injection, antiovalbumin not until 125 days later; a response to S. *typhi*, diphtheria toxoid, or BCG (an attenuated form of the tubercle bacillus used in human immunization) not being elicited until some time after the lambs' birth. Capacity to reject homografts developed at about 80 days of gestation. In other species as well, capacity for forming immunoglobulin and antibody has been shown to exist at a time when tolerance may readily be established. Thus the general tendency to consider the immunological apparatus undeveloped at birth is not solidly grounded.

Graft Versus Host Response

One major problem in tolerant animals is termed the GRAFT VERSUS HOST reaction. Thus a radiation chimera has no immunological apparatus of its own to destroy the transfused cells, but since the latter—especially those from spleen—are themselves immunologically competent they may not only proliferate but even react against the antigens of their host. The foreign immunocompetent cells of newborn mice that are made chimeras may also react in the same way; nonimmunocompetent cells such as red blood cells, epithelium, kidney, and so forth are not involved; it is the cells of the lymphoid system that are responsible. The graft versus host reaction gives rise to a syndrome in growing mice called RUNT DISEASE (or in the irradiated adult HOMOLOGOUS DISEASE) (Fig. 14.3) characterized by diarrhea, stunting of growth, loss of hair, skin sores, and atrophy of lymphoid cells throughout the body. Hemolytic anemia is common except in the mouse. The difficulty runt disease creates for experimentation on tolerance is evident in that the CBA$\longrightarrow$A system described above is considered especially advantageous because the mortality from runt disease, even with spleen cells, was only 50 percent. Graft versus host reactions are a major obstacle to the therapeutic use of bone marrow transplantation in man.

Fig. 14.3 Runting mouse (6.5 grams), together with normal litter-mate (17 grams). The runt is a forty-day ($C_3H \times ST/A)F_1$ that was injected when two days old with 20 million spleen cells from adult C_3H (From Simonsen, M. Progress in Allergy, vol. 6, p. 349 [Karger, Basel/New York, 1962].)

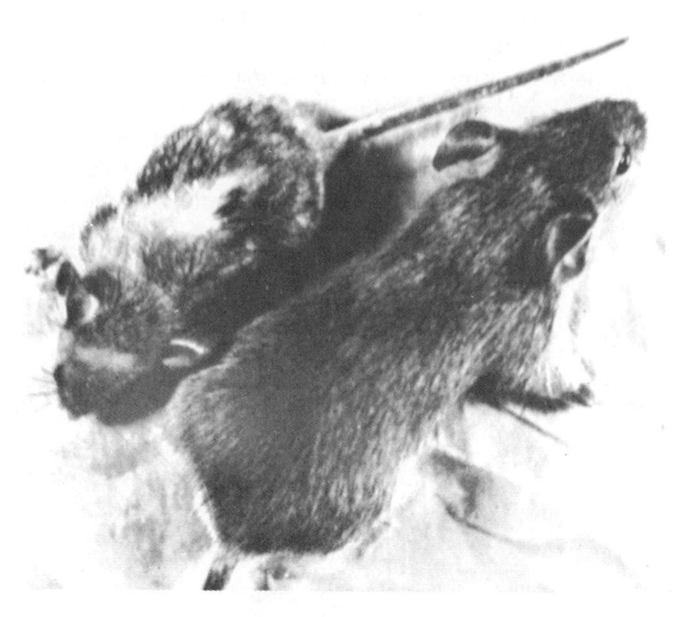

The avoidance of graft versus host reactions may be accomplished by the observance of certain genetic principles. Thus, if hybrid F_1 mice are obtained, such hybrids will be incompatible to both parental strains since they each contain antigens lacking in either parent. However, the F_1 cells will not be able to induce graft versus host reactions in the parent lines since they possess antigens from both parents. Induction of tolerance to F_1 hybrids in parental strains is readily accomplished in newborns and in irradiated animals without accompanying runt disease. In the inverse case the F_1 hybrids will tolerate cells or skin grafts from either parent, but parent cells introduced into the F_1 may react to the antigens they lack to cause graft versus host disease. Thus a system is available for studying each phenomenon in the absence of the other.

The graft versus host reaction has been developed into a method for the assay of immunologically competent cells. The injection of chick embryos or newborn chicks with immunocompetent incompatible cells results within eight to ten days in substantial enlargement of the spleen (Fig. 14.4) and also of the liver, both from multiplication of the foreign cells and by a stimulating effect on the recipient's cells which leads them to proliferate more rapidly. These animals would subsequently develop runt disease with accompanying atrophy of the spleen. With this technique lymphocytic cells, and not monocytes or polymorphonuclear leucocytes, were shown to be the responsible cells. F_1 hybrids are widely used as recipients not only for the advantages previously mentioned but because they can be used for 10 to 14 days after birth as compared with 1 day for random incompatible lines. Enlargement of the spleen occurs at an early stage (eight to ten days after incompatible cells have been given) in other species as well.

Another useful modification of the graft versus host reaction is obtained by inoculating incompatible cell suspensions from blood, thymus, spleen, and so forth on the chorioallantoic membrane of the chick embryo, a widely used technique for viral cultivation. If a small section of shell and egg membrane is removed from a fertilized avian egg the chorioallantoic membrane, which contains a highly vascular network, is exposed. This can be dropped back from the inside of the shell to form a large flat surface, and dilute cell suspensions may be spread upon it. The hole in the shell is covered, and the egg incubated. After four to seven days at 37°C the membranes are removed and examined. A large number of small nodules may be seen (Fig. 14.5); very few are found if the cells are from compatible strains. Quantitative studies indicate that about ten thousand blood leucocytes are required to produce a single nodule. Many large confluent areas are also seen

Fig. 14.4 Splenomegaly in three-day-old chicks injected intravenously at three days before their hatching with adult chicken spleen cells. Controls above. (From Simonsen, M. Progress in Allergy, vol. 6, p. 349 [Karger, Basel/ New York, 1962].)

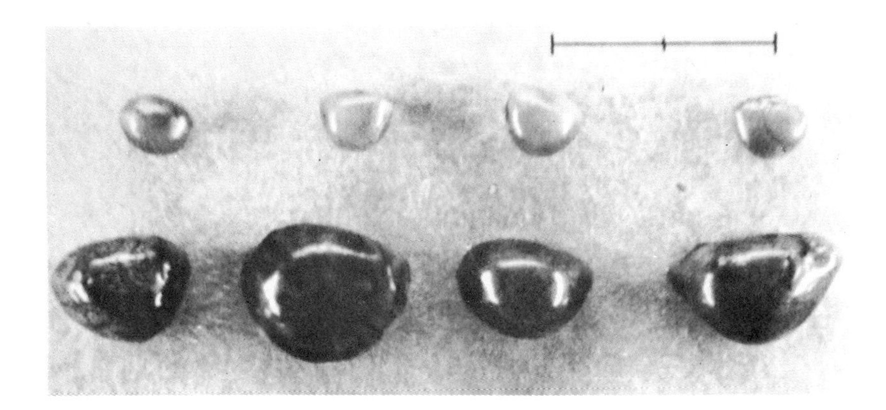

and these may represent secondary foci (Fig. 14.5). It was at first thought that the effective cells are the large and medium lymphocytes, and estimates of the number required to produce one nodule range from 40 to 1000; but others consider the small lymphocyte to be the important cell, and these are present in much greater number. Many investigators believe that a single cell induces each nodule and that the others may not be immunocompetent with respect to the antigens of the chorioallantoic membrane. This point is an important one in terms of the number of antigens to which a single cell can react and, hence, in judging the validity of certain theories of antibody formation.

The effective cell in the induction of graft versus host reactions as well as in the rejection of grafts by tolerant animals seems to be the small lymphocyte, since thoracic duct lymphocytes (see Chapter 10) caused both these phenomena.

Factors Affecting Tolerance to Living cells

The dose of cells necessary to establish tolerance in newborn mice depends upon the histocompatibility differences involved. Table 14.1 shows that with incompatibility at the strong H2 locus, 1.25 million cells induced tolerance in 43 percent of the recipients, while with a combination involving incompatibility at weak loci as few as

Fig. 14.5 Chorioallantoic membrane from a chick embryo inoculated at twelve days with a suspension of adult fowl leucocytes and harvested after six days incubation at 38°C. Typical large nodules are shown with many small foci that may be of secondary origin. (From Boyer, G. Nature **185:** 327 (1960); by permission of the copyright owner, Macmillan [Journals], Ltd., London.)

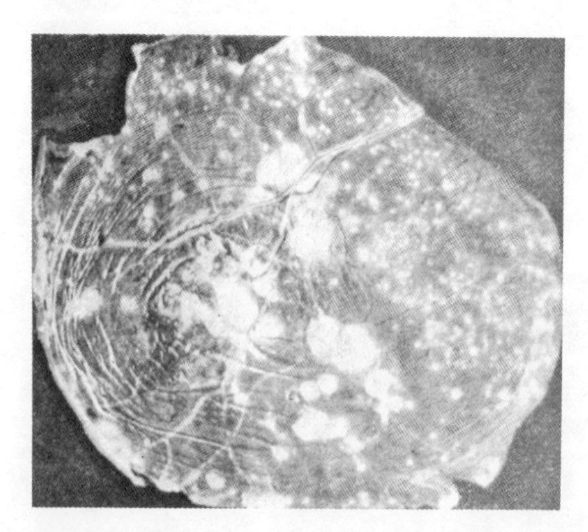

TABLE 14.1

Effect of Histocompatibility Differences on Induction of Tolerance by Intravenous Injection

Donor Cells	Recipient	Histocompatibility Loci Differences Involved	Number of Cells Injected × 10^6								
			5.0	2.5	1.25	0.62	0.31	0.16	0.078	0.037	0.018
			Percentage Highly Tolerant Animals [a]								
(CBA × A)F_1	A	H2 (strong)	100	70	43	0	0				
CBA	C3H	H1 and H3 (weak)					100	79	42	22	0

Data from G. Rowland, Brit. Med. J. **21**: 123 (1965).
[a] Highly tolerant denotes animals in whom a test skin graft survived in a healthy state 5 times the median survival time in normal controls.

78,000 cells give a similar degree of tolerance. The dose required increases rapidly with the age of the recipients, the 5 million cells giving 100 percent tolerance in the newborn for the (CBA × A) F_1 cells into A recipients produced only 35 percent tolerance when two-day-old recipients were used and no tolerance in four-day-old animals. If the dose were 5 million cells per gram body weight to compensate for the growth of the mice, 27 percent tolerant animals were found at six days and none at eight days of age. Very large doses of spleen cells and multiple injections can produce tolerance in older mice; 650 million cells in twelve injections to 34 thirteen-day-old animals gave 20 recipients tolerant to the combination showing H2 incompatibility. With very weak histocompatibility differences between the strains, transplantation tolerance may be produced in adult animals. Such adults tend to be chimeras and are essentially no different than neonatal tolerant animals. In inducing tolerance the same dose is more effective intravenously than intraperitoneally and it is ineffective if given subcutaneously. Immunosuppressant drugs and x-radiation facilitate induction of tolerance and prolong the time of survival of homografts.

The induction of tolerance in animals is an important tool in the study of transplantable tumors that cannot be transferred to nonhistocompatible strains except by inducing tolerance.

The injection of serum containing antibodies produced in chicks by repeated skin grafting, and by the injection of bone marrow and spleen suspensions in Freund adjuvants, induced rapid and total rejection in tolerant ducks of heterografts of the strain of chicken used to produce the antiserum. Loss of chimerism also resulted.

TOLERANCE TO INANIMATE ANTIGENS

With tolerance induced to living cells, there is no question of the persistence of antigen in the tolerant animals. Moreover there is no doubt about the absence of an immunological response in such animals, since the adoptive transfer of lymph node aborts tolerance. A variety of other types of immunological nonreactivity have been produced in different ways. These involve contact with nonliving antigens, with resulting subsequent failure of an immunological response. Some of the methods used are explained below:

1. Oral administration of various chemicals such as dinitrochlorobenzene prevents subsequent induction of delayed sensitivity and of antibody formation to these substances for 11 to 13 months in a very high percentage of animals; intravenous injection is less effective.

2. While minute doses (*ca* 0.01 μg) of pneumococcal type-specific polysaccharides induce active immunity in mice, large doses (500 μg) fail to immunize and the mice succumb to infection with very few pneumococci; this was termed IMMUNOLOGICAL PARALYSIS and can be readily produced in adult mice.

3. The injection of large amounts of protein antigens in adult rabbits results in their failure to form specific antibody for prolonged periods (IMMUNOLOGICAL UNRESPONSIVENESS).

4. The administration of antimetabolites such as 6-mercaptopurine, cyclophosphamide, and amethopterin, at the time of initial contact with the antigen results in specific failure to form antibody or to develop delayed hypersensitivity on second contact with antigen without further administration of the drug.

These findings together with those indicating that tolerance to living cells can be induced with cell extracts have led to the conclusion that the tolerant state is maintained by action of the antigen in inhibiting antibody formation and that this applies to all forms of tolerance. The amounts of antigen needed in adults are of the same order on a body weight basis as those in newborns, and massive doses of antigen can induce some degree of tolerance against unrelated antigens.

The absence of antibody formation in animals tolerant to protein or polysaccharide antigens may be established in two ways. One of these is by showing the absence of immune elimination—in addition to the failure to find circulating antibody—for example elimination of an intravenous labeled dose of antigen at the rate characteristic of that of homologous antigens. This technique is most frequently employed in studies on tolerance to serum proteins. The second method is to demonstrate by fluorescent antibody studies that antibodies are not present in the cells of tolerant animals. Both techniques are widely used, but one does not have a clear idea of their sensitivity. In the first instance one would like to know how much antibody an animal could be producing, and at what rate, to shift detectably a curve from the nonimmune elimination type. This would obviously vary with the dose of labeled antigen used in the assay, and data do not appear to be available. The fluorescent antibody technique has a high sensitivity in detecting cells producing a good local concentration of antibody, but the minimum amount detectable has not been established; it also would have low sensitivity for detecting a large number of cells each of which produces little antibody, although the total amount in the organism might be substantial. It is often difficult to distinguish between a tolerant animal, that is, an animal that has reacted to the initial dose of antigen by becoming tolerant, and an animal that fails to react to antigen in any way.

Within these limitations in newborn or adult mice that received 0.5 mg of bovine serum albumin (BSA) per gram of body weight per day for 60 or 40 days respectively plus weekly injections of 2 mg of alum-precipitated antigen, neither antibody nor antibody forming cells could be seen, although a single injection of 2 mg of alum-precipitated antigen gave rise in controls to substantial antibody with many cells showing antibody by fluorescent techniques. Similarly, 1 μg of pneumococcal polysaccharide gave rise to cells with antibody by fluorescent staining, while with 500 μg no such cells are found.

A single dose of 500 mg of BSA in neonatal rabbits regularly induced tolerance lasting for at least six months, with no further contact with antigen being required. This tolerance could be broken by the injection of cross-reacting antigens. Thus horse or human serum albumin, which show 15 percent cross reactivity with anti-BSA, given to such tolerant animals was highly antigenic inducing not only antibody to itself but also the formation of anti-BSA in over 80 percent of the tolerant animals, as evidenced by an immune elimination curve, precipitating and hemagglutinating antibodies to BSA. Pig serum albumin, which shows 32 percent cross reactivity, broke tolerance in only one third of the animals, while sheep serum albumin, with 75 percent cross reactivity, did not cause loss of tolerance.

The mode of administration of antigens is also important in whether tolerance or immunity will result. Thus 2.8 μg of human serum albumin injected into newborn rabbits within 36 hr of their birth gave no detectable antibody response during the following four weeks, and 28 percent of the rabbits showed nonimmune elimination. If, however, the same quantity of antigen was incubated at 37°C with cell suspensions containing largely macrophages from an allotypically different donor and was then injected into newborn recipients, antibody was formed which was of the the recipient but not of the donor allotype, although nonantibody γG immunoglobulin of the donor allotype could be detected in 8 percent of the recipients for a considerable period and reached levels comparable to those found in heterozygotes.

The coupling of simple substances such as picryl chloride, or of antigens such as bovine gamma globulin, to erythrocyte membranes (stroma) or to white blood cells gave products that were very effective in inducing tolerance in adult guinea pigs as measured both by delayed hypersensitivity and by circulating antibody response. The duration of this unresponsiveness has not been established.

There is evidence that the state of tolerance is not absolute. Tolerance induced by feeding picryl chloride can be broken by intraperitoneal injection of a picryl conjugate with a heterologous protein with production of circulating hapten-specific anaphylactic antibody; if the antigen was adsorbed on aluminium hydroxide, precipitating antibody was formed and the injection of picrylated guinea pig stromata with Freund adjuvants plus several cutaneous applications of picryl chloride led to some delayed hypersensitivity.

Tolerance induced by immunosuppressive drugs is greatly affected by the dosage and time of administration of the drug, which apparently are related to the status of the cell population that can react to the antigen. Thus, small doses of 6-MP given simultaneously with a protein antigen in Freund adjuvants inhibit delayed sensitivity while they do not affect the synthesis of circulating antibody. Somewhat longer administration of 6-MP inhibits γG antibody synthesis while not affecting γM antibody. An enhanced antibody response can be obtained by administering the drug for one week followed by the administration of antigen a week later. The compensating lymphoid cell proliferation in recovering from the effects of the drug apparently provides a more responsive cell population.

The specificity relationships in tolerance are not too unlike those involved in the antibody response, in delayed hypersensitivity, and in homograft rejection, although some differences exist. The dissociation of delayed hypersensitivity from γM and γG antibody formation by different dosages of drugs suggests the involvement of different cell types in these phenomena. Similarly, the finding of a case of myasthenia gravis with accelerated homograft rejection but no delayed hypersensitivity, makes it unlikely that the latter provides the basis for homograft rejection. Studies with synthetic polypeptides indicate that a substance may induce tolerance without itself being immunogenic. Thus a multichain polymer poly-D-L-alanine on poly-L-lysine, containing 91 percent alanine residues, injected at birth into rabbits resulted in failure to form antibodies to the polyalanyl determinants of poly-D-L-alanyl human serum albumin or poly-D-L-alanylribonuclease, although antibody to the other determinants of the protein was obtained. Similarly, injection of nonimmunogenic polyglutamic acid into neonatal rabbits gave unresponsiveness to the weakly antigenic poly-Glu^{60}-Ala^{40}, but not to the stronger antigen poly-Glu^{42}-Lys^{28}-Ala^{30}. In all these phenomena, the exact role of antigen has yet to be determined. There are many other interesting aspects of tolerance which could not be considered here. These and a discussion of theories of tolerance, antibody formation, and delayed hypersensitivity may be found in the Suggested Readings.

Immunological Enhancement

Another phenomenon closely associated with graft rejection and tolerance is termed IMMUNOLOGICAL ENHANCEMENT. It is most frequently demonstrated with transplantable tumors in mice, but may also be of broader significance. A typical experimental design to demonstrate enhancement is as follows: If a mouse of strain B receives a transplantable tumor of an incompatible strain A, the tumor will be rejected. However, if the recipient B mouse receives injections of lyophilized tumor cells or of other tissue cells of strain A prior to the tumor transplant, the tumor will grow in the recipient despite the incompatibility between the two strains. This facilitation or enhancement phenomenon is associated with the formation of circulating antibodies, since it may be produced by the passive transfer of serum from another mouse of strain B which had been immunized to strain A tissues. Electrophoretic studies have shown the antibodies responsible for enhancement to occur in different electrophoretic fractions than did the hemagglutinating or cytotoxic antibodies. The exact mechanism by which these antibodies facilitate tumor growth and suppress graft-rejection processes remains to be established. Isolation of the antigens associated with enhancement and the determination of whether the same antigens are responsible for graft rejection and enhancement is also of primary interest.

SUGGESTED READINGS

Billingham, R. E., L. Brent, and P. B. Medawar. Quantitative studies on tissue transplantation immunity. III. Actively acquired tolerance. The Royal Society (London). Philosophical Transactions **239**: 357 (1956); *a detailed presentation of the techniques of homografting and establishing tolerance.*

Wolstenholme, G. E. W. and M. O'Connor [eds.] Cellular aspects of immunity. Ciba Foundation Symposium, London. (1960) Little, Brown & Company, Boston.

Hašek, M., A. Lengerová, and M. Vojtíšková [eds.] Mechanisms of immunological tolerance. (1962) Publishing House: Czechoslovak Academy of Sciences, Prague.

Bussard, A. [Organizer]. Tolérance acquise et tolérance naturelle à l'égard de substances antigéniques définies. Colloques Internationaux du Centre National de la Recherche Scientifique. Editions C.N.R.S., Paris, No. 116 (1963); *contains important papers on tolerance, many in English.*

Brent, L. [Scientific ed.] Transplantation of tissues and organs. British Medical Bulletin **21**: 97-182 (1965).

The four symposia listed above have much detailed background material.

Humphrey, J. H. and R. G. White. Immunology for students of medicine. (2d ed.; 1964) F. A. Davis Company, Philadelphia, Pa.

Simonsen, M. Graft versus host reactions. Their natural history and applicability as tools of research. Progress in Allergy **6**: 349 (1962). [S. Karger Basel].

Dausset, J. and F. T. Rapaport. Role of ABO erythrocyte groups in human histocompatibility reactions Nature **209**: 209 (1966); *initial efforts to evaluate the role of an antigen of defined structure in homograft rejection.*

Šterzl, J. [ed.]. Molecular and cellular basis of antibody formation. (1965) Publishing House: Czechoslovak Academy of Sciences, Prague.

Samter, M. [ed.]. Immunological diseases. (1965) Little, Brown, & Company, Boston; *a comprehensive survey of immunology, tissue transplantation, and diseases with associated immunological phenomena.*

Chase, M. W. [Chairman]. Symposium on immunological tolerance to defined antigens and haptens. Federation Proceedings **25**: 145-168 (1966).

Seventh International Transplantation Conference, New York Academy of Sciences, Annals, **129**: 1-884 (1966) and earlier conferences; *a good source for various view points and recent developments on tissue transplantation, tolerance, and related subjects.*

Voisin, G. A., R. G. Kinsky, and F. K. Jansen. Transplantation immunity: Localization in mouse serum of antibodies responsible for hemagglutination, cytotoxicity and enhancement. Nature **210**: 138 (1966); *a source of references on immunological enhancement.*

15

Whither Immunology and Immunochemistry?

Perhaps the best way to summarize the perspective this book has tried to create is to outline a number of the important directions that fundamental immunological and immunochemical research may take in the next few years—based on our existing knowledge—as well as some of the more long-range and more difficult problems for which new leads are needed.

1. Important major developments should flow from determination of the complete sequences and structures of a sufficient number of Bence Jones proteins and myeloma globulins to establish the extent of the variable regions of their chains. From these data one would hope to obtain some insight into the structural changes caused by this variation, which may have direct application to the structure of the antibody combining site. It will be very important to determine the structural basis for the chain heterogeneity of the myeloma globulins. Knowledge of sequences and the availabiltiy of the various peptides that are obtained in their determination should make possible the identification of those sequences responsible for other allotypic determinants (Gm groups and so forth) and for the antigenic determinants associated with heavy and light chain specificity. Of special interest will be the location of the groups in the heavy chains which permit attachment to skin in reverse passive cutaneous anaphylaxis and the

determination of the differences associated with heavy chain subgroups, K and L specificity on the light chains, and individual specificity. Delineation of the variable region may permit a choice among various genetic mechanisms as the basis for formation of the different immunoglobulins. Studies on the three-dimensional structure of the Bence Jones proteins and myeloma globulins by x-ray methods, if correlated with sequence might give a spatial picture of the region formed by the variable portions of the heavy and light chains which might be directly transferable to work on the structure of antibody combining sites. Does the disposition of the side chains in a myeloma globulin make clefts or sites similar to the lysozyme cleft into which an antigenic determinant could fit? A knowledge of the number of different myeloma globulins could provide an estimate of the different kinds of cells making these proteins, which would set the stage for studies on the differentiation during embryogenesis of these different cell populations. It would be most useful to know whether the mutation leading to the extensive multiplication of myeloma cells and the synthesis of myeloma globulin has in any way affected or limited the synthetic capacities of the neoplastic myeloma cells, as compared with their precursor normal immunoglobulin-synthesizing cells. Do some myeloma cells make a relatively homogeneous myeloma globulin while others make several?

2. The extension of such sequence studies to antibodies will require preparations of greater homogeneity than are currently available. Substantial consideration should be given to developing methods of providing antibodies of more restricted specificity, for example, to produce antibody to single antigenic determinants and with a limited size range of antibody combining sites. Choice of antigen and the development of selective methods of providing such antibodies either in animals or in tissue culture might simplify the problem of fractionation. If the size ranges of γM antibody combining sites prove to be less than those of γG antibodies they might be more amenable to study. The various myeloma globulins with antilipoprotein, antistreptolysin, anti-DNP, and other specificities may provide another lead; and their specificity and heterogeneity require further characterization. Since a human antilevan has only one type of heavy and one kind of light chain and two bands in starch gel at acid pH, studies of its heterogeneity with respect to antibody combining sites would be informative.

3. Fractionation of the γM, γA, and γG antibodies will permit considerable progress to be made in evaluating differences in properties and their relationship to valence and sizes of combining sites. Improved methods are needed for the preparation of antibody to single determinants of greater homogeneity with respect to size of antibody combining site. Measurements of binding and other ther-

modynamic constants for such fractions obtained from antibodies to single antigenic determinants of simple structure will be of great importance, as will correlation with biological properties such as protection, capacity to sensitize for anaphylaxis, and so forth. The basis for the variations in affinity of antibodies produced at different periods during immunization requires further investigation.

4. Intensive study of various protein and heteropolysaccharide antigens will be carried out to isolate single antigenic determinants and to evaluate the exact size ranges of antibody combining sites. A major aspect of this will be the establishment of whether, within a single antigenic determinant of a protein, each of the several amino acids can function as an immunodominant group–as is true for linear heteropolysaccharides–thereby further increasing the heterogeneity of the antibody response. Another important line is the evaluation of the role of conformation of the antigenic determinant on antibody specificity and heterogeneity.

5. Establishment of the role of antigen in the biosynthesis of antibody. Does antigen influence translation and synthesis of the chains, or does it act at the cellular level as a selecting agent? An experimental approach into this area is sorely needed.

6. Studies of the genetic factors in animals which are involved in the synthesis of specific antibody combining sites. This will depend upon breeding and the selection of suitable lines.

7. Efforts to understand the nature of the hemolytic and other actions of the C′ components at the molecular level, for example, definition of the specific groupings on the molecules with which the components react, the nature of the substrate for those components with enzymatic properties, and the chemical nature of the degradation leading to the hole in the cell. The availability of various highly purified components and the ability to carry out certain reactions in solution should make an attack on this problem feasible. A very important area is the study of other sequelae of antigen-antibody interaction through triggering of enzymatic reactions, the evaluation of their effects on cell surfaces, and their relation to immunopathological changes.

8. A major endeavor should be the purification of the reaginic antibodies from various species, primarily from man, and the establishment of their chemical properties, especially whether they are distinct from the other classes of antibodies as now seems likely. The extremely small amounts of these antibodies usually formed and the short period during which they are present in some species makes this very difficult. A myeloma globulin that may be related to the human reaginic immunoglobulins has been found. Efforts to enhance specificity of antisera and to increase the relative proportions of re-

aginic antibodies should be made. Identification of the type of cell producing reaginic antibody is of great importance.

9. Fractionation from diphtheria or tetanus antitoxins of those antibodies with neutralizing power, and identification of the determinants with which they react, should lead to an understanding of the mechanism of neutralization and of the sites associated with their toxicity and antitoxic activity.

10. The isolation and characterization of antigens associated with homograft rejection and histocompatibility.

11. Resolution of the basis for delayed hypersensitivity as either a property of a unique type of antibody or a cellular phenomenon.

12. The role of antigen in the establishment and maintainance of immunological tolerance.

13. Determination of the antibody forming potentialities of individual cells and of factors limiting production, if any, not only in terms of the individual antigens but also with respect to the various parameters of heterogeneity which have been established for antibody to single antigenic determinants.

APPLICATIONS TO OTHER SCIENCES

The scope and power of immunological and immunochemical methodology makes it of great value when applied to problems in many other fields of science. Whenever a protein is purified or even partially purified, antibodies to it should be prepared if possible, since such antibodies may facilitate its further purification and characterization. This approach is widely used in examining enzymes and other tissue proteins from plant and animal sources. Specific antisera permit the investigator readily to follow the appearance of these substances during embryogenesis or their elaboration in tissue culture or cell-free biosynthetic systems. By fluorescent antibody techniques they may be localized in particular cells and tissues, and by ferritin-labeling techniques their distribution within cells may be established. They will thus become increasingly valuable in attacking the major problems of the future such as understanding the basis of embryogenesis and cell differentiation and the storage, retrieval, and transmission of information in the nervous system.

For example, with a specific antiserum, a cationic protein from brain could be shown histochemically to be localized around, but not in, the nuclei of glial cells of the central nervous system as well as in the nuclei of neurones in certain areas of the brain. In a cell-free system, 10 to 15 percent of the newly synthesized soluble protein was specifically precipitable by the antiserum to this cationic protein.

Another protein isolated from mouse submaxillary glands, mouse sarcoma, or snake venom is called the NERVE GROWTH PROTEIN. It stimulates development of the sensory and sympathetic nerve ganglia. Antisera to this protein not only inhibit its action but if injected into newborn mice results in the specific disappearance of all of the sympathetic nerve cells; indeed, it is possible to raise animals lacking a sympathetic nervous system.

In another area the enzyme lactic dehydrogenase has been shown to be of two types that differ in their antigenic specificity, one found in skeletal muscle and the other in heart muscle. Both enzymes are built up of four subunits, and hybrid molecules that contain both types of subunits in varying proportions (isozymes) are also found in different tissues. With specific antisera to each, the enzyme in the breast muscle of a 6-day chick embryo could be shown to be identical with that of heart muscle. During subsequent embryonic development, the amount of skeletal muscle specificity rose, while that of heart muscle specificity declined so that in the 21-day embryo the breast muscle contained predominantly lactic dehydrogenase of the skeletal type. Between 6 and 21 days, the intermediate forms were precipitated by both antisera and were probably hybrid molecules. These antigenic changes are paralleled by changes in the electrophoretic mobility in starch gel, indicating differences in the proportions of the various isozymes during development.

With carbohydrate-containing substances such as glycolipids and glycoproteins, the recognition and identification of component monosaccharides and their linkages may often be greatly expedited by using antipolysaccharide sera to determinants of known specificity. For this purpose, the type-specific antipneumococcal sera, antidextran sera with specificity for the different α-glucosyl linkages, antisera to the determinants of the O antigens of Salmonella and other microorganisms, as well as antisera to conjugated carbohydrate-protein antigens constitute an invaluable collection. Identifications by cross reactions may often be made with minimal quantities of the carbohydrate materials (Chapter 7). These antisera have great potentialities for the localization of carbohydrate determinants in developing tissues and in cells by fluorescence and ferritin-labeling technics.

Antisera to purines, pyrimidines, oligonucleotides, and nucleic acids will undoubtedly have many uses in biology. Already purine and pyrimidine specific antisera have been shown to arrest embryonic development of the fertilized sea urchin egg. Antisera specific for single stranded bacteriophage T4 DNA were useful in establishing that the usual renaturation that takes place on slow cooling of heat-denatured T4 DNA is never complete—as much as 20 percent of single stranded regions remaining. Such antisera should prove of great value in hybridization studies. The occurrence of anti-DNA antibodies of different specificities, for example, specific for double or for single-stranded DNA, in sera of patients with lupus erythematosus makes a reference panel of such sera a valuable research resource.

Immunochemical studies will also play a very important role in evaluating conformational factors, quarternary structure, and so forth in the biological activity of proteins. A study of interspecies hybrids of mouse and human A hemoglobins showed that the mixed hybrids such as $\alpha_2{}^{Mou}\beta_2{}^{A}$ and $\alpha_2{}^{A}\beta_2{}^{Mou}$ reacted less well in C′ fixation and in inhibition assays with antisera to human or to mouse hemoglobins. Antisera to the isolated α- and β-chains of human hemoglobin precipitated and fixed C′ with their homologous chains, but did not react with the heterologous chain. The antisera reacted with hemoglobin A by C′ fixation to a lesser extent than did the isolated chains, indicating that the determinants on the chains were accessible in the intact molecules, but that steric or conformational factors were involved. Antisera to the individual chains were especially useful in detecting mutational differences among hemoglobins involving only single amino acid substitutions.

References to these various applications are given in the Suggested Readings. Examination of current journals will provide dozens of other striking examples of the applications of immunology and immunochemistry.

SUGGESTED READINGS

Hydén, H. and B. McEwen. A glial protein specific for the nervous system. Proceedings of the National Academy of Sciences **55**: 354 (1966).

Levi-Montalcini, R. and B. Booker. Destruction of the sympathetic ganglia in mammals by an antiserum to the nerve growth protein. Proceedings of the National Academy of Sciences **46**: 384 (1960).

Levi-Montalcini, R. The nerve growth factor: Its mode of action on sensory and sympathetic nerve cells. Harvey Lectures **60**: 217 (1964-65).

Cahn, R. D., N. O. Kaplan, L. Levine, and E. Zwilling. Nature and development of lactic dehydrogenases. Science **136**: 962 (1962).

Rosenkranz, H., B. F. Erlanger, S. W. Tanenbaum, and S. M. Beiser. Purine and pyrimidine specific antibodies: Effect on the sea urchin egg. Science **145**: 282 (1964).

Levine, L., E. Wasserman, and W. T. Murakami. Immunochemical studies on bacteriophage DNA VI Renaturation of T_4 DNA. Immunochemistry **3**: 41 (1966).

Reichlin, M., M. Hay, and L. Levine. Immunochemical studies on interspecies molecular hybrids of hemoglobin. Immunochemistry **2**: 337 (1965).

Reichlin, M., E. Bucci, C. Fronticelli, J. Wyman, E. Antonini, C. Ioppolo, and A. Rossi-Fanelli. The properties and interactions of the isolated α and β chains of human hemoglobin IV. Immunological studies involving antibodies against the isolated chains. Journal of Molecular Biology **17**: 18 (1966).

Index